The Scientist

and the Soul

Frank F. Rupert

KAUMAGRAPH COMPANY

WILMINGTON, DELAWARE

1965

53997
July, 1966

Printed in the United States of America

Preface

I HAVE TRIED in this book to present the results of reading and thinking about a number of publications on the subject of the relation of science to religion. My working lifetime has been spent in the field of science, but the subject of religion has always been present in my thoughts. I have by no means read all that has been written on this important subject, but I am assuming, because I lack much more time to read other publications, that those which I have reported cover the subject in general. I have also endeavored to present my own reactions to these ideas. I am not and could not be an evangelist, or indeed a propagandist of any kind; I have no strong belief on any subject that allows me to think that I know much more than the person I am addressing. Rather the emphasis to me is always on the immensity of the things that I do not know. Therefore the reader will look in vain for an easy solution of any of the problems presented; but I believe that one can perform a service by showing the immensity of a field and the inadequacy of other solutions of the problems.

Most of my attention has been given to Protestant thought. Catholic and Jewish beliefs have been considered incidentally, but I have not tried to present them in full, nor to argue for or against them.

I have written largely in the first person, which I think is befitting in a book of this kind.

It is not my primary purpose to present my own views; however, in any book of this character the author's beliefs are more or less evident, whether or not they are frankly stated, and they depend to a great extent upon his environment and personality. Therefore I feel that a brief account of myself is in order.

My family was Presbyterian, but at the time I united with the church at the age of sixteen, neither my father nor my stepmother was a member. I thought that joining the church was a duty. I was hardly aware of the "conflict between science and religion", and my belief in so far as it could be expressed at all was practically fundamentalist, although some questions about that belief had arisen in my mind. I had read a little about evolution, but I thought that evolution and history according to the Bible should probably be easily reconciled. At one time I considered becoming a minister, but fortunately for the church and for me, my family and friends were decidedly cool to the idea and directed me away from it. One reason was that I would be the world's worst salesman and therefore the world's worst evangelist. Moreover, it was much easier to think about things than to be aware of people. I decided to study science, and my choice of chemistry was influenced by having had an opportunity to read about it and to experiment a little with it. My crude philosophy was that, since I was inclined to be intellectual, and on the intellectual side God is truth, therefore I would serve God best by learning as much truth as possible and extending it if I could. It is easy now to find gaps and inconsistencies in that reasoning, but that is what I believed at that time.

My religious environment was mostly fundamentalist; but when I began to attend a state university in the middle West, I was greatly surprised to learn that there were additional acceptable beliefs besides fundamentalism. I learned that there were Presbyterians who did not believe in the inerrancy of the Scriptures, and even some who did not believe in the Virgin Birth, although the latter disbelief was expressed rather quietly. I began to realize that denial of fundamentalist doctrines was not equivalent to denial of Christianity; rather, that the denial opened the way to a fuller understanding of its meaning. I also had broader and more naive thoughts. I had visions of a world based on cooperation; that is, a world in which each inhabitant was aware of his duty to help the others, and practiced it. I had no idea of compulsory cooperation in the form of socialism, and when I learned about it I could not see its logic. Since my inclination was to be aware of the material world more fully than of persons, it took several rude awakenings to get into my mind a realistic picture of the human world: but I retained some of the ideal of world cooperation; when ministers speak of "giving to God" when they simply mean giving to the organized church, I feel as if I were taken into the vestibule of a house and left there.

Naturally I thought it was my duty to follow the precepts of Christianity, and almost as urgent a duty to think about the intellectual problems of religion. One of my fellow-students once said: "Why do you worry about these religious questions? Why don't you leave them to experts in those fields?" My reply would have been, if I had thoroughly elaborated it, that the scientific and logical aspects of religion are fully as interesting as those of sciences in which I am not directly engaged, and perhaps more so since religion is a subject of interest to almost everyone. I know there is a time to think and a time to trust; I know that sometimes one should "be still and know that I am God", as Julian Huxley as well as more orthodox religionists have used the quotation. But at the same time I think that questioning of religious beliefs is as definite a part of the religious life as prayer and obedience.

There have been many times when I misapplied my religious knowledge; sometimes it was the fault of the teaching and sometimes it was due to my personality. The teaching to which I refer is that given in some Sunday School literature. The printed word always made more impression on me than did speech. One of these teachings is the excessive emphasis on altruism; that is, on the point that one should always be giving up one's self for the benefit of others; one should love one's neighbor better than one's self; this is a meaning not intended by Jesus or any other authority, and possibly the statements in which it is implied were exaggerated for emphasis. After being exposed to this over-emphasis, it was refreshing and relieving to hear a noted preacher say that Christianity called for a proper balance between self-love and love for others; but it took a number of hard knocks in the way of personal experience to free me from the misinterpretation that I had accepted. I avoided some of the conscious and obvious sins, but committed others of which I was not aware until much later. Now if any of these wrong teachings and wrong interpretations had been in the field of science, it would have been easy to correct them by experiment; but experiment is so much more difficult in the field of religion that it can hardly be applied.

If thinking independently about religious matters is a heresy and a sin, I am still guilty of it. The president of a theological seminary assured me that the students are taught to think for themselves. That must be true in most modern seminaries, and it is a great improvement over the situation which existed one hundred years ago. Still, you can lead a student to the thinking trough but you cannot make him think. Moreover, that encouragement to think on religious matters rarely reaches laymen. Ability to think on religious subjects naturally requires some knowledge of biblical criticism. John Knox (a modern writer) says:[1] "One of the most distressing features of church life is the theological gulf between the seminaries and graduate schools on the one hand and great multitudes of lay people on the other. Why is it that so many theologically trained leaders have theologically illiterate congregations?

Why is it that, eating bread and meat ourselves, we have continued to feed our people only milk? To answer these questions adequately would involve consideration of the whole educational technique of the church."

Roy L. Smith, commentator on the International Sunday School lessons, says on the same subject: [2] "Quite unfortunately, the great world religions have been, for the most part, afraid of the inquiring mind, the inquisitive youth, the exploring individual who persists in askng 'Why?'

"It is a part of the divine image in which every man is created, that he finds himself forever seeking explanations."

"The word 'Why' is responsible for every research laboratory in the world, for the discovery of every scientific principle and for the proof of every spiritual law."

"A young lad of 14 went to his pastor and asked a very serious and deep question. That mistaken man replied, 'My lad, that is a question you do not need to ask. You are, in fact, too young to ask it. The Church has faced your problem a long time before you ever thought of it, and men who are wiser, perhaps than you will ever be, have answered it. Therefore, do not trouble yourself to try to think the matter through. Take what the Church tells you, and you will be forever on safe ground.' "

"With that the youth turned away from the pastor, from the Church, and from religion. His was a brilliant mind, and he might have rendered the cause of religion a signal service, if that pastor had known the mind of an inquiring boy, and the real principles of his faith."

It is possible that the result of a frank discussion might not be entirely satisfying intellectually; but at least the boy would have learned what others had thought on the subject and would have been ready to ponder it for himself and to realize that there is much to be known and that religious leaders are aware of it.

Religious thinking, of course, is not synonymous with religious experience. It is sometimes very difficult to distinguish real religious experience from the products of a strong imagination.

To return to my personal history, there have been times when all the world seemed beautiful and I felt at one with the world and with God; and I have been subject to the constant alternation of sin and repentance that is characteristic of most Christians. I have on occasions felt the sense of the holy, to which I shall allude later. There was one crisis in which I sought help and received it in a manner which I am convinced that either God or telepathy or both had a part, but I cannot prove it.

At a graduate school in the East my experiences with a liberal kind of formal religion were continued. After finishing my school work, however, I settled in Pittsburgh and joined a Presbyterian church there. I found that much that I had learned about the Bible and related subjects over the preceding decade was taboo. In a Bible class my questions relating to Biblical criticism were not welcome, and a similar attitude prevailed in the church in general. Persons outside my scientific environment—and many of them were intelligent—were shocked when I mentioned evolution. Statements which were made in the school atmosphere in the ordinary course of discussion horrified hearers outside that field.

I am sure that I could have found a more liberal (non-Presbyterian) and more congenial church to attend, but distance was a factor, and also it seemed to me that there was something fundamentally right in my remaining in that church, although what I called fundamental was much different from what the people of the church called fundamental. I continued my studies of higher criticism and theological differences while participating to some degree in the work of the church. Sermons and lessons in which I do not agree with the speaker are more stimulating than those with which I agree thoroughly. Moreover, one should not depend completely on the church for spiritual nourishment. I stimulated my thinking further by reading religious and philosophical literature with various viewpoints. Bergson was a better antidote for a creeping materialism than any strictly religious instruction or literature, although I would not defend all of Bergson's ideas. At a later period in Pittsburgh the situation was much the same, but when I retired I found a church with a broader outlook which was more satisfying.

PERSONAL ATTITUDES

The following paragraphs are concerned with my attitude toward some practices of the churches. The first concerns the Apostles' Creed.

For the past twenty years or so the recitation of the Apostles' Creed has become an increasingly important part of the ritual in Protestant churches. For several years I have abstained from repeating the Creed, and I have found that I am by no means alone in that abstention. The plans that are being considered for the union of several Protestant denominations are very commendable in some respects, but I regret that the use of the Apostles' Creed is one of the bases of the proposed union. The Creed can be understood literally or symbolically; it is probable that it is intended to be interpreted symbolically, but in practice most of those who recite it are thinking of it as being literally true, if they are thinking at all, and I wish to avoid the impression that I am so doing.

There are minor variations in the Creed as now recited, but one of the common versions reads as follows: "I believe in God the Father Almighty, maker of heaven and earth; and in Jesus Christ His only son, our Lord: who was conceived by the Holy Ghost, born of the Virgin Mary, suffered under Pontius Pilate, was crucified, dead, and buried; he descended into hell; the third day he rose from the dead; he ascended into heaven and sitteth on the right hand of God the Father Almighty; from thence he shall come to judge the quick and the dead. I believe in the Holy Ghost; the holy catholic church; the communion of saints; the forgiveness of sins; the resurrection of the body; and the life everlasting. Amen." The principal variations in other versions include the substitution of Spirit for Ghost, and differences in punctuation and capitalization.

I shall first state the objections to the literal understanding of the Creed and then discuss explanations based on its origin and early meanings. The strongest objection to the Creed is that it implies belief in an abandoned conception of the physical universe. Even most fundamentalists have ceased to think of heaven as a material place in the universe, although it has been imagined as existing on a very large planet of a distant star, and also as a place beyond the farthest galaxy. It was simple for the ancients to think of Jesus as ascending to a heaven just above the clouds, and there to sit on the right hand of an objective Father; but it is very difficult now. The Russian astronaut mockingly said that he did not find God in his travels; the irony of his statement is that no one over ten years old would expect to find God there; yet the Creed implies that a material God and a material Christ would be found somewhere out in space. Most of us believe, I think, that Christ is in the spiritual dimension, right with us, and is judging all the time, and does not have to come from a distant realm. (Even here is symbolism.) The Virgin Birth will be discussed in a later chapter.

Two difficult statements are "He descended into hell" and the "communion of saints". One interpretation of the former is that Jesus went to hell to convert Jews and pagans such as Socrates who had approached Christianity in their thinking and their lives.

To others it simply means that he was in the abode of the dead. The communion of saints, likewise, has more than one interpretation. The lay belief, at least, is that it means simply the fellowship of Christians. The literal resurrection of the body is at variance with some Biblical teaching. The Resurrection, the forgiveness of sins, and the life everlasting will be discussed in other chapters. The Creed says nothing of the deeds and teachings of Jesus, which many Christians consider most important of all. Possibly it was not considered necessary to mention them, because if Jesus was divine his sayings were unquestionably true, but on the other hand there was little resemblance between many of the official practices of the church, then and later, and the Beatitudes. These objections may be summarized by saying that the Creed is too materialistic to express the fundamentals of Christianity.

Some of these objections may be countered by an explanation of the origin of the Creed. It cannot be traced back to any of the Apostles; but a creed apparently used by Justin Martyr about 150 A.D. contains some of its statements. In the opinion of scholars additions and changes were made from time to time but the present creed contains the vital points of the different versions. Many variations in belief were held during the first four centuries of Christianity. They were called heresies except when one of them was largely accepted; then it became the truth and the former truth became heresy. Two of the most prominent heresies were Gnosticism and Arianism. There were variations in Gnosticism, but two essential features was the denial of the humanity and materiality of Christ, and insistence upon his divinity. Arianism, on the other hand, made Jesus less than God; in other words, it denied his divinity in the accepted sense. According to Hordern the Apostles' Creed was primarily directed against Gnosticism. He says: [3] "If the Gnostics had triumphed, the message of Christianity to all men would have been replaced by a message for the chosen few . . . Christianity rose up to cast out this heresy, and in doing so solidified its orthodox position. The Apostles' Creed, which is still repeated in many churches, arose at this time, and can best be understood as a refutation of Gnosticism. First, it affirmed belief in 'God, the Father Almighty, Maker of Heaven and earth'. That is, it repudiated the idea that the created world is evil or the work of an evil god. This material work is good and worthy to be used and enjoyed by man.

"The Apostles' Creed next affirms belief in 'Jesus Christ His only Son our Lord: who was crucified, dead, and buried'. Many a modern man has been stopped by the phrase 'born of the Virgin

Mary'. He cannot believe in the Virgin Birth. But, ironically, to the early Gnostics, the problem was not 'Virgin'; it was 'born'. The modern man sees a red flag because he hears 'born of the *Virgin* Mary'; the Gnostic saw a red flag because he heard '*born* of the Virgin Mary'. Actually, this phrase, together with the ones about suffering, death, and burial, are the Church's method of asserting its belief in the complete humanity of Jesus. Whatever orthodox Christianity had to say about the divinity of Jesus, it retained a firm hold on its belief in his humanity.

"In the same light must be understood that other phrase of the Creed that causes trouble to many moderns—'The Resurrection of the body'. Are we to believe, they ask, that the atoms of this earthly body will be regathered and made to live again? Actually, anyone who has read the 15th chapter of the First Corinthians would not suppose that this is what the doctrine means. But it was a method of asserting to Jewish faith that man is a whole; he is not divided, as the Gnostics and many other Greek philosophers believed, into a good soul and an evil body. The Gnostic doctrine of the immortality of the soul is based on this belief, and implies that the soul is naturally immortal and only needs to be freed from the flesh. This also implies that the body is at best a burden and at worst an obstacle to the salvation of the soul. Christianity denies this, asserting the value of the body and thereby the importance of this earthly life."

Apparently not all authorities agree with Hordern that the Apostles' Creed was directed primarily against Gnosticism; but there is no doubt that the target of the Nicene Creed was Arianism. On account of the strife which Arianism was causing in the church the Emperor Constantine called the Council of Nicaea in 325 to decide upon an official creed. Athanasius was the chief opponent of the Arian belief, and Arius and his associates were on hand to defend it. The tone of the Council was political rather than dialectical; its foregone conclusion was the adoption of what has become the Nicene Creed. Arius and his prominent disciples were exiled. Some puzzling questions remained, but in the Council of Constantinople held in 381, general agreement on the remaining problems was reached and the doctrine of the Trinity in substantially its present form was established. No convocation can give final answers to problems of opinion, but it is evident that if the Arian views had been adopted, the position of the Church would have weakened and it might have become only one of the historical mystery cults. The Creed, therefore, had a survival value for the

Church, whether or not it was nearer absolute truth than the "heresies".

Whatever the historical value of the Apostles' Creed, it has little relation to present-day belief, except perhaps that of the extreme fundamentalists. There are unofficial creeds in the literature of some denominations which are more consistent with many shades of present belief, but perhaps the best solution is that of the denominations which hold no creed at all.

The language of the Lord's Prayer is also to some extent symbolic, but I do not hesitate to repeat it. It is not a statement but an expression of desire. In church I take communion in spite of a suspicion that its origin was outside Christianity rather than at Jerusalem just before the Crucifixion, and in spite of the absence of any belief that the bread and "wine" in themselves do anything to me. To me it is a symbol of which daily learning and exercise of Christian principles are the reality.

Hymns are an important part of religious service, and their contents give a clue to the religious thought of the time in which they were written and to the beliefs of the people who sang them at the time. Eventually, however, many hymns become obsolete in thought while remaining in the hymn book. Finally, they are no longer sung and in a later edition they are omitted. This is true especially of a small number of hymns but not of the great ones which have a permanent and universal appeal. One that is still popular in some churches is:

> "There is a fountain filled with blood
> Drawn from Immanuel's veins;
> And sinners plunged beneath that flood
> Lose all their guilty stains."

A humanist friend once told me that he had asked his daughter to read it. She thought it was ridiculous, but when it was sung she recognized it as one which she had often joined in singing. Of course it is highly symbolical; but symbols gradually change. The story of the Adonist origin of the symbol, in which persons were actually bathed in blood, now makes it impossible for me to sing the song. "Nearer my God to Thee" is a great and beautiful song but its use is declining. The verse:

> "Or if, on joyful wing,
> Cleaving the sky,
> Sun, moon, and stars forgot,
> Upward I fly."

has an entirely different implication for a modern space-minded youth than it did for the people who sang it years ago. There are a few other songs that I cannot bring myself to sing, but I believe that most of them are slipping out of use. A psychologist once said that one of the difficulties of liberal Christianity is that it has no songs to express its ideals. His statement has been denied by liberals; but essentially a song is an expression of emotion rather than of factual belief; and hence I may be unduly critical of songs. Most congregational singers give no thought to the words they sing, which may be good or bad.

One more religious practice to be considered is that of giving. If church membership is worth while the church deserves to be supported financially. Some of the methods of raising funds for the church, however, antagonize me rather than enlist my support; that is, the argument that everything one has is a gift from the Lord, and one should repay at least ten per cent. The idea of "giving to the Lord" to support the church is materialistic. One "gives to the Lord" when one does a bit of kindness or helps another to see the truth of a situation but if one is conscious of "giving to the Lord" in any of those situations he is guilty of a sort of idolatry. The motive must come from deep within him. "Let not your left hand know what your right hand does." Giving to the church or to any other religious, charitable, educational, or scientific cause should be a spontaneous but reasoned act with the specific view in mind.

Fortunate is he who can select causes to which he can give generously with the knowledge about the definite benefit that will result. Any act of dedication to one's work, or to one's daily duties, in a cheerful mood, is a more religious act than the simple giving of a few dollars to an institution. We are too likely to assume that our whole duty is accomplished when we do the latter. Of course the giving of money may encourage someone to be a better Christian, but this giving is not to be substituted for personal devotion. Too much publicity is often given in religious literature to conscious giving. Of course there is need for organization so that various worthy causes will share without too much duplication.

CONTENTS

Chapter I

Night Under The Stars

COME WITH ME out into the night and look upward at the bright stars and the newly risen moon. For ages people have thus watched the heavens and been awed by their beauty, even long ago when the stars were thought to be bright points somehow suspended in the sky, or as others have thought, holes in a balloon-like membrane stretched far above us, revealing bits of the brilliance beyond. The moon was a larger light or hole the purpose of which, according to Genesis, was "to rule the night." Now, however, we know more about the stars and the sky. We know that the stars are at vastly greater distances from us than the ancients thought; we know that some groups of stars which appear to be close together are at various distances from us as well as from each other; we know that most of the stars are much like the sun and radiate light and heat as the sun does; we know that a few stars are planets which shine only by the reflected light of the sun and are much nearer than the "fixed" stars; we know that the diaphanous drapery stretching across the sky which we call the "Milky Way" is an aggregation of millions of individual suns; we know that the Milky Way and the visible stars constitute a definite group called a galaxy, which light at its enormous speed takes 100,000 years to traverse; we know that far beyond our own galaxy are millions of other galaxies, most of them too far away to be seen without a telescope; we know that all these stars are composed of the same chemical elements that we have here on earth; we know that the apparent motion of the heavenly bodies across the sky is really due to our own motion as the earth revolves on its axis and we ride around on it; we know that all the stars and galaxies also have their own movements according to fairly well known laws and that their courses can be predicted by knowing those laws; we know that the moon is a body like the earth but with very little atmosphere and very little water, very hot in the sunlight and very cold in the shade.

These statements constitute only a small portion of our knowledge of the distant portions of our universe. You will ask me.

1

"How do we know these things?" The answer is that scientists
have learned them, a little at a time, not by going out into space
and closely observing each star, but by applying the same principles that they have verified here on earth. For instance, it is
well known that spectroscopic examination of an incandescent
solid surrounded by hot vapor shows dark lines at definite places
which are characteristic of particular chemical elements in the
vapor. The stars and the sun similarly examined show dark lines
at the same places. Therefore, the scientists reason, the sun and
stars contain the same chemical elements.

Some of these astronomical facts are almost within reach of
personal experience and direct measurement. For instance a satellite has given us a rather hazy but reasonable photograph of part
of the other side of the moon; and possibly in the early future
persons will be landing on the moon. On the other hand, near
the other extreme of thought there are hypotheses, that is, guesses
based on incomplete observation. For instance there are three
views about the creation of matter: (1) that matter was never
created but always existed; (2) that the universe began at a
definite time and place and has been expanding ever since; and
(3) that the universe is expanding but matter is constantly being
created. Most astronomers now favor one of the last two views,
with the hope of finding conclusive evidence in favor of one or
the other. Similarly in each branch of science there are points so
well confirmed by observation and a small degree of reasoning
that we call them facts; there are beliefs about groups of facts so
consistent that we call them theories; there are others about which
our reasoning appears to be good but the confirmation is not so
complete, and they are called hypotheses; beyond these there are
regions in which the factual evidence is meager or contradictory
and we can only speculate. The lines between fact and theory,
between theory and hypothesis, and between hypothesis and speculation are often so indefinite that the scientists differ on what category includes an individual belief or statement.

Whatever the state of these unsettled questions, or whatever
the details of our present knowledge of the universe, such a look
at the stars always reminds me of the insignificance of the earth
and its inhabitants, with their aspirations and their troubles, their
industries and their sciences, their politics and their wars, and
above all, the insignificance of *me*. This feeling of insignificance
has been experienced by so many people that it is perhaps trite to
mention it; but complementary to that thought is another: "But

here I am." Here I am, standing here and now, and knowing all these things that I have mentioned, most of which were unknown a mere 400 years ago. Likewise, when I contemplate the short span of my life compared to the billions of years that scientists tell me the universe has existed, the answer is, "here and now, I am." Although in one sense I am greatly inferior to the physical universe, in another sense I am superior to it, because I know about the universe but so far as I am aware it does not know me.

But let us forget the stars for the present and "come down to earth." I can see in the pale light the house from which we came, other houses, some trees, some other features of the landscape, and you. As with the stars, I know many things about these objects, partly from my own observation and reasoning, and partly from what others have told me. I know that the trees, the grass, the houses, and you and I each began to exist at different times, and that we grew according to definite patterns. I also believe, in common with most educated persons of our time, that the trees and grass and you and I exist as the result of a growth called evolution, involving many individuals of many kinds, and beginning many millions, if not billions, of years ago; and we are what we are now as the result of the lives of many predecessors. But, as I said before, "here I am," knowing all these things. The philosopher Descartes began his reasoning about the world with "I think, therefore I am". Many other philosophers think that it is not so simple as that and have offered various objections to his statement. Some modern philosophers would simply begin "I am." Without being told by anyone, I feel that there is something about me that is independent of birth or evolution. This "I" or "me", this soul, ego, mind, personality, this consciousness, or whatever it may be called in various contexts, is independent of all science, and I am conscious that in the very process of using those words I have crossed a line separating things from non-things.

I have been considering *you* as part of my environment. No amount of scientific knowledge can tell me that you also are conscious. Chemists can analyze your tissues; physicists can measure your energy; biologists can determine what happens in all parts of your body; psychologists can measure your reaction to every stimulus; to some extent psychologists and physiologists can tell what parts of your brain are associated with particular experiences; but so far as science goes you could be an automaton, and so could everyone else, except me; I know that I am not. I can, however, use my reason and imagination, in a process called projection, to convince myself that you are like me in knowing the world somewhat as I do.

This account of a brief look at the stars has raised a number of questions, some of which have never been answered and probably will not be, at least for many years to come. Harold E. Kuhn has related this incident[1]: Naturalist William Beebe has told of visits he made to Theodore Roosevelt at Sagamore Hill. Often, after an evening's visit, the two men would walk over the spreading lawn and look up into the night sky. They would vie with each other to see who could first identify the pale bit of light-mist near the upper left-hand corner of the Great Square of Pegasus, and then either Roosevelt or Beebe would recite: "That is the Spiral Galaxy of Andromeda. It is as large as our Milky Way. It is one of a hundred million galaxies. It is 2,500,000 light years away. It consists of one hundred billion suns, many larger than our own sun." Then, after a minute of silence, Theodore Roosevelt would grin and say: "Now I think we are small enough. Let's go to bed." Similarly after our own experience, having made ourselves sufficiently small, not only in comparison with the physical universe, but also to the philosophical questions that have puzzled many people, we can sleep on the information and questions, and then consider the following subjects separately: What is a scientist like? What is science? How did it come about? What is the scientist's function in society? What is the "soul"? Since the use of the word "soul" brings up the subject of religion, what are scientists' attitudes toward religion? What are the attitudes of religious authorities toward science? What is the nature of the "conflict between science and religion", if there is one? What are the fundamentals of religion? What else has been said about the "I-you" relationship? To discuss these questions thoroughly would be to discuss the entire field of philosophy, which I am not qualified to do. However, I shall try to summarize the thoughts of a number of authorities on these questions, without attempting the impossible task of settling them.

Chapter II

Scientists

IN THIS BOOK we shall be much concerned with the deeds and thought of scientists, so the first questions are, what is science and who is a scientist? The word science is derived from the Latin word "scire," to know; originally science meant knowledge and a scientist was "one who knew." The total range of knowledge is so broad that one cannot have extensive knowledge in more than one field or at most in a few related fields, therefore knowledge must be specialized. One who has extensive knowledge of one subject without reference to how he obtained his knowledge is called a scholar. For instance a scholar may know Greek history thoroughly by reading most of what has been written on the subject; he may even have an extensive knowledge of chemistry or other sciences by reading numerous textbooks on the subject; but that does not make him a scientist, unless he acquires first-hand knowledge by observation and experiment. Webster's most applicable definition of science is "accumulated and accepted knowledge which has been systematized and formulated with reference to the discovery of general truths or the operation of general laws." Conant supplies a gap in that definition and emphasizes the dynamic character of science by saying that science is [1] "that portion of accumulated knowledge in which new concepts are continuously developing from experiment and observation and which lead to further experiment and observation."

The first classification of science is into pure or fundamental science and applied science. Delahay throws the following light on this distinction: [2] "Three groups of motives for scientific inquiry are readily distinguished: intellectual curiosity and aesthetic motives; utilitarian ends and improvement of human condition; and personal factors such as ambition and escape from daily life. These motives are combined with varying degrees in an individual, and the predominance of one motive varies with the age of the individual." Science is applied in many fields, among which are indus-

5

try, medicine, pharmacy, engineering, aviation, war, and agriculture. Science applied in industry is called technology.

There is much polemical conflict between the advocates of pure and applied science. One extreme is represented by the proverbial mathematics professor, who in demonstrating a theorem which he had discovered said, "the greatest beauty of this theorem is that it cannot possibly be applied." On the same side of the question but more reasonably, Simons has said: [3] "Science and technology are frequently classed together. This is unfortunate, because they are so vastly different. Science is passive; technology is active. Science deals with knowledge; technology is concerned with the work of the world. It is true that the practitioner and technologist use science, but so do other people, and the practitioner uses many things that are not science. The physician in treating the sick cannot be limited only to the use of science. It seems to me that science is related more to the aesthetic arts than it is to the practical arts. It has all the aspects of one (of the aesthetic arts): the emotional appeal, the beauty, the opportunity for the use of the imagination, and the satisfactions of creation. Whenever science and technology are taken together, one can be sure that it is almost entirely technology with very little science."

At the other extreme is the following statement by Du Ruen-Sheing, in describing the "Great Progress Made in the Natural Sciences in China during the Last Decade." He says: [4] "To know Nature is for the purpose of transforming it to satisfy the requirements of production. Some maintain that 'scientific research would not in the least tolerate utilitarian considerations'. In saying this, they forget that all the current scientific inventions in the world are without exception directly related to social requirements and therefore inseparable from conceptions of utility. In the world of today, the difference in the question of utility lies only in whether it is for the capitalist or for the people. It is either this or that, but no other. The slogan 'science for science's sake' is incorrect." This extreme view may eventually prove to be an inherent weakness in Chinese science.

It is difficult to draw a sharp line between the scientist and the technologist. A scientist may be defined as one who conducts, or at some time has conducted scientific research. The meaning of the word research, however, has become broadened and sometimes thereby degraded so that Simons proposes the term "creative scholarship" for the true type of research as conducted in a university or college. Research consists in attempting to find out something that has not been known before and then trying to correlate the resulting data with known facts. Simons gives the original meaning of the word "research" as employed in academic circles as [5] "a quest leading to an increase in human knowledge." He gives the following example of the misapplication of the word: "One of the largest soap manufacturers had for many years the important research project of trying to achieve the largest bar containing the least soap." The improvement of a product so that it will better satisfy the user is more ethical than the case just described, but it may or may not be research within the terms of its original meaning, depending upon whether the improvement may consist of adding a little of this and taking away a little of that or of finding that some scientific principles are directly related to some of the properties of the product under observation. So the question of "who is a scientist?" and "What is research?" must remain somewhat indefinite. It could be said that one who is engaged in industrial research is a scientist if in his training he has conducted research in pure science and thereby absorbed some of the scientific spirit.

Traits of Scientists

Most traits of scientists vary in about the same proportion as they do in the general population. A scientist may be short or tall, stout or thin, pleasant or unpleasant, aggressive or retiring, and so on through a list of personal qualities. A certain degree of intelligence is of course necessary. A study of the technical men at a large atomic energy laboratory showed, contrary to what one might expect, that a larger percentage of them were interested in civic projects and church activities than the average. The report of the study, however, did not disclose how many of the personnel under examination could be strictly classed as scientists.

Essential attributes of the scientist are curiosity and intellectual honesty. A third that is not absolutely essential but is highly desirable is creativity.

Curiosity is one of the earthy constituents of human behavior. When unrestrained it may lead to the fate of the proverbial cat, but when qualified by restraint and experience it is valuable in scientific investigation. Curiosity is present even in the most primitive people and is a heritage from our animal ancestors. As necessity is the mother of invention, so is curiosity the mother of science. According to popular legend, true or not, Sir Isaac Newton's curiosity as to why the apple fell led to the discovery of the law of gravitation. Many other examples could be given; in fact, every discovery and every stage of a learning process is preceded by a question of what happens or why it happens. Curiosity, however, must be accompanied by the knowledge of what to look for. Curiosity that is the forerunner of science is not the kind that flits hither and thither, but curiosity controlled by thought and persistence until it is completely satisfied.

As mentioned previously creativity is a desirable trait. The routine work of science can be accomplished without much creativity, but the most successful scientists are the most creative ones. The general opinion is that creativity is inborn and there is nothing much to be done about acquiring or improving it. A paper by Walkup, however, presents a different view. He says: [6] "One of the creative mind's greatest contributions to the success of the scientific method is that of carrying out the whole process in the imagination, without time-consuming experiments, tedious data-taking, or the awkward drawing of conclusions. The creative intellect can and does perform many experiments in the 'twinkling of an eye'. Without this ability, many scientific searches would have so greatly exceeded the patience and energy of man that they would never have been completed at all. In a sense, the sum total of these extra-logical activities constitutes what has been called 'creativity', that most elusive of all man's varied abilities." This does not mean that a solid factual basis need not underlie every scientific conclusion. A theory developed by this creative process may be wrong, but an opportunity is given to check the conclusions and, by a fresh creative effort, to arrive at correct results.

Walkup continues: "Many attempts have been made to isolate creativity, with little success. It is an almost mystical ability possessed in large measure by gifted people but which most of us exercised as children; exercise now, to a limited extent; and could exercise more effectively if only we appreciated its elements and would practice its development. William N. Sheldon in *Psychology and the Promethean Will* and A. H. Maslow in *Motivation and Personality* have pointed out that most children are highly creative but that, tragically, their creativity vanishes sometime between adolescence and maturity in something Sheldon calls 'dying back of the brain'. This tragedy happens to so great a percentage of mankind that it is scarcely noticed. In fact, the few who escape it are considered a little queer. Fortunately, the few who escape this wilting of powers seem to continue to improve their creative powers up to the onset of senility."

Walkup also points out that creativity seems to have little relation to intelligence as measured by IQ. On the other hand, creative persons have strong imaginations and power to visualize situations. Walkup also believes that creativity can be improved by freedom from attention to details and concentration on the subject under consideration. "Provide yourself with a lot of clean paper and pencils, along with slide rule and perhaps a few handbooks or texts, depending upon the field of your problem. Then THINK, AND THINK, AND THINK." In other words the exercise of free play of the imagination is more effective than the pursuance of a logical routine sequence. Creativity plays an even more important part in the arts, especially in the fine arts. In that field it does not have to be checked by reference to facts, but rather by established canons of form. Creativity especially in the fine arts is often called inspiration. The meaning of the two words is the same so far as results are concerned; but inspiration carries the implication that something from outside is breaking through to the artist, while creativity implies merely that the artist does the creating.

Intellectual honesty is the most important attribute of the scientist. Intellectual honesty is not defined by Webster, and it is a pity that there is not a shorter word to express its meaning. A strict line of demarcation cannot be made between intellectual honesty, or personal honesty, and "plain" honesty or social honesty. A rough distinction is that a socially dishonest person deceives or tries to deceive others, but an intellectually dishonest person unknowingly deceives himself. On the other hand, the line between self-deception and ignorance is also fuzzy. A person can easily form an opinion on a subject about which he knows very little, based on preconceptions, prejudices, and wishes. He is ignorant rather than intellectually dishonest. If, however, he is presented with facts contrary to his opinion and still holds to that opinion, he is intellectually dishonest.

Intellectual honesty is absolutely essential to the success of the scientist, and conversely the study of science contributes to intellectual honesty. Delahay says: [7] "A scientist of doubtful character may not hesitate to borrow ideas ruthlessly without acknowledgement, but he will not falsify or invent data in the reporting of his work. He would otherwise face almost inevitable punishment. The rules of the game cannot be flouted in science, and scientific reports have a stamp of authenticity unequaled in many other human documents."

Objectivity and intellectual honesty are not exactly synonymous, but objectivity is a spur to intellectual honesty. "Objectivity"
is defined as "emphasizing the nature of reality as it is apart from
self-consciousness, treating events as external rather than as affected
by one's reflections or feelings; expressing facts without distortion
from one's personal feelings or prejudices." Objectivity in any
particular case is recognition of this situation. In science there is
always something to be regarded as objective; and though our
knowledge of it is imperfect, the opportunity to determine whether
it is objective is always present. That is often not true in other
fields; hence objectivity does not exist as a bulwark against intellectual dishonesty.

Integrity is a trait or habit closely related to intellectual honesty. According to Bridgman, integrity is broader than intellectual
honesty. He says: [8] "For me, integrity in the individual implies
'intellectual honesty', but it is more than this. It is a frame of
mind. Integrity demands that I *want* to know what the facts are
and that I *want* to analyze my mental tools and know what happens
when I apply these tools to the facts. . . . If I have a new vision of
something which I did not appreciate before, I may not put the
vision back and pretend that I did not have it and refuse to admit
that there may be consequences."

Humility and dedication belong together as constituents of
intellectual honesty. The following quotation from Thomas H.
Huxley is applicable: [9] "Science seems to me to teach in the highest
and strongest manner the great truth which is embodied in the
Christian conception of entire surrender to the will of God. Sit
down before a fact as a litle child, be willing to give up every pre-
conceived notion, follow humbly whenever and to whatever abysses
nature leads, or you shall learn nothing. I have only begun to learn
content and peace of mind since I have resolved, at all risks, to do
this." The abysses which the scientist encountered in the past, but
less at present, include rejection, ridicule, incredulity, oblivion, and
sometimes persecution. A word in Huxley's statement that requires
comment is "fact". Huxley did not say: "Sit down before theory
as a little child." If one does so reverence a theory, he may find
later that someone else has discovered additional facts that disprove
the theory. Therefore risking the abyss is unjustified. But where
does fact end and theory begin? It was almost universally accepted
as a fact before Copernicus that the heavenly bodies revolve around
the earth, and no doubt many "sat down before this fact as a
little child." According to modern conceptions they were wrong.

The new fact to which Huxley refers is a new belief for which the scientist thinks he has found conclusive evidence in spite of opposition, as did Copernicus and Galileo. Pragmatism, the belief that a theory is true if it works, to put it crudely, and the theory of relativity have asserted that neither the revolution of the heavenly bodies around the earth nor the rotation of the earth which gives the illusion of their motion is an absolute fact; the advantage of the Copernican view is its simplicity.

Huxley did not mean "sit down" in the sense of stopping there; I do not know in just what context his statement was written, but to the scientist a conclusion at which he has come to rest is the beginning of another search for knowledge. Moreover, it may be well to balance Huxley's admonition with another famous quotation, this from Sir Isaac Newton: [10] "I do not know what I may appear to the world; but to myself I seem to have been only like a boy playing on the seashore, and diverting himself in now and then finding a smoother pebble or a prettier shell than ordinary, whilst the great ocean of truth lay undiscovered before me."

Following are some famous cases of intellectual honesty. When Cavendish conducted an experiment in which he had removed the oxygen, nitrogen, carbon dioxide, and water vapor from a sample of air by chemical and electrical means, and according to all expectations no gas should remain, a "small bubble" was left. He faithfully reported this occurrence, but little attention was paid to the "small bubble"; many years later, however, the discovery of argon and other rare gases in the air in very small quantities confirmed his observation.

When Linnaeus, the naturalist, had finished his classification of species and was about to publish it, he found a plant that did not fit into his classification. He was on the point of abandoning the publication of his book, but on the advice of his friends who saw much value in it, the book was published with the exceptions noted and became a classic. Now of course Linnaeus' classification is outdated and the troublesome case has been explained but his admission of the defect added to his prestige. The feared abysses do not always appear.

When J. A. R. Newlands presented a paper at a meeting of the British Chemical Society in 1864, showing that certain properties of chemical elements vary periodically with their atomic weights, he was met with unbelief, and someone in the audience asked: "Did you every try comparing their properties with their positions in the alphabet?" All nuclear science as well as much of ordinary modern chemistry is founded on those relationships which the audience ridiculed. In this case there was a brief abyss; but the point emphasized here is the lack of intellectual honesty on the part of the audience; one ingredient of intellectual honesty is the willingness to consider new viewpoints. There have been many cases in which obscure observers reported their findings to well-known authorities and were told that they were wrong, but later they were proved to be right. In these cases it was the obscure scientist who was intellectually honest and the man of experience who was not. With advancing age and increasing prestige a scientist may to some extent lose his early objectivity and rely too much on his store of knowledge. On the other hand, objectivity may be slow in developing in a student, and often it is the young scientist who is overconfident of his knowledge. Exaggerated claims for science and misstatements about science often come from immature scientists and science writers who have not thoroughly learned objectivity. True intellectual honesty often forces the statement "I do not know."

Another foe of intellectual honesty is pressure for results, which is to be avoided in all fields of scientific endeavor. In schools where the value of a science teacher is rated according to the number of his papers which are published, these papers are often written at the expense of thorough investigation and accurate presentation of the results. A similar situation may prevail in scientific work for a government, as the value of a department and hence its appropriations, is often judged by its published material. Many applied scientists are employees of manufacturing corporations, where the conflict between immediate profit and honesty may be acute. Even when "fundamental research" is conducted by an industry, as Simons says in the paper previously cited: [11]"These terms (fundamental and research) have already been degraded by the industrial companies, for they use them for investigational activities the results of which are expected to produce profits next year or the year after. This distinguishes them from ordinary research, the gains from which are expected this year." The industrial scientist is free from this pressure only in a few of the most progressive companies. Sometimes the small companies which are new in the field of research want to have the reputation of supporting research without knowing exactly what research means, and therefore tend to consider the scientist as an adjunct of the advertising department. When the research is conducted under the auspices of an independent research institution, one of the functions of the institution is to protect the scientist in such cases and to insist upon absolute honesty. If the scientist is directly in the employ of the company it is his first obligation to be true to the interests of his science. This does not mean that the scientist is always right in a conflict between his ideas and those of the advertising and promotion departments. The applied scientist must be aware of the practical aspects of production and selling; but he should never sacrifice scientific ideals to commercial demands.

Another possible foe of scientific honesty is politics in the form of ideology. The Russian biologist Lysenko conducted experiments which appear to confirm the theory that acquired characteristics are transmitted by inheritance—a theory that had long ago been repudiated by biologists. Most biologists detected flaws in Lysenko's reasoning, but his results were welcome to the Soviet government because the theory was entirely consistent with its ideology; that is, with the idea that people may be changed and their descendents will remain so. For some time Soviet scientists appeared to accept his theory, but they finally repudiated it. Thus science triumphed over ideology. Science knows no ideology or political theories. It is hoped that eventually even the Chinese will realize that.

Scientists do not always carry over their intellectual honesty into their daily lives. Conversations between scientists reveal as strong prejudices as those held by their non-scientific friends. Many are the heated disputes that have been held between scientists and between groups of scientists about credit, priority, and such matters, in which a patient search for the facts would have settled the disputed points. On the other hand, nothing that has been said here about intellectual honesty is intended to imply that it is an exclusive possession of the scientist. Intellectual honesty existed long before modern science. Its enemies are prejudice and wishful thinking on the part of the individual, and "brain washing," which involves both the washer and the washed.

Is intellectual honesty as important in art as it is in science? The term "art" is so broad as to include all human activity, at least all systematic activity. Industrial art is synonymous with applied science. Its immediate object is to produce a tangible result, although the ultimate object is human satisfaction. The results are subject to the laws discovered by the application of pure science, and hence the same awareness and the same honesty are as necessary as in the pursuit of pure science. In human terms the necessity may be greater; for instance a little inattention to a detail

in the manufacture or design of an airplane may result in the loss
of many lives. In the practice of medicine, likewise, the life of the
patient may depend upon the knowledge of the doctor and his
conscientious use of that knowledge; but here the human relationship is another factor.

In other arts the most important purpose is persuasion. These
arts include business, law, and politics. Their aim is to convince
people that certain views are facts and to influence them to act
accordingly. In business, especially in promotion and selling, the
practice of social honesty, and therefore of intellectual honesty,
varies greatly. At one extreme is the fly-by-night salesman whose
goods are worthless. At the other extreme is the salesman who
must undergo a course of training, partly scientific, in the properties
of the materials he is to sell to manufacturers and other users who
will not be satisfied if the materials do not measure up to certain
standards. The more exacting the requirements of the customer,
the nearer the truth the claims of the salesman must be.

Many television commercials are examples of flagrant dishonesty of both kinds. Everyone is familiar with the persuasive
man or woman who must interrupt the program at frequent intervals to recount the virtues of a cigarette, a hair lotion, an automobile, or almost anything. These people work for reported sal-
aries beyond the wildest dreams of scientists; basically they are
actors trained for their parts, and are not necessarily responsible.
This brand of dishonesty is usually originated by the sponsors'
advertising organizations, who do not seem to realize that one
failure of the product to give the promised results teaches the
purchaser to avoid that product thereafter, and that two or three
such failures on the part of different products cause hesitation to
purchase any material so advertised. There are not many cases of
outright deception, because the Federal Communications Commission would easily become aware of them; on the other hand,
very few products can ever be as good as they are purported to be.
Often the attack is psychological; the use of the sponsor's product
makes "a lovelier you" or "you can feel the difference" or "smoking
satisfaction", etc. but in many cases the buyer can apply an objective test, and often does. The apparent success of television advertising seems to indicate that many watchers are not critical.
Commercials are the price that the public must pay for the illusion
of free entertainment. It is small wonder that in such an environment rigged quiz shows and payola have flourished. Education,
especially in science, should have sales resistance as one of its results.

In the field of law, the main purpose of a court trial is to establish facts and motives. In many cases the facts can be established by scientific inquiry. The scientific way of approaching the question would be for an unprejudiced scientist to perform experiments with the sole object of finding the facts. This method has often been advocated and in comparatively few cases applied; but the method is not in accordance with legal tradition. Each party in the suit hires an investigator who produces results favorable to that party, and the judge and the jury, usually all non-scientists, are to determine which results are right. In other cases the question is, who was where at a particular time and what did he do? Reliance is altogether on the testimony of witnesses, although scientific methods could sometimes be applied here also. Whether or not any science is involved, the separate presentation of a case as practiced does not encourage intellectual honesty or aid in the attainment of justice.

Closely associated with law is politics, a field in which the standard of honesty is especially low. Though the politician is more often accused of social dishonesty, it is evident that many politicians actually believe in their superficially conceived plans and panaceas. As in other areas, the constant repetition of a statement leads to belief in its truth, on the part of its propounder even more than on the part of the listener. Khrushchev gave a revealing clue to Soviet philosophy when he said, "Repetition is the soul of education." We all admit that repetition is necessary at the beginning of education; but if the student continues to be taught by repetition alone when he should be thinking for himself, this method of teaching leads to the dwarfing of the judgment or to intellectual dishonesty. The leaders of the Soviet Union are masters of self-deception and brain-washing; but these qualities are not entirely absent in the politics of any country. Bridgman says: [12]"From the point of view of the individual, it is evident that the political arena is no place for the practice of individual integrity. It seems to be more and more the case that political success is achieved at the cost of personal integrity." The only remedy for dishonesty in this field is the development of a factual and critical attitude in the people at large; this goal is far distant.

The function of the fine arts is to give the individual pleasure in its highest form and to "lift him above himself". The full import of these ideas is discussed in the next chapter, but the role of intellectual honesty may be discussed here. In the field of the fine arts it is no longer synonymous with objectivity. In literature for instance, without reading what the critics have said, I consider an intellectually honest piece of literature one that corresponds with my own sense of truth; that is, for instance, the people in a story act as I see people act and as I might act. In literature which is not intellectually honest, there may be a happy ending, or on the other hand an unhappy ending, that is not justified; or the characters may be activated by motives not present in actual human beings or by fewer motives than actually exist. An error in facts in a biographical novel or play does not make it dishonest; Shakespeare's many errors such as his reference to the seacoast of Bohemia are very minor matters. Of course literature is a condensation of life, and we cannot expect to find persons described fully; but when literature is intellectually honest the facets of human nature that are presented represent reality. The honesty of Shakespeare's best plays lies in our feeling of a sense of justice in the sequences of conduct, although we have never seen the same situations in life. Is there a little wishful thinking still left? The answer must be left to the critics.

The same considerations apply to the stage and screen as to the book. Unfortunately when a screen play is made of a book it is usually less true to life than the book. Even the central theme of the story is often changed, usually for the worse.

Intellectual honesty in poetry is a more difficult subject. I cannot often distinguish "good" from "bad" poetry, and I think that most scientists feel as I do; but it can be said that when a poem awakens the feeling that something in it is eternally true, no matter in how fanciful language it is cast, the poem is intellectually honest. There are scientists who make a hobby of music, and some who paint. Rarely, however, is there a scientist who writes poetry. Harrison says: [13]"Scientists usually make poor poets, for they are likely to depend too much on reason, and their product to invoke undesired emotional responses. Sir Isaac Newton called poetry 'ingenious nonsense'. But science is beautiful for the same reasons as poetry because it contains symmetry, pattern, and harmony. The poet, painter, and musician have no monopoly on the creation of beauty, for the ardor of the creative artist fills the scientist also when he pursues a discovery, and longs for the perception of previously unknown truths. To a mathematician the orderliness of numbers can bring feelings of great beauty. One mathematician called the algebra of determinants 'a beautiful garden open on every side to expansion.' " In going to the subject of beauty are we straying away from intellectual honesty? Not entirely. Suppose there were a flaw in the scientist's honesty? Would that not destroy the beauty of the conception? We feel that integrity and beauty are two phases of a fundamental entity. Although the fields of science and poetry require different attitudes of mind, they have a common ground.

The following quotations may be of interest in this connection: [14](1) "I think Americans, perhaps more than other people, are impressed by what they don't understand, and the poets take advantage of this." E. B. White. (2) "Irresponsible poets who simulate inspiration trample down the flower of language as brutally as politician and journalists, with their slovenliness, blunt and enfeeble the common run of words." Cyril Connelly. (3) "Any poem not written to free the poet from an emotional burden is only a piece of craftsmanship." Sara Teasdale. (4) "A man would have to be a positive genius, with a vision of old truths and a great technical competence to seem a modern poet today if he were clear and rational. Most of those who honor me with thin copies of their cryptic visions are all for economy of expression as exposition and concentrated pellets from which the miraculous intuition of the reader is expected to elicit vast landscapes of tumultuous but silent passion." George Santayana. (5) "People are exasperated by poetry which they do not understand and contemptuous of poetry which they understand without effort." T. S. Eliot. These quotations aid in understanding that poetry can be honest or dishonest in addition to possessing other qualities.

In painting, concealment and deception are necessary to the impression desired. The illusion of depth, in other words the illusion of three dimensions when there are really only two, is produced by techniques in the application of the paint. Sculpture and architecture also embody concealment and deception. This kind of deception, however, does not involve intellectual dishonesty. The only real deception would occur in the trick used in some museums and elsewhere, in which a realistic painting is placed in the path of the visitor so that he almost stumbles into it before he realizes that it is a painting. Honest art is that which satisfies the competent observer, whom I shall not presume to define. In the case of many types of "modern" art, competent observers must constitute a very limited group. In none of the fine arts is there the objective punisher of dishonesty that there is in science.

Harrison has this to say about illusions: [15]"The discoveries of science show that we all live in worlds of illusion, as Eastern mystics long have held. But once we understand what an illusion is, we find that this is a perfectly reasonable sort of a world to live in. We must learn to live with illusions while recognizing them for what they are, for through them lie our only approaches to reality."

Are philosophers intellectually honest? Or rather, is there any way by which the presence or absence of intellectual honesty in the assertions of a philosopher can be assessed? Critical study may show whether his propositions are mutually consistent; but there is no objective test as there is in science; that is, several philosophers may deal with the same set of facts but arrive at different conclusions according to the underlying assumptions whether stated or implied. Objectivity, therefore, may be ruled out as a test. Yet there is no doubt that most philosophers are sincere. If they are consistent we shall have to grant them belief in their intellectual honesty although there is no objective test. Bridgman's definition of integrity is partly repeated here: "Integrity demands that I *want* to know what the facts are and that I *want* to analyze my mental tools and know what happens when I apply these tools to the facts . . . If I have a new vision of something which I did not appreciate before, I may not put the vision back and pretend that I did not have it and refuse to admit that there may be consequences." This statement applies to the philosopher as well as to the scientist, with the limitation that the philosopher has all the mental tools except experiment and observation; the philosopher should always be conscious of his limitation. The philosopher may reply that the scientist must also be aware of *his* limitations.

The reader may have become aware by this time that there is another field, an art if you will, that has not been mentioned, namely religion. The reason for its omission is that there are many phases of religion to be considered before it can be discussed in relation to intellectual honesty.

The foregoing discussion has been concerned mainly with the virtues of the scientist. What faults do his critics find in him? A questionnaire taken among high school students a few years ago brought out some opinions that scientists are not practical and pay little attention to the affairs of ordinary life. Such opinions were not held by the majority, but by a substantial percentage of the replicants. Some of these students probably retained their opinions in adult life. Some psychologists have said that people become scientists to escape from the bustle and competition of the world, because they feel inferior. This idea would bring the scientist's choice of a vocation under Delahay's classification of motives previously mentioned; that is, "personal factors such as ambition and escape from daily life". It may be admitted that there are some scientists to whom these descriptions apply; but from my personal observation and that of others, I believe that the great majority of scientists are normal human beings. As Walkup has said, a person who has retained his youthful creativity in a full degree may seem "queer"; but not many scientists are highly creative.

The Sciences

In the discussion so far, science has been considered as a whole. Every scientist, however, is a specialist; he is a chemist, an anthropologist, a geologist, a psychologist, or a worker in some other limited scientific field. It is not my purpose to catalogue the sciences completely, but merely to point out the chief differences in method and outlook between certain group of sciences.

The ideal progress of a science consists of these steps: (1) gathering a fund of facts by observation; (2) classifying those facts; (3) framing hypotheses that are consistent with as many of those facts as possible; (4) testing the hypotheses by experiment; (5) accepting the hypotheses as theories; and (6) continuing to accumulate facts, constantly checking against theory, and when necessary formulating new hypotheses.

The study and progress of physics involves all the above steps. Physics is the most highly developed of the sciences. Standen calls physics "science at its best" and says further: [16]"Physics is not about the real world; it is about 'abstractions' from the real world, and this is what makes it so scientific. It has all the proper attributes—the importance of exact measurement, the reduction of everything to mathematics, the carefully defined and precisely used terms, the pitilessly rigid trains of logical thought—that are commonly ascribed to everything that goes by the name of science. . . . Other sciences are scientific in so far as they approach the dignity of physics, and it would be only a slight exaggeration to say that physics is science." This quotation and others to follow were taken from *Science Is a Sacred Cow*, a best-seller of about 1950 by Anthony Standen, a chemist. It is refreshingly iconoclastic and is worth occasional reading by anyone interested in science. No scientist will agree with everything that Standen says, especially when he deals with the scientist's own specialty, but his provocative statements will make the reader think and will keep him humble.

Regarding the above quotation, one may ask without attempting to answer, "What is the real world?"

Standen says about chemists: [17]"Chemists are, on the whole, like physicists, only less so. They don't make the same wonderful mistakes, and much of what they do is art, related to cooking, instead of true science." Chemistry, like physics, is an experimental science. The chemist deals with substances as entities, while the physicist is not concerned so much with individual substances. Physical chemistry is considered almost synonymous with theoretical chemistry; at least all the theory underlying the various branches is gathered into physical chemistry. Beyond the basic classification of chemistry into inorganic, organic, physical, and analytical, most subdivisions are related to the applications of chemistry; examples are petroleum, agricultural, food, plastics, polymer, geochemistry, and pharmaceutical chemistry.

Other physical sciences include geology and astronomy and their subdivisions. Both geology and astronomy are concerned to some extent with occurrences in the remote past, and to the degree that they are, the step of experimentation must be lacking. In astronomy most of the material to be studied is too far away for experimentation. The branches geophysics and astrophysics are concerned with attempts to make the parent subjects as nearly experimental as possible. In geophysics, for instance, experiment shows what happens when chemicals such as those constituting the earth are subjected to high pressures such as must occur in the interior of the earth; and in astrophysics the spectra of distant stars are compared with those of known elements. The time may come when astronomy will be more experimental, but that time appears to be far distant. The photographing of the other side of the moon is not experiment; it is observation by an ingenious method.

The biological sciences are less subject to experimentation than the physical sciences, but the role of experiment is increasing. The experiments on Heredity involving the study of many generations of short-lived and quick-breeding Mediterranean fruit flies are well known. For most animals and plants, the biological processes are too slow for experimentation. The same limitation has restricted the development of theories. Some of the theories of the biologist have been merely accumulations of facts; the cell theory, for instance. Standen says: [18]"The truth is that biologists don't think, at least not in the sense of making formal conclusions. Their mental processes go by analogy. Analogy is a wonderful, useful,

and important form of thinking, and biology is saturated with it.
. . . The physicist, with his facts, seeks reason; the biologist seeks
something like rhyme, and rhyme is a kind of analogy. . . . This
analogy, this fine sweeping ability to see likenesses in the midst of
differences, is the great glory of biology, but biologists don't know
it, and praise themselves for the wrong reasons. They have been
so overawed by the superior prestige of exact physical science that
they have to imitate it, and they solemnly announce that what they
are doing is 'framing hypotheses' and 'testing them', in the manner
of the physicist."

To whatever extent Standen's criticism is valid, and whether
logic or analogy is the more important in biology, his views are
thought-provoking. There are two rival hypotheses concerning the
relation of the biological to the physical sciences. The first is
mechanism, which assumes that the phenomena of life involve only
physical forces and chemical reactions, no matter how complex
their interactions may be. The second is vitalism, which assumes
the presence of other powers which are restricted to the living
world. The sum of these powers has been called vital force, elan
vital, telefinalism, or telism. There is no experimental or obser-
vational evidence for either belief, and so far as we can see, there
cannot be. The question is philosophical, not scientific.

One comprehensive theory, of course, is always in evidence;
that of evolution. Evolution purports to be a history of life and its
varied developments, and since it is to be regarded as history, it
cannot be checked experimentally to any serious extent. Evolution
is accepted by nearly all scientists and by most educated persons;
that is, it is accepted as a reasonable explanation of the existence
of the varied forms of life, including man's. Evolution can be
interpreted on a purely materialistic basis or as the result of purpose; this question, too, is philosophical.

Whatever is the philosophical status of the contrasting explanations of life, it is admitted that mechanism is the more useful
scientifically. Progress is continually being made in the explanation of biological facts in terms of physics and chemistry. An
example is the relation of ribonucleic and deoxyribonucleic acids,
the molecules of which have long spiral structures, and which
cohere on account of that structure to become units of viruses and
bacteria, and are factors in protein synthesis. Another example
is histone, a simple protein that has been found to be the chemical
key that locks and unlocks the activity of the genes which regulate
the processes of life. Biological facts are thus closely related to

the mechanical structure of the molecules of organic compounds. Where the experimentation on this subject will lead, we do not know.

Still farther away from the exact experimental basis and precise statements of the physical sciences is psychology, which means literally "science of the soul." It originally was taken to mean just that; but later it was realized that "soul" is too indefinite a term to be used in a science. Until the nineteenth century the field covered by the science was open only to speculation, but it gradually emerged as a modern science. Its outlooks and subject matters, however, are still controversial. Late in the nineteenth century Titchener's school of thought accepted introspection as a method, but insisted that an introspectionist must be properly trained. "Functional" psychology originated with James and Dewey about the beginning of the present century; its premise is that the proper method of psychology is the study of the functions of the nervous system. Behaviorism, introduced by Pavlov and in America by Watson, abandoned the introspective method. According to the behaviorists, if you have measured by an appropriate instrument the response of a person to anything done to him, you have learned something about him, more than if he had told you what his feelings were. Two other developments occurred at about the same time. Kulpe discovered that thinking itself, such as creative problem solving, is largely or entirely unconscious. Freud and others discovered that motives are largely unconscious. Thus psychology became and is largely a matter of measuring responses without reference to individual consciousness, although there are many controversies regarding methods and interpretations. It is now defined as the science of behavior. Whatever its philosophical status, psychology has many useful applications, including therapy and counseling, industrial psychology, human engineering, and applied social psychology.

In contrast to psychology, which is the study of the individual, the social sciences, the chief of which is sociology, deal with people in the mass. Methods are necessarily at the other extreme from those used in the physical sciences. Experimentation in the physical sense cannot well be used. In general its conclusions must be presented in the form of statistics. A perennial debate is conducted in the literature, between the social scientists and their critics, on whether sociology is really a science. Without going into the details of the argument, I shall summarize the main points involved as indicated in several papers on the subject. Its opponents claim: (1) that much of sociology is scientism or pseudo-science; (2) sociology deals with living and erratic man rather than with the definite and predictable matter of physics; (3) sociologists fall into a meaningless jargon which is accepted as scientific; and (4) sociologists claim to be able to reorganize society. Its supporters answer with some justice that: (1) sociologists are as aware of their limitations as are their opponents; (2) carefully conducted investigations have yielded valuable statistical information on the true state of society, often disproving popular misconceptions; and (3) their opponents confuse science in the narrow sense, as in physics, with science in the broader sense. Paul F. Schmidt puts the case thus:

[19]"But there is no reason why the social sciences should 'hamstring' themselves with the method of physics. No method has been presented to show intrinsic reasons why they cannot seek and progressively attain the goals of scientific method in the broad sense, although the path be slow and long. To deny this is to limit scientific method to the narrow sense. On the other hand, to reject the social sciences as sciences because one rejects the goals of scientific method in the broad sense begs the question, for it rejects science in toto. Such rejection cannot be argued on pain of contradicting onself. Thus I can see no inherent limitation on what subject matters can be treated scientifically in the broad sense, and I consider this lack of limitation a distinct merit of scientific method."

Sociology is the comprehensive social science. Others include economics, group psychology (although this may also be claimed by psychology), political science, anthropology, ethnology and philology.

Mathematics stands apart from the other sciences. It does not involve experimentation in the usual sense of the word. Some mathematicians hold that it is founded primarily on the experience of counting, but others disagree. A. N. Whitehead and Bertrand Russell spent many years in developing the idea that mathematics is founded on logic. That doctrine is opposed by a school led by L. J. Brouwer and Hermann Weyl, who maintain that logic is based on mathematics. The series of natural numbers is held to be given intuitively and to be the foundation of all mathematics. Whichever view is true, the data of mathematics depend neither on experiment nor observation in the usual sense. The Greeks studied mathematics for its own sake, and looked down upon those who studied it for its applications; but in many ways mathematics is the servant of the other sciences. Euclidean geometry was suf-

ficient for thousands of years, but the scientific developments of
the late nineteenth and the twentieth centuries called for the use
of different kinds of mathematics which were ready to be developed. As every schoolboy knows, certain axioms are assumed and
other truths are developed logically from them, explicitly in geometry and implicitly in other branches. Until these recent scientific
developments these axioms were considered to be unquestionable
truths, but in the nineteenth century several mathematicians found
that other geometries could equally well be devised with the use
of different axioms, some of which contradicted the conventional
ones. [20] "The recognition that an axiom is a statement which is
assumed, without any necessary belief in its truth, brought a great
relief to mathematicians; for intuition had led the older workers
to believe in the truth of many particular assertions which were
shown in the latter part of the nineteenth century to be false."

Standen says: [21] "There is one science, and only one, that is
actually true. That is mathematics. The others, from physics
downwards do not lead to known truth, but only to probable opinion." The criterion of truth here is that everybody agrees to it.
Standen continues: [22] "Scientists like to define their terms, but
mathematicians have realized that it is almost impossible to define
some of their very simplest conceptions. If you try to give a really
precise definition of a point, you get bogged down in a morass
of difficulties. Mathematicians can go in for very abstruse definitions of these ideas without arriving at satisfactory definitions.
Yet the strange thing is that although points and lines are excruci-
atingly hard to define, they are exceptionally easy to understand.
Even rather dumb pupils understand them at once. The stupider
members of a geometry class have all sorts of difficulties in understanding the propositions, and following the proofs, but these
difficulties never depend on any serious misunderstanding of what
a straight line is. They understand it as 'just straight—that's all',
and this utterly unscientific understanding is sufficient for complete
agreement."

Education of Scientists

Multitudes of papers have been written during the past few
years about education in science. The progress of the Russians
in science, especially in those sciences which are necessary to the
conduct of war and defense, has shaken the complacency of
American educators and students, insofar as they may have been
complacent. One educator reports that in his school the students

showed an increased interest in the physical sciences and a more serious view of them after the first Sputnik was launched. The following points are evident: (1) if education in science in the Soviet Union is actually more advanced than in America, it is forever too late and no crash program will enable us to overtake it; (2) more and better science instruction is needed, but science must not be taught to the neglect of other studies; (3) the long range program rather than the apparent immediate crisis should be kept in mind; and (4) science teaching must be oriented both toward the training of future scientists and their teachers and the inculcation of science-mindedness in as many people as possible.

The beginning of science teaching should consist of the awakening of the student, consciously and subconsciously, to the realization of something that proceeds independently of his own will and everybody's will, and to the knowledge that the behavior and rules of this outside something must be understood in order to live to the best advantage. Systematic contact with this reality in the form of observation and experiment is necessary, and it should begin at an earlier age than has been customary. Moreover, the conventional experiments by which high school science students are introduced to science do not interest them sufficiently. Progress is being attempted, however, in improving science teaching in both these respects. Children in the lower grades are taught elementary science by the use of textbooks adapted to their ages; they are taught to observe the world around them, and to perform experiments so simple that they do not know that they are experimenting. In many schools they participate in science fairs even in the second grade.

Books for young readers have been introduced recently entitled "Chemistry is Fun", "Painting is Fun", and so on through a list of arts and sciences. These titles have drawn some protests on the ground that too much attention has been given to fun and not enough to discipline. Without having read the books in question, I would say that the value of these books depends upon the meaning of "fun". If it means that the subject is interesting for the moment and that soon afterward the child's attention wanders off to something else, such books have little value. On the other hand, if "fun" means that the child enjoys the subject to the extent that he is willing to spend many hours on it day after day, such books provide a real benefit. When a student realizes that science is worth while, even fun, the rest of his scientific education is comparatively easy, and consists largely in learning many details

until he is ready for creative work. In other words, teaching that
anything worth while can be accomplished without work is dangerous, but teaching that work may be enjoyable is inspiring.

There are a number of motives that may guide a young person in the direction of scientific work. It may be a natural curiosity that leads him to experiment; it may be a habit of reading
and the inclusion of scientific subjects in his reading; it may be
enjoyment in learning long hard words; it may be acquaintance
with a scientist and acquisition of interest in his work. It may even
be hope of financial success, although it is questionable whether
this motive leads to the best scientific work; it often ends in dis-
appointment.

The limitations of science must also be learned. Introduction
to beauty, to the sense of history, and to religion, also begin with
an awakening, in some cases to a "rebirth", followed by the longer
but easier absorption of details. Of course one cannot attain maximum proficiency or maximum enjoyment in all these fields, but
if interest in science is not to some extent balanced by these other
interests, the student will have that one-sided picture of science
which is held by many scientists and science-minded people. Only
time will tell whether the present attempts to improve science
teaching will be successful.

Intellectual honesty has been discussed as a necessary virtue
of the scientist. The question arises whether the student acquires
intellectual honesty as a result of his training, especially if he is
studying science without the idea of practicing it. It is easy to be
overenthusiastic on this point. Standen quotes Stewart Cole: [23] "The
scientist is a man of integrity who trusts the basic laws of nature and
intelligence to lead him in the paths of truth. His loyalty to truth is
unquestioned; his capacity for patient and sacrificial inquiry is limited only by his powers of endurance; his devotion to the scientific
method is unwavering; his objective is the welfare of mankind;
and his discoveries, whether of medicine, mechanics, psychology,
or what not, are free possessions of democratic peoples." Standen
also quotes Professor Hendren, of the University of Georgia:
[24] "The success of the scientific method . . . is based upon an absolute
honesty of mind and love of truth. . . . Dogmatic prejudice, lying,
falsification of facts and data, and willful fallacious reasoning are
all out of harmony with the spirit of the sciences. It is writ large
on the history of science that the most heinous offense a man can
commit is to falsify his data and let his prejudice and his desires
color his reasoning. It has never been given to such a type of mind

to discover any of the important truths of nature. If a student leaves his course in physical science with the typical scientific point of view, he has obtained a moral value which will be a distinct asset and which will help to lead him to a happy and successful life." There is no question of the ideals that are outlined in the above expressions, but Standen voices doubts of their actual existence in the minds of most students: "If this is the effect of studying science in Georgia, it does not seem apparent in the rest of the population. Vast masses of people, all of whom had biology I in college, or at least 'Introductory Science' in high school, are not in the least distinguished, either by absolute honesty of mind, or by the absence of dogmatic prejudice, nor are they particularly happy or successful. How did this happen? Weren't they taught enough science? Or were they taught so badly that it didn't stick? Or can it possibly be that science—at any rate the kind of science they were taught—isn't all it is cracked up to be?" One possible answer would be that the teachers had not enough sense of humor, or even intellectual honesty, to teach also the limitations of science. Moreover, it must be admitted that the acquirement of intellectual honesty by a course in science is a slow process unless it is already present to a considerable degree or strongly inculcated by the precept and example of the teacher.

Standen goes on to say that students come out of a science course with one of three possible reactions: (1) they hated the course, and have depressing memories of cutting up dogfish and of "doing" experiments and trying to make the results come out right; (2) they found the subject interesting but the teacher dull, and nourish for the rest of their lives a wistful yearning to know more; and (3) they believe that science can solve all the problems of the universe. They learn cocksureness, not humility. The first essential to be taught by science is useful information. [25] "The more of this kind of information everybody has the better, but it is only those who dish it out that are fooled into thinking that it has anything to do with moral values and sacrificial inquiry." It must be admitted, however, that there are many science teachers to whom Standen's pessimistic assertions do not apply.

The first function of science instruction is to provide useful information about the world, and at the same time to instil the habit of careful observation. The tendency to begin science teaching at an earlier age and to improve methods of instruction should have these effects to an increased degree. Then, as instruction continues, the student is led to closer observation and more refined experiment. Intellectual honesty will come with that process, without bravado on the part of the scientific writer. When the student is ready for his own research work, he will have the intellectual honesty to be successful in that work. Naturally, the increase in intellectual honesty in a class of students is caused in part by the weeding out of those who are persistently dishonest. For those students who learn only a little science and then go to other occupations, we must conclude with Standen that their honesty will not have been much affected by their science courses. There are other ways of inculcating honesty that are equally effective or even more so.

As I have said, science is being taught at an earlier age than formerly. Clifton Fadiman has suggested that philosophy be taught in the elementary schools at the ages of 8 to 12. [26] "All I suggest he says, "is that somewhere along the route the child's fresh, active, inquiring mind be led to *wonder* about the universe, the world, his place in nature, and some of the statements that wise men have made about these matters." This plan should not interfere with early science instruction. It might even enhance it.

A subject that has not been considered is science as a cooperative effort or community project. That depends upon some other relations that will be considered later.

Chapter III

The Soul

T HE TITLE "The Scientist and the Soul" calls for a definition of the highly controversial word "soul". The word has been given many objective meanings throughout the history of philosophy and near-philosophy. The most primitive people thought of the soul as the breath, a manikin residing in the human body, a shadow, a reflection, or some other materialization. These beliefs all implied a mysterious something at the center of each person. Many believed that the soul was free to leave and reenter the body, and that it did so during sleep. Frazer's[1] *Golden Bough* and some later books describe such beliefs in detail. As thought became more sophisticated and philosophy developed, the grosser attributes were discarded. The soul was conceived of as fire, as air, or as finer atoms than those of material things. According to Plato the soul of the individual is immortal, uncreated, and an imperfect copy of the soul of the universe. Aristotle defined the soul as the final and efficient cause of the human body, but not immortal. The Hebrews had no philosophers, and their idea of the soul was less definite than any of those held by the Greeks. The early Christian conception of the soul, down to the third century, was that of a lighter, subtler material than our gross bodies. Origen and Tertullian shared this view in the third century. Later St. Augustine combined the Christian and Aristotelian views, and taught the simple, immaterial, and spiritual nature of the soul. Augustine's view was incorporated into scholastic philosophy and into Christian theology. According to this and some of the earlier conceptions the soul in regarded as immortal; that is, it persists as some kind of entity after the body is dead. To that extent the soul, although called "spiritual", is in a way, objective in our thoughts.

Early in the seventeenth century Descartes developed a new philosophy which began: "I think, therefore I am." He did not mention the soul in that connection; but the soul in the sense in which it is frequently used and will be used in this discourse is the

29

subject of "am". Descartes thus laid the ground for some modern conceptions. Without going into the intricacies of philosophy, it may be said that there are three general systems of belief about the relation of the "soul" to the body: (1) idealism, in which the soul is the primary entity, and all the material world is derived from it; (2) Materialism, naturalism, positivism, and dynamism, in which the physical world is primary and the soul can be disregarded or reduced to a material basis; and (3) dualism, according to which both soul and matter exist, independently of each other but with some sort of relation between them. The nineteenth century saw the development of modern idealism from Descartes through Kant, Fichte, Hegel, and a number of their followers. It came as a reaction to the materialism based on the scientific discoveries of the preceding period. Science has been influenced to some extent by idealism, but many scientist accept critical naturalism, which is more moderate than materialism. Another philosophy that fluorished in the early twentieth century is pragmatism, the main tenet of which is, stated roughly, that a belief is true if it works. That is, problems that have no bearing on possible action do not exist. Another philosophy, now popular in Europe and given some attention in America, is existentialism.

The professional philosopher, having embarked upon a particular system of thought, must for the sake of consistency pursue it to the bitter end. When the edges of his system become fuzzy he may reach conclusions that are satisfactory to him but are pounced upon by his fellow philosophers. Then he may write another book either elaborating or modifying his original views, and so on. The amateur philosopher, and most of us are amateur philosophers, is much freer than the professional. in the choice of a belief, as he is not bound by the need of consistency. He may be a little of a materialist, a little of an idealist, a little of a dualist, and may wander in and out of a number of philosophies. In doing so he may be a sort of a pragmatist, but we are warned that pragmatism, like the others, may not be carried too far. If I pay more attention to existentialism than to others, it does not mean that I am a consistent existentialist, but that some of its advocates present pictures that may be enlightening.

Existentialism has been said to be not so much a philosophy as a label for several widely different revolts against traditional philosophies, but even this statement has been denied by some of its advocates. Kaufmann puts it thus: [2] "The refusal to belong to any school of thought, the repudiation of the adequacy of any body of

beliefs whatever, and especially of systems, and a marked dissatisfaction with traditional philosophy as superficial, academic, and
remote from life—that is the heart of existentialism. Existentialism
is a timeless sensibility that can be discerned here and there in the
past; but it is only in recent times that it has hardened into a sus-
tained protest and preoccupation." The soul and other conceptions
were in the older philosophies something to be thought about and
they became abstractions; the thinker was not considered.
Descartes' announcement "I think, therefore I am" was revolutionary; but his method of approach has since been discounted.
One hypothesis has been advanced that the thoughts are the
thinkers. The existentialists, however, at least those with whom
we shall be concerned, go farther back. The philosophy begins
with "I am;" here I am in the present situation, aware of many
things around me, of my body, and of the past. The ultimate reality is not the system of facts leading to the concept of the outer
world in which science operates or of beliefs leading to the concept
of the soul, but simply the present moment as experienced. The
existentialist authors who will be discussed do not use the word
"soul" in this connection; but there is justification for its use as
meaning the fundamental entity, the "I", and it will be so used.

The first hurdle to be mounted by any form of existentialism
is solipsism, which is the conclusion that everything in the world
consists of *my* ideas. You and the material world exist only in my
thought. Solipsism is well dramatized in *Alice in Wonderland*,
where Alice was told by the Red King that she existed only in
his dream and would cease to exist if he awoke. Philosophers
have made various further assumptions to escape this trap. One is
the independent assumption of an outside world (which to some
extent denies idealism) and another is the assumption of the existence of other personalities.

The existence of other personalities may seem so obvious and
so generally realized that it is unworthy of mention; but philosophy, which sometimes lags thousands of years behind human life
and experience, did not give it expression until fairly recently. In
1923 Martin Buber published a book entitled *I and Thou,* in
German. It attracted little attention at first and was slow to penetrate world thinking. The first English translation was published
in 1937, and translations have been made into several other languages. Dag Hammersköld, at the time of his death, was at work
on a Swedish translation. Buber is considered one of the existentialists, but his work is also regarded as a step beyond existential-

ism. The theme of "I and Thou" is that each of us has two outlooks on the world, namely the I—it and the I—thou. I—it is one's relation to any of the *things* of the world; one's relation to any other person is both I—it and I—thou. As an "it" you are simply a part of my environment; you may be of possible use to me, as something that supplies me with food, with comfort, with an opportunity for material success; on the other hand, you may be in my way and even an enemy. As a "thou", however, you are a creature like me, sharing my interests and my ideas and receiving my empathy and cooperation. (The translators of Buber and of Heim use the word "thou" because it more nearly expresses the German "du," and I have used it accordingly.)

Buber's translator says: [3] "To the reader who finds the meaning (of Buber's text) obscure at first reading, we may only say that the book "I and Thou" is indeed a poem." I may add that I find many things obscure even after several readings, and I am willing to accept it as a poem rather than as formal philosophy. Possibly the following quotation will serve as a summary of the philosophy: [4] "The world of *It* is set in the context of space and time. The world of *Thou* is not set in the context of either of these. The particular *Thou,* after the relational event has run its course, is bound to become an *It.* The particular *It,* the relational event, may become a *Thou.* . . . Without *It* man cannot live. But he who lives with *It* alone is not a man."

Karl Heim, German theologian and philosopher, has amplified and clarified the fundamental statements of existentialism and Buber's I—it and I—thou conceptions. The first existentialist proposition according to Heim is: [5] "I stand with respect to certain quite definite, concrete, and easily distinguishable and circumscribable contents of the objective world of experience in the relation which we express with the word 'my.' . . . The second proposition is that I cannot change that relation. I can imagine being someone else; but I am indissolubly bound to my own situation. This necessity is not a logical one, like 'twice two is four;' nor is it a physical one. It cannot be objectivized. This reality lies outside the three-dimensional plane."

A significant paragraph by Heim on the I—thou concept reads: "The picture of the whole world which I necessarily form for myself from this central vantage point is all at once disturbed and called in question by the coming of a second ego which is as irremovably and unchangeably welded to another position as I am to mine. From this arises a world that has two centers and which logically can have only one center. The non-objective seeing-point is located in two positions, yet it *can* be located in only one position and can be only one seeing-point. Two 'egos' is an impossible expression even from the linguistic point of view. The word 'ego' can be used only in the singular; for otherwise it loses its subjective character and becomes an object possessing number like other objects. And we are forced to use 'ego' in the plural We are so accustomed to this paradoxical situation that in everyday life we are already scarcely aware of the contradiction which it involves."

The problem is but little further complicated by the presence of not only one "thou" but of millions of others with which the ego may have actual or possible relations. Heim continues: "Previously, in the period of idealism, only one person sat in the darkened auditorium and watched the cosmic drama unfolding on the brightly lighted stage of objective reality. Now the darkened auditorium is filled and contains many persons; they cannot indeed see one another but each of them is nevertheless aware of the presence of his neighbor. They push each other this way and that. Each one lays claim to the one favored position in the middle of the stalls exactly opposite the middle of the stage. . . . And yet, although each one tries to exclude and invalidate the other, they have need of each other and cannot exist without each other."

In order to give the picture of the "I—thou" relations, Heim uses the concept of an additional dimension of reality. A number of authors, including philosophers, theologians, and scientists, have employed the concept of a dimension of existence in addition to the three to which we are accustomed; but Heim takes the idea more seriously. A digression to explain the idea of additional dimensions may be in order here.

On a common-sense basis we live in a world of three dimensions. Late in the nineteenth century some mathematicians considered the idea of additional dimensions, in purely mathematical terms. During the present century, however, the work of Einstein and others has shown that four dimensions of space-time are necessary to account for observed phenomena of nature, and there are suggestions of the necessity for more than four. Although the applicability of time as a fourth dimension can be easily imagined, the concept becomes increasingly necessary in dealing with high velocities, such as those comparable with the velocity of light. Seven dimensions are needed for some of the most advanced work on nucleonics.

Long before the advent of the theory of relativity, attempts

had been made to picture life as it would be in a world of more or
fewer dimensions than three. As early as 1884 a book entitled
[6] "Flatland" by Edward Abbott was published. The book describes
a race of people living in Flatland, which has only two dimensions,
unaware of anything outside the only plane in which they lived, and
unable to move off its surface. The assumed narrator, A Square (I
have wondered whether the much more recent slang use of "square"
was to any extent inspired by this book) relates a dream in which
he visited Lineland, a country of only one dimension, and fails
utterly to give its king an idea of a second dimension. Later he is
visited by an inhabitant of the three-dimensional world, who had
the form of a sphere (all the characters in the book have simple
geometric forms). The sphere-man can be recognized by Mr.
Square only when he is in the latter's plane. As the three-dimensional man passes through that plane, he first appears as a point,
then as an ever-widening circle until a maximum size is reached,
then as a narrowing circle, as a point again, and then disappears. Finally the visitor lifts Mr. Square out of the plane to see
Flatland as a surface. A Square loses favor with his visitor, however, by his persistent inquiries about a fourth dimension, and is
pushed back into the Flatland plane. For his attempts to convince
the other Flatlanders of the existence of a third dimension, he is
imprisoned—in a two-dimensional jail of course; he is not rescued
by the visiting sphere with whom he had quarreled. The story is
in part a satire on society; but its chief implication is that all our
experience is in three dimensions, and happenings in an additional
dimension would be very puzzling to us. At the time of its publication the book did not attract the attention it deserved, and it was
not until mathematicians paid attention to the implications of
additional dimensions that it became popular.

   Heim does not use the word "dimension" as much as "space":
"I—thou" and the "I—it" spaces are spaces containing the additional dimension of the same name, in addition to the ordinary
dimensions. This term, also, has been used by others to a slight
extent with a meaning suggesting the one used by Heim. "Conquest
of inner space" is an example. Heim nowhere mentions an "it—it"
space or dimension. Many scientists and naturalistic philosophers
would insist that that could be the only real space. But Heim's
spaces are metaphysical, not scientific, and are in accord with the
idea that science is a human activity.

   A number of scientists, apparently largely physicists rather
than psychologists, have discussed the "inner picture" and the

"outer picture" of knowledge. Heim continues: [7] "The difference between these two aspects becomes clearest to me in relation with 'my' own body. I can look at my body from the outside. I can look at it in the mirror, in order to have the view of it which other people receive who look at it from without. If I happen to be a doctor or a scientist myself, I can examine parts of my body anatomically, I can carry out a blood test and subject the specimen to chemical analysis. I can X-ray my lung and so arrive at the most exact possible diagnosis. In all this I am concerned with forming an 'outside picture'. I join in the work of examining my body, but, in general, other people, and particularly specialists, who can look closely at every part of it under the magnifying glass as disinterested spectators, are far better qualified for this than I am. But this forming of an 'outer picture' of me reaches a quite definite limit at which the competence of my fellow human beings ceases, no matter how earnestly they may strive to advance further. There is an innermost area to which I myself alone have direct access, and at which nobody else can look. I alone know what I suffer and what joys I experience. Others may endeavor, by means of their imagination, to put themselves in my place and to share in my joys and sorrows. Yet anyone who does not know from his own experience the pangs of hunger, for example or what it means to have toothache or migraine, can indeed very accurately analyze the nervous disturbances which these pains cause, but he has no knowledge whatsoever of the 'inside picture' of these processes. None of us can look directly into the sphere of consciousness of another. Nor can I see into the world-picture in which reality is mirrored in your consciousness, and, what constitutes a still greater obstacle to mutual comprehension, I cannot even see into the memories, conceptions, and thoughts which arise in your mind or into the joys which exalt your soul, or the pains which inwardly torment and convulse you."

These statements are not to be taken to mean that the "I" can be an object of direct experience. William James, in the conclusion of his classic chapter on the I and the Me, says: [8] "In a sense, then, it may be truly said that, in one person at least, the 'Self of selves', when carefully examined, is found to consist mainly of the collection of those peculiar motions in the head or between the head and throat. I do not for a moment say that this is *all* it consists of, but I fully realize how desperately hard is introspection in this field. But I feel quite sure that these cephalic motions are the portions of my innermost self of which I am most intimately aware. If the dim portions which I cannot define should prove to be like unto these distinct portions in me, and I am like other men, it could follow that our entire field of spiritual activity, or what passes by that name is really a feeling of bodily activities whose exact nature is by most men overlooked."

No later observations, experiments, or speculation on the subject have made it any clearer; it remains evident that the I, the ego, or as I have called it, the soul, cannot be found in the field of direct experience. But still, I know that I am. We may then call the idea of the existence of the I, the I-hypothesis. Also, since I can have no direct experience of you, let us say that my awareness of you is the you-hypothesis. Since, however, the you-hypothesis depends upon the I-hypothesis, we may combine them into the I-you-hypothesis. The term "social hypothesis" has been used by at least one author, and it is substantially the same concept. This hypothesis cannot be proved by any manner of experimentation, but it works. Bridgman says on this subject that [9] "instead of saying I am conscious I should say I am 'mescious'. . . . The same scheme could be adopted in speaking of others. I can say that you are 'youscious'. I can also say that only you are 'youscious'. Similarly I can invent the word 'hescious', but 'wescious' or 'theyscious' would make no sense."

To some persons the viewpoint which has been discussed is too obvious to be considered; to others it is pure nonsense. The second group includes some scientists, especially psychologists of the behavioristic school. Their goal is to eliminate the "inner picture" altogether. One psychologist has discussed the evolution of consciousness; others have called consciousness an "epiphenomenon", which means "an accompaniment of brain processes, dominated by them but incapable of exerting any influence upon them"; some have called it simply "a relation". To these views I can reply with the existentialists, that all the externals accompanying consciousness may be the result of evolution, but *I* am not; I know that I am neither an epiphenomenon nor a relation. A young behaviorist once told me that the aim of behaviorism is to reduce the individuality of persons to the individuality of grains of sand; but I know that *my* individuality is something more than that of a grain of sand. Some sociologists have called the ego "nothing;" an existentialist has written several volumes about this "nothing." In their efforts to eliminate the "soul" or "ego" altogether, what these psychologists have accomplished is to confess the limitations of their science. Literally their difficulty is that they forget themselves.

Not all scientists, however, ignore the "inner picture;" but those who have expressed their views are not psychologists but physicists. Among the eminent physicists who have written about the human aspects of science are Bridgman, Eddington, and Jeans. Bridgman in a recent book deals with the relationship between the inner and outer pictures and suggests a possible method of reconciling them. He says: [10] "The outer picture of human behavior becomes more and more amplified and sharpened with the progress of psychology. It is becoming increasingly evident that every thought or action is accompanied by definite molecular configurations in a number of locations. The behaviorist would be satisfied if he could know these configurations for any mental situation, and is not concerned to the slightest extent with the inner picture.

Parenthetically it may be said regarding these "molecular configurations" that it is considered practically proved that memory is a process of storing in the body all the impressions received through the senses in such a shape that they can be recalled for examination at any time. In other words, the human brain is very much like a man-made computer but very much more complex. The process has been considered a building-up of brain cellstructure; but recently the idea has gained ground that the process is on the molecular level rather than on the cellular. One evident reason for the newer belief is the complexity of the process. When I consider the numerous details of an instant of my life which I remember, including the colors of various objects around me, the direction in which I was going, sometimes my emotional attitude at the time, though admitting that I have forgotten some of the details and many of my experiences, I marvel at the number of separate units and the number of molecules that must have been involved; it must have been astronomical. Someone has truly said that the human personality is more wonderful than the greatest nebula.

Bridgman, like other scientists, is not content with this outer picture. He imagines "a record kept in two parallel columns. In one column is a complete analysis of my brain as a function of time. . . . This atomic analysis column will have to be made by someone else. Paralleling the atomic analysis column is a column which I myself make, in which I record all my conscious activity, including in particular a record of the occasions when I recognize that I am conscious. If that record is carried through, . . . then I have a method for getting my private consciousness, with which I started, onto a completely public level. . . . The thesis of atomic analysis now enables a meaning to be given to the 'inaccessible event', a combination of words from which one point of view is self-contradictory." Bridgman admits that such a procedure is highly theoretical and impracticable. If there were such a method of "atomic analysis" that could be performed without killing the subject, the experiment would not be feasible, even if we had much more advanced knowledge than we do, mainly because the investigation and recording would take longer than the events themselves, and would therefore lag in increasing periods of times behind them.

Several authors have called attention to the great diversity in human behavior, caused simply by the great diversity in physical factors involved. The individuality we have been discussing, however, involves differences of another order of magnitude. Some examples in amplification of Heim's discussion may be useful here. For instance, I do not know that the red you see in a particular rose is the same red that I see. In one type of color blindness the subject cannot distinguish red from green. The question arose among psychologists as to whether the color seen was red or green. [11] Finally a case occurred (one of a very few such cases) in which a woman was color blind in one eye only. It was easily discerned that the color that she saw with the affected eye was red. But even such a case does not get to the heart of the problem under consideration. There was still no way of determining whether the red that she saw was the same that another person would see.

One of the best examples of the impossibility of communicating sensations is the sense of direction. It has been said that about one-third of all people have no sense of direction, and will not know what any discussion of this sense is about. Roughly another third have a sense of direction that is easily upset and therefore unreliable. In another third the sense is well developed, though never perfect. Each person with a sense of direction has a set of mental coordinates on which his surroundings are laid out independently of the position of his body. "North", for instance is conceived of as a definite direction on the reference axes. The sense is more or less capable of improvement by training, but can be easily "thrown off" by traveling along a winding road or sleeping on a train. Sometimes when one enters a building that is very similar to another building that is familiar to him he will find himself applying the same directional pattern as that of the building remembered. Persons with a sense of direction will extend it to their mental maps. For instance, most of my mental maps are consistent with my general set of coordinates; however, probably because I was sitting in the wrong direction when I first studied the map of Africa, Asia, and some parts of Southern Europe those countries were upside down from my general directions, and though I have many times tried to put them in their proper mental places, Palestine and some parts of Africa have persisted in being upside down. On a practical basis, the confusion is of no consequence, and is only slightly annoying when I picture those countries when reading of events which happen there. A sense of direction has only a limited practical value, because it can be so easily confused. An aviator can fly for thousands of miles and light at the right spot, simply because he relies on his instruments and not on his sense of direction. In *The Spirit of St. Louis,* Lindbergh relates that after arriving over Ireland, he turned back over the Atlantic, unwittingly depending upon his sense of direction rather than the instruments. He then corrected his course after reading the instruments. Some of us remember "Wrong-Way" Corrigan, who left New York to go to Washington, but eventually found himself off the coast of Ireland. I do not remember his explanation, but it is easy to suppose that he was depending upon his sense of direction. Unreliable as that sense is in present human experience, the possibility occurs that it is a remnant of a more reliable sense that guided our remote ancestors as it now guides birds in their migrations. That, however is only speculation; the point of this discussion is the utterly individual character of sensations. I do not see how the sense of direction could be investigated in Bridgman's parallel self-examination process.

Some years ago I read a poem whose author and source I do not remember. The first two lines were:

> "Each one a world, to other worlds unknown,
> Revolves in a tiny circle of its own."

This individuality of sensation affects our thinking and is a barrier to our understanding of each other. Bridgman reports a seminar in which representatives of various sciences participated, and in which[12] "the discussion was centered around a few concepts of social importance, such as 'community', 'morality', 'justification', and 'rights'. . . . The one outstanding impression that I got from the experience was of the unfathomed complexity of the verbal background of each one of us and the fact that no two backgrounds were alike. . . . In some cases even prolonged effort did not avail to secure agreement or to isolate the sources of disagreement." He suggests the possibility of minimizing these differences by education, but still the differences must be at least partly individual as well as cultural. In fact, every word we use has individual emotional connotations from experience. In spite of all these individual differences, people do have ideas understandable to each other and are able to cooperate to a large extent. Mathematics is an illustration of mutually understandable concepts.

Heim provides a pictorial representation of the I—thou and I—it relationships. Like all such pictures, it has its limitations and should not be pursued too closely, but it helps to illustrate the relations. It is part of the "I—thou" idea that we can communicate only through the medium of the objective world. The part of the objective world by which we communicate is represented as an opaque wall separating two cells in a prison.[13] "Neither of the two prisoners can see into the other one's cell. Neither knows what the inside of the other's cell looks like. And so each one sees only one side of the party wall which separates the two cells. And yet it is one and the same wall and is part of both cells, even though it presents a different side to each of the two prisoners. It is because of this that the party wall serves the two lonely captives as an invaluable medium for communicating with each other." The analogy is then modified by assuming that the medium of communication does not consist of solid material, but of a soft mass of wax so thin that the prisoner can produce in it an "impression" which then becomes visible in the next cell as a corresponding "expression". In the discussion so far only two prisoners are concerned. Taking into account the existence of many more than two persons, the picture becomes more complicated. "The number of solitary prisoners has greatly increased. And yet it is the same party wall which forms the medium, common to them all, through which they affect one another."

Another feature of the existentialist philosophy is the recognition of the "now". Existence is like a mower running through a field, cutting down the future and making it into a dead past. Thus the "I" or "thou" of the immediate present becomes an "it" of a moment ago. The mower may not be an exact symbol, because it emphasizes the destructive aspect of existence but not the constructive.

As was noted in the discussion of Buber's philosophy, to any person another may be an "it" or a "thou" and is usually both. The following quotation from Toynbee may serve to introduce this subject:[14] "When a self is yearning in this self-devoting way, it is treating the object of its yearning, not as an 'it' which is fair game, but as a 'thee' who is sacrosanct because this 'thou' is another self.

In feeling a desire of the self-devoting kind, the loving self is treating everything in the Universe as a society of selves like itself; in feeling a desire of the self-centered kind, it is treating everything outside itself as a soulless set of waves and particles. It is a fact of human experience that every human self can and does have desires of these two different kinds, and that the two are not only different but are at the opposite poles of the spiritual gamut. Here we have a further manifestation of the paradoxical union, in human nature, of opposites that conflict yet are inseparable. And the unceasing struggle which is an unescapable accompaniment of human life in This World is, in truth, a struggle to extinguish our self-centered desires at whatever the price may be. The price turns out to be suffering in an extreme degree."

The imaginary projection of one's own consciousness into another being is called "empathy". It is also expressed as "putting yourself in another's place" and leads to "doing unto others as you would that they should do unto you". An example of empathy is the affirmative answer to the question, "Are _____ people?" where the blank means Negroes, Russians, Chinese, children, or whoever is under discussion. Empathy is at its highest degree in the family, and the word "love" is universally accepted as appropriate in that situation. "Love" as it is used in the New Testament has the same implication, and it is a pity that there is not another acceptable term, on account of the sentimentalized connotation generally given to "love".

The killing of another person, whether as murder or legally as in war and capital punishment, means the abandonment of the "thou" attitude. The victim is an "it" who is not wanted, either as an "it" or a "thou". Long after a war, however, participants on both sides may meet and talk over their experiences with mutual interest. In the Crusades and other religious wars, the "heathen" or other opponents were things which should be exterminated unless they became converted into people. The early Spanish conquerors of America who converted Indians and then killed them had a false idea of conversion; the Indians were still "its".

Games provide interesting illustrations of the dual nature of human relations. In games in which the contest is directly between persons, in checkers and chess as in war, the opponent is only an "it". One tries to predict and forestall the action of the other, and although he tries to think what the other would do under the particular circumstances, it is simply in relation to his own success. But, after they finish the game, they may discuss it. In considering possible plays they might have made, they are thinking of each other as fellow creatures. In games in which each player contends directly with nature instead of an opponent, as in golf, the "it" relation while playing does not necessarily hold.

The field of business is an interesting example of the interplay of the two ways of regarding others. Success in business depends on the sales made to others as "its". On the other hand, the ideal of business is service; that is, one is in business because he can furnish his customers with things they want. Therefore his success depends upon his putting himself in his customer's place to determine what he wants, or at least to pretend to. All advertising consists of building up an image in the prospective customer's mind of something greatly desirable. The emphasis on "you" in radio and television commercials is an example; for instance: "This is what you want for *your* car." Business people vary greatly in this respect. Some do not bother about the "you"; dealings are entirely impersonal; many more are courteous but with gain almost exclusively in mind; but there are a few who, you feel, are really interested in serving you.

Closely related to the subject of business is that of labor relations. Those relations are almost altogether "I—it". To the employer, his employees are "hands", to them he is the "boss". No matter how their relations are settled, whether by compromise or strike, or however, those distinctions still hold. Business men fear they will lose something if they consider the employees as persons or "souls"; workers do not want to recognize the "boss" as a fellow-being. Just a few labor questions have been settled on the basis of mutual recognition, the only permanently satisfactory settlement. No amount of negotiation leads to peace so long as they remain in the category of enemies.

Interest in any one of a number of activities can be a unifying factor and contribute to the I—you relationship; besides those mentioned are welfare work, religion, education, and many others. The most unifying pursuit of all is science. Students of science tend to forget their differences in other fields. Killian has said: [15]"The concepts of science cross all national and ideological boundaries. It is the one language understood the world around. It is a means to common understanding and joint action. In response to these benign characteristics of science, we have seen successful patterns of cooperation between nations with deep ideological differences. . . . The professional discourse among Soviet and American scientists, now fortunately extended beyond the domain of atomic science, is a dialogue of hope in the tense pessimism of the cold war. It should be encouraged by both nations, as should the whole array of cultural relations." Science is a community activity. Pollard, in his book *Physicist and Christian,* stresses the importance of the scientific community in the progress of science, and shows how the scientific spirit grows out of the scientific community. That subject will be considered later in more detail.

Some essentials of the various sciences were discussed in the preceding chapter. The subjects of all these sciences, even mathematics, are in the it-world. History could be added to that list if it were only a study of external events; it is a science to the extent to which scientific methods are used in its study but history which treats people merely as "its" would be a dull subject indeed. What makes good history interesting is its presentation of the individuals and groups who fill its pages, just as fiction is thus made interesting.

Important as the sciences are as part of education, the humanities are also essential; that is, ancient and modern literature, and the language instruction which is necessary to appreciate it. Also, these subjects are primarily concerned with the I—you relation, and should not be neglected.

It can be said that the purpose of religion is to make the "I—thou" relation supreme; as God loves us, so should we love each other. In the Calvinistic and similar theologies, however, there are the unredeemed who, as "its", are consigned to eternal torment. That attitude, however, if it was ever held to that extreme, is disappearing. Toleration in the true sense is the extension of the "I—thou" attitude.

In the preceding chapter intellectual honesty was emphasized as the chief virtue of the scientist as a scientist. According to the foregoing, "love" is the chief virtue of anyone, scientist or not. We cannot say that either is the more important, because they do not conflict. A difference between the applications of the two is that intellectual honesty is demanded of the scientist at the beginning, while love does not come full-blown; it is difficult to achieve, partly on account of physical restrictions and partly on account of the non-physical hindrances that have been discussed. Are the two virtues antagonistic, complementary, or independent, or is one included in the other or a necessary consequence of the other? Two nations may be imagined, one with intellectual honesty but without love, and the other with love but without intellectual honesty. The former could attain high material standards, but its people could be cruel, hostile to each other, and dishonest in the

ordinary sense of the word. They could unite in spite of differences
only when they knew it was necessary. The people of the other
nation might be full of love and sympathy for each other, but have
little knowledge of the material world such as that given by
science, and would go bumbling about trying to do good but
accomplishing nothing in the conquest of disease or other ills.
Such a nation might have hospitals and all sorts of welfare plans,
but they would be ineffective on account of lack of scientific knowledge. The latter condition was approached in medieval times, but
not so simply as I have indicated. Our modern civilization is based
on the presence of both virtues, although both are far less prevalent than they should be. Our schools, our hospitals, our facilities
for travel and culture, and other elements of our civilization result
from a combination of the scientific and altruistic spirits, although
both are applied only imperfectly. Of course much of our business
and other activities are conducted with an assumed altruism which
goes as far as courtesy but has "enlightened selfishness" as its basis.

Can an "I—thou" relationship exist between persons who are
not contemporary? The answer is "yes", because the relation is
not necessarily mutual. The mother thinks of her child as a "thou"
although the child does not reciprocate. I can read the work of an
author who lived a thousand years ago and enter into his thoughts;
I think of him as a person like me.

So far only relations between human beings have been discussed. The question naturally arises whether there can be an I—
thou relation between a person and an animal. On this subject,
Buber says: [16]"An animal's eyes have the power to speak a great
language. Independently, without needing cooperation of sounds
and gestures, most forcibly when they rely wholly on their glance,
the eyes express the mystery in its natural prison, the anxiety of
becoming. This condition of the mystery is known only by the
animal, it alone can disclose it to us—and this condition only lets
itself be disclosed, not fully revealed. The language in which
it is uttered is what it says—anxiety, the movement of the creature
between the realms of vegetable security and spiritual venture.
This language is the stammering of nature at the first touch of
spirit, before it yields to spirit's cosmic venture that we call man.
But no speech will ever repeat what that stammering knows and
can proclaim.

"Sometimes I look into a cat's eyes. The domesticated animal
has not as it were received from us (as we sometimes imagine) the
gift of the truly 'speaking' glance, but only—at the price of its

primitive disinterestedness—the capacity to turn its glance to us prodigious beings. . . . But with this capacity there enters the glance, in its dawn and continuing in its rising, a·quality of amusement and of inquiry that is wholly lacking in the original glance with all its anxiety. The beginning of this cat's glance, lighting up under the touch of my glance, indisputably questioned me: 'Is it possible that you think of me? Do you really not just want me to have fun? Do I concern you? Do I exist in your sight? Do I really exist? What is it that comes from you? What is it that surrounds me? What is it that comes to me? What is it?' ('It' is here a transcription for a word, that we do not have, denoting self without the ego; and by 'it' is to be imagined the streaming human glance in the total reality of its power to enter into relation). The animal's glance, speech of disquietude, rose in its greatness—and set at once. My own glance was certainly more lasting; but it was no longer the streaming human glance." I am assured by a longtime owner of a pet cat that Buber has very well expressed her thoughts. We have not been able to get the cat's comments.

W. G. Pollard relates another instance. His son had acquired a pet mouse, which he named Stewart. The mouse became quite tame and would run up and down the boy's body and over the surroundings. The boy was much interested in the mouse, but the interest usually was that directed toward an "it". [17] "Every now and then, however, when my son was playing with Stewart something different would take place. It might be when the mouse, having run down his arm, would stop still in the palm of his hand and look at him. For a moment then these two totally different beings, with no means whatever of communicating with each other, would simply face each other, confronting each other across the void. My son, who a moment before had been laughing with delight over the antics of the mouse, would in such a moment become very still and a profoundly solemn look would come over his face. For just a moment these two beings would stare at each other as though to say, 'Who are you? What is the mystery of existence like for you? Do you care about me? Do you *know* me?' Such a moment would never last very long; one or the other would soon break it up and they would be playing again as before. But who can doubt that in that moment something very different from the subject-object relationship had occurred? These two creatures were meeting each other; two unique beings confronting each other across the void of non-being. In that moment neither one was experiencing, observing, enjoying, or fearing the other. Neither was merely the other's object. The new dimension of the *I and Thou* was revealed in it."

As we descend in the scale of the animal kingdom the attention paid to the I—thou relation decreases, but it differs among individuals. Most of us do not wish to do unnecessary harm to lower animals; but that reluctance disappears when the creature is likely to cause us harm. Many people in India will not harm any animal, because they believe that the animals embody deceased persons, one of whom may be an ancestor. There are persons of other faiths, however, who are filled with reverence for life to the extent that they would not harm a mosquito.

Buber extends this I—thou consciousness to a tree. His concluding paragraphs read: [18]"The tree is no impression, no play of my imagination, no value depending upon my mood; but it is bodied over against me and has to do with me, as I with it—only in a different way. Let no attempt be made to sap the strength from the meaning of the relation: the relation is mutual.

"The tree will have a consciousness, then, similar to our own? Of that I have no experience. But do you wish, through seeming to succeed in it with yourself, once again to disintegrate that which cannot be disintegrated? I encounter no soul or dryad of the tree, but the tree itself." Heim concludes, as Buber suggests here, that consciousness may exist, not only in the lowest forms of life, but even in inanimate objects.

Having attempted an explanation of the word "soul" as used in this book, we shall return to the subject of science, first relating its history as a struggle against strangulation or retardation by religious and pseudo-religious forces, and then consider what effect that development and triumph had on religion, and especially on Protestant Christianity. I have studiously avoided references to religion in this chapter, and it has been fairly easy to do so because Heim has logically separated the *thou* of other persons from the *Thou* of religion. The extension of this philosophy to religion will be discussed later.

Chapter IV

Science's Struggle
For Existence

K NOWLEDGE IS CUMULATIVE. In that respect it differs from other
human mental activities. Physically, wealth is cumulative,
and the debris left by human beings is cumulative. Civilization is
usually cumulative because the acquisition of knowledge is an
important activity of civilization. Philosophy, ethics, esthetics, and
religion are only to a slight extent cumulative, because each individual must largely begin afresh. Although the individual may be
awakened to new spheres of beauty or goodness as he develops, he
can pass them on only to a limited degree. The highest ideals of
ethics were enunciated less than two thousand years ago. It is
barely possible to imagine still higher standards, but in practice
we have not caught up with those we have. The history of religion,
whether considered apart from or in conjunction with ethics, shows
little progressive development. A few religious thinkers disagree
with that statement but apparently they are thinking of cumula-
tiveness as a possibility and agree that it has not occurred in fact.
History is cumulative in its very nature because each generation has
learned something which can be called positively established
and has put it into a form which the next generation can absorb
without going through the entire learning process again. Occasionally some of this positive knowledge proves to be wrong; but
it is only a small part of the whole and the error can be corrected.

Inventions were a feature of the early history of mankind but
they were made gradually and often at widely separated intervals.
Examples are the use of fire, agriculture, domestication of animals,
the wheel, language, and writing. Every invention may presuppose
some rudimentary science; but one of the barriers to more rapid
progress in invention was the absence of objective thinking.
Primitive man was conscious of the impact of other people on him;
therefore he thought of the material world as composed of beings

like himself. He was benefited or hurt by what people or animals did to him. Therefore when something happened to him and no human agent was visible, he invented one. Every place and every object was either a sort of person in itself or the tool of one. In the full development of this belief, for instance in Canaan every place had its baal, and in Greece and Rome every spring had its naiad, every hill had its oread, and every wood had its dryad, and at a more advanced stage every nation had its god. These beings could help or harm, and just as human enemies might be propitiated by presents and other signs of respect, so might these invisible beings. Thus arose the ideas of sacredness, taboo, and worship. The stars were not regarded as objects in the sky, distant and neutral to any human consideration, but rather as demons who could affect human beings beneficially or adversely. Thus the pseudo-science of astrology arose. In Babylonia at least, the progress of astronomy was furthered as much by astrology as by observation of the progress of the seasons.

According to Sarton, [1]"The total evolution which prepared the dawn of science must have taken tens of thousands of years. By the beginning of the third millenium before Christ it was already complete in at least two countries, Mesopotamia and Egypt, and possibly in two others, India and China. The people of Mesopotamia and Egypt had then attained a high degree of culture including the use of writing and a fair amount of mathematical, astronomical, and medical knowledge. ". . . As early as the middle of the fourth millenium B. C. the Egyptians were acquainted with a decimal system of numbers. . . . By the middle of the following millenium Sumerians had developed a highly technical system of accounting. The astronomical knowledge of these people was equally remarkable. The Egyptian calendar of 365 days was established in 4241 B. C. Babylonians accumulated planetary observations for astrological purposes; e. g. their elaborate observations of Venus go back to the twentieth century. They compiled lists of stars and were soon able to predict eclipses."

Medicine may be considered the first experimental science, because even the first medicine men must have been guided by knowledge of various herbs and other medications. But even in the case of medicine the witch doctor or medicine man thought of these drugs as personal or god-given, and relied, or at least made sure that his patients relied, on his incantations and his cooperation with the healing powers more than on the medicines. Thus both in medicine and in astronomy progress was made in spite of erroneous theories; this sequence is by no means confined to the ancients. The study of papyri from the early Egyptian period shows that scientific knowledge was not only abundant but also highly systematized. The tradition of Imhotep, the Egyptian god of medicine, can be traced back to a real person, a learned physician who lived at the beginning of the twentieth century B. C. There are other cases on record in which actual persons became legendary gods.

We do not know how the Egyptians' early knowledge of mathematics and medicine and the Babylonians' knowledge of astronomy were transmitted to the Greeks, but we do know that long after the decline of science among those early peoples it began to flourish among the Greeks, as did also literature and art. Whatever influence those early cultures had on Greek science, it soon blossomed into an excellence previously unknown. The sciences may have been applied to the same extent in other countries, but this was the period of the great philosophers, and science had some effect on their thinking. The Greek philosophers were lucid thinkers, freed by their social position from the details and unpleasant practical aspects of everyday life. Bernal thus states the situation: [2]"The Greek genius at its height was contemplative; it sought to understand the world only to admire eternal truths. The very idea of using intellect to further change was abhorrent to Socrates and Plato; they had seen too much of it in the destructive rivalries of the city states, and of the classes within them."

Naturally, then, the Greeks were concerned most with mathematics and astronomy. It is well known that Euclid's text on geometry was still used in the nineteenth century, and that most of the modern texts rely on his method. Hippocrates and others contributed greatly to the advance of medicine. A beginning in mechanics was made by Archimedes and others. Thus there were exceptions to the interest in "heavenly" things only. Practical scientists, however, were not popular with the philosophers. According to Sedgwick and Tyler, [3]"Eudoxus and Archytas, the originators of the art of mechanics, solved some intricate geometric problems by measurement. To solve the problem of finding the two mean lines of a proportion when the extremes are given, they used certain curves and sections of lines to make measurements, much to the disgust of Plato. He objected to that process as the mere corruption and annihilation of the one good of geometry, which was thus shamefully turning its back upon the unembodied objects of pure intelligence to recur to sensation, and to ask help (not to be obtained without base supervisions and derivation) from matter; so it was that mathematics came to be separated from geometry and, repudiated and neglected by the philosophers, took its place as a military art." From Plutarch's account of the siege of Syracuse, it is evident that Archimedes, who lived a century later than Plato, would likewise have incurred his wrath, although he was a thinker as well as an inventor. He first discovered the principles of the lever and the screw, although those instruments had been used for ages, and also made the first determination of specific gravity when he showed that a certain king's crown was not pure gold as it had been represented.

Sarton discussed the question of the cause of the decadence and fall of the Greek spirit. He concludes tentatively that [4]"what happened to Greece is that the intellectual activities of its people were needlessly out of proportion to their political wisdom and their morality. A house divided against itself must necessarily fall, a body rent by internal strife is foredoomed to destruction, above all such a body is incapable of any kind of creation. It was not simply Greek science that disappeared, but Greek art and literature as well." Regarding Rome, he says: "Roman science at its best was but a pale imitation of the Greek. The Romans were so afraid of disinterested research, the excess of which had been one of the causes of Greek corruption, that they went to the other extreme and discouraged any research, the utilitarian value of which was not immediately obvious." Sarton does not mean research in the modern sense; this the Greeks did not conduct. The Romans did not encourage abstract thinking.

The state of science among the Hebrews was no different from that among the other "barbarian" countries. Their scientific accomplishments were not notable. They accomplished some engineering feats but they were fewer and on a smaller scale than those of the Egyptians and Babylonians. They had no philosophers until Greek influence pervaded their thinking. Their religious development, however, was unique. In Greece and some other countries religion had advanced to the polytheistic stage. In Israel, however, it had progressed from the idea of place deities through polytheism and henotheism (belief in many gods, one of whom is supreme) to some degree of monotheism, although polytheism and idolatry persisted until the captivity of the Jews by the Babylonians in 586 B. C.; their captivity helped to unite them in a monotheistic belief. Throughout the rest of their National history, they were independent politically for only a brief period, at the time of the

Maccabean rebellion. Political freedom is essential to the progress of science and philosophy. Moreover, their religious attitude was a deterrent. God caused the sunshine and rain; God gave the crops; God blessed or punished with misfortune both the individuals and the state. There was no need for further investigation. Medicine was not unknown; but the priests were responsible for the diagnosis of leprosy and probably of other diseases.

During the early Christian era many cases of healing by spiritual means are recorded, but neither Jesus nor the early disciples opposed the practice of medicine so far as we know. In fact, Luke, the reputed author of the third Gospel and the Acts of the Apostles, was a physician. On the other hand, by the fourth century, when Christianity had triumphed politically and deteriorated spiritually, the belief prevailed that diseases should be healed only by prayer and spiritual means, and medicine was not only discouraged but even forbidden. Many humanitarian reforms in the spirit of Christianity had been established; but the heretics who were persecuted included those who suggested the possibility of healing by physical means.

According to White, [5]"The influence of Christianity on the healing art was twofold; there was first a blessed impulse—the thought, aspiration, ideals, example, and spirit of Jesus of Nazareth. This spirit, then poured into the world, followed down through the ages, promoting self-sacrifice for the sick and wretched. Through all those succeeding centuries, even though the crudest, hospitals and infirmaries sprang up all along this blessed stream." In the time of the Crusades great organizations like the Order of St. John of Jerusalem were founded, and thenceforward every means of bringing the spirit of Jesus to help afflicted humanity was used. There was another influence, however, which somewhat offset this one, a "theology drawn partly from prehistoric conceptions of unseen powers, partly from ideas developed in the earliest historic nations, but especially from the Hebrew and Christian sacred books. The theology developed out of our sacred literature in relation to the cure of disease was mainly twofold: first, there was a new and strong evolution of the old idea that physical disease is produced by the wrath of God or the malice of Satan, or by a combination of both, which theology was called in to explain; secondly, there were evolved theories of miraculous methods of cure, based upon methods of appeasing the Divine anger, or of thwarting Satanic malice. . . . Along both these streams of influence, one arising in the life of Jesus, and the other in the reasonings of theologians, legends of miracles grew luxuriantly. It would be utterly unphilosophical to attribute these as a whole to conscious fraud. Whatever part priestcraft may have taken afterward in sundry discreditable developments of them, the mass of miraculous legends, century after century, grew up mainly in good faith, and as naturally as elms along water-courses or flowers upon the prairie." Legends of miracles grew about the lives of saints and benefactors of humanity. An example is St. Francis Xavier. All evidence from his writings and others of the time show nothing that he considered miraculous, but soon after his death these accounts of miracles were numerous, and in 1682, 130 years after his death, his published biography contained many additional miracles, including healing and the gift of tongues.

It is now realized that healing depends upon both physical and psychic factors. At one extreme are cases where the administration of a remedy cures the disease, no matter how skeptical the patient may be. On the other hand some conditions yield to placebos or suggestion without any real medication. In the Middle Ages the physical factor was ignored completely as it is today among members of a number of cults. It can be supposed that there were many "miraculous" healings; but there were probably more cases in which the method was not effective. The failures were mostly attributed to lack of faith, or sin, or the persistence of the demon. Some Christians, including Charlemagne, Alcuin, Frederick II, and Roger Bacon, promoted honest medical studies, but they were decidedly in the minority. The Lateran Council about the beginning of the thirteenth century forbade physicians to undertake medical treatment without calling in ecclesiastical advice. Scientific men were generally classed with sorcerers and magic makers. These conditions persisted throughout the Middle Ages. After the Reformation, Protestants were no more favorable to science than were the Catholics.

Hygiene was not encouraged to any greater extent than was medicine. Epidemics were supposed to be caused by the wrath of God. Comets, meteors, and earthquakes were considered portents of epidemics. To some extent Jews escaped pestilences that prevailed among other peoples, because sanitation was inground as part of their religion; but, as White says: 6"The public at large could not understand so simple a cause, and jumped to the conclusion that their immunity resulted from protection by Satan, and that this protection was repaid and the pestilence was caused by their wholesale poisoning of Christians." Thousands of Jews died by persecution, although Pope Clement VI stood against this popular unreason. Witchcraft was considered another cause of epidemics, and witches were persecuted by both Protestant and Catholic. It was not until the nineteenth century that plagues were minimized by scientific methods.

Since for the reasons given there was no progress in the science and art of medicine in the Middle Ages and the period of the early Reformation, it was not surprising that other sciences were also at a standstill. The same was not altogether true of Greek philosophy. The philosophy of Plato had considerable influence on the ideas of the early Christians. The much later re-discovery of the philosophy and knowledge of the Greeks was accompanied by a gradual assimilation by the churchmen of some of the Greek philosophy, especially that of Aristotle. At first his beliefs were considered a serious danger to the Christian church; for instance his definition of the soul was far from the Christian definition and did not imply immortality. Eventually, however, in the thirteenth century, Thomas Aquinas welded together most of Aristotelianism with Christian theology without sacrificing any of the essentials of Christian faith. Greek science, however, had much less influence on Christianity than did philosophy. Augustine, in the sixth century, considered science as the handmaid of philosophy, and his view was accepted even by Roger Bacon in the thirteenth century. Although the Greek philosophers had achieved some degree of freedom of thought, they were not entirely free from the belief in the divinity of the heavenly bodies. Even though this belief was in conflict with the Christian religion, traces of this pagan idea persisted up to the time of Galileo.

Jews and Mohammedans had no objections to the study of science or any type of philosophy. The rapid spread of Islam and the thirst for knowledge on the part of many of its leaders led to search for old manuscripts and translators for them. Now the Oriental Christians, out of favor with the Byzantine government, furnished valuable aid in making translations. Sarton says: [7]"The immense cultural importance of Islam lies in the fact that it brought finally together the two great intellectual streams which had flowed independently in ancient times. Previous attempts . . . had failed. Jews and Greeks had mixed in Alexandria but in spite of the fact that the former had learned the language of the latter and that one of their learned men, Philon, had made a deep study of both traditions, there had been no real fusion. The Christians had not succeeded any better, because of their single-hearted devotion to the

new Gospel, which reduced everything else to futility in their eyes.
Now for the first time in the history of the world Semitic tradition
and Greek knowledge actually combined in the minds of many
people. Nor was that integration restricted to any single city or
country; the new culture spread like a prairie fire from Bagdad
eastward to India, Transoxiana, and farther still, and westward to
the very edge of the world."

According to Sedwick and Tyler, [8]"the preservation and transmission of portions of Greek science through the Dark Ages to
the dawn of science in western Europe about 1200 A.D. was mainly
effected through three distinct, though not quite independent,
channels. First, there was to a limited extent a direct inheritance
of ancient learning within the Italian peninsula, through all its
political and military turmoil; second, a substantial legacy was
received indirectly through the Moors in Spain; while, third, additions of great importance came later through Italy from Constantinople." During the period of the Crusades, about 1100 to 1300,
though Christendom was at war with the Muslim world a large
part of the time, peaceful contact between the eastern and western
countries increased. During the eleventh and twelfth centuries the
beginnings of some of the modern universities were made. The
history of science through this period is a record of slow but
steady progress in several sciences, but with no brilliant accomplishments. The Indian or Arabic system of numerals came to be
generally adopted. Algebra in a crude form was introduced. Some
progress was made in astronomy. The Muslims made some contributions to medical science but their medical knowledge hardly
went beyond that of Galen. Alchemy received some attention. The
value of Mohammedans to science lies in their preservation of
ancient wisdom. Their lack of positive achievement was largely
the result of their temperament, which was inclined toward the
occult, the mystical, and the fantastic, rather than toward the
practical aspects of life.

The Revival of Learning

In the twelfth century there was a great stimulation of new
knowledge. Arabic versions of many Greek texts were discovered
and translated into Latin. The Jews also had a part in the preservation of ancient learning; but the net result was that, whatever
the intermediate process, some of the works of the ancient Greeks
were not available in Latin, the language of educated people. This
literature was gradually assuming greater importance. Astronomy

was the first science finally to break through the period of dormancy. A number of ancient people had believed that the earth is round; in fact, it had been practically proved to be so. One result of scientific progress during the Renaissance was easier navigation. The rotundity of the earth was nearly established by the voyages of Columbus and practically proved by that of Magellan. In the third century B. C. Aristarchus had gone much further; he postulated that the earth revolves around the sun. His statement brought upon him the charge of blasphemy by the Greek religious and political leaders, under much the same conditions as those that led to the death of Socrates. The cloud of prejudice, on the part of Christian as well as Greek, that followed hid the truth until the time of Galileo. Thus the antagonism between theological and scientific methods did not originate with Christianity. The early Christians were not interested in astronomy, because they interpreted the teaching of Jesus and his disciples to mean that the world would soon be destroyed. Later anyone with radical ideas in astronomy as well as in any other field was effectively suppressed in the interest of the god of things as they are understood, whether that god was disguised as pagan or Christian.

Measurements of the motions of the heavenly bodies around the earth had been attempted in very ancient times. Their paths were not found to be the simple circles that were expected. The complications of their orbits were among the facts that led Aristarchus to propose the heliocentric theory. When that theory was rejected by his contemporaries, he invented epicycles, or loops, in the planetary orbits. The Egyptian astronomer Ptolemy systematized and corrected the work, and the Ptolemaic hypothesis remained the orthodox system of astronomy until the Renaissance. Copernicus (1473-1543) revived the idea that the earth is spherical and rotates, and that it and the other planets revolve around the sun. His work was theoretical; he did not have the instruments to check his theory. Tycho Brahe (1546-1601) was above all an accurate observer, and his measurements, though without benefit of telescope, substantiated the theory of Copernicus. Kepler (1571-1630) discovered the laws of motion of the planets. Galileo, through the use of the telescope, gave final confirmation to the views of Copernicus, and greatly extended the knowledge of astronomy.

Sedgwick and Tyler say: [9]"In this age it is almost impossible to realize the extent of the opposition to each new conclusion, on the part of organized conservatism, although there are remnants of that opposition today. Copernicus, Tycho Brahe, and Kepler had, for various reasons, not incurred the serious opposition of the Church, but Galileo, because of the greater publicity given his work and the frankness with which his conclusions were stated, could not avoid intense opposition. The Aristotelians rejected his views on philosophical grounds; one professor of that school refused to look at the moon and planets through the telescope, and tried to convince Galileo of the error of his ways. His principal opponents, however, were the churchmen, and the final consequence was his appearance before the Inquisition. The text of the condemnation and of Galileo's recantation cannot now be read by the scientist or Christian without horror."

According to White, Galileo's work fulfilled [10]"one of the most touching of prophecies. Years before, the opponents of Copernicus said to him: 'If your doctrines were true, Venus would show phases like the moon.' Copernicus answered: 'You are right; I know not what to say; but God is good, and will in time find an answer to this objection.' The God-given answer came in 1611; the rude telescope showed the phases of Venus."

Parts of the Condemnation and Recantation of Galileo may be of interest: [11]"Whereas you, Galileo, son of the late Vincenzo Galilei of Florence, aged 70 years, were denounced in 1615 by this Holy Office, for holding as true the false doctrine held by many, namely, that the sun is immovable in the center of the world, and that the earth moves, and also with a diurnal motion; also for having pupils whom you instructed in the same opinions; also for maintaining a correspondence on the same with some German mathematicians; also for publishing certain letters on the solar spots, in which you developed the same doctrine as truth; also for answering the objections which were continually produced from the Holy Scriptures, by glozing the said scriptures according to your own meaning; and whereas thereupon was produced the copy of a writing, in the form of a letter, confessedly written by you to a person formerly your pupil, in which, following the hypothesis of Copernicus, you include several propositions contrary to the true sense and authority of the Holy Scripture:

Therefore this holy tribunal being desirous of providing against the disorder and mischief thence proceeding and increasing to the detriment of the Holy faith, by the desire of His Holiness, and of the Most Eminent Lord Cardinals of this supreme and universal Inquisition, the two propositions of the stability of the sun, and the motion of the earth, were qualified by the Theological Qualifiers as follows:

The proposition that the sun is the center of the world and immovable from its place is absurd, philosophically false, and formally heretical, because it is expressly contrary to the Holy Scripture.

The proposition that the earth is not the center of the world, not immovable, but that it moves, and also with a diurnal motion, is absurd, philosophically false, and, theologically considered, at least erroneous in faith."

(The text goes on to recite repeated publications of the heresy, and subsequent actions taken by the Inquisition.)

"We pronounce, judge, and declare, that you, the said Galileo, by reason of these things which have been detailed in the course of this writing, and which, as above, you have confessed, have rendered yourself vehemently suspected by this Holy Office of heresy; that is to say, that you believe and hold the false doctrine, and contrary to the Holy and Divine Scriptures, namely, that the sun is the center of the world, and that it does not move from the east to west, that the earth does move and is not the center of the world; also that an opinion can be held and supported as probable after it has been declared and finally decreed contrary to the Holy Scripture, and consequently that you have incurred all the censures and penalties enjoined and promulgated in the sacred canons, and other general and particular constitutions, against delinquents of this description. From which it is Our pleasure that you be absolved, provided that, first, with a sincere heart and unfeigned faith, in Our presence, you abjure, curse, and detest the said errors and heresies and every other error and heresy contrary to the Catholic and Apostolic Church of Rome, in the form now shown to you.

But, that your grievous and pernicious error and transgression may not go altogether unpunished, and that you may be made more cautious in the future, and may be a warning to others to abstain from delinquencies of this sort, We declare that the book of the Dialogues of Galileo Galilei be prohibited by a public edict.

We condemn you to the formal prison of this Holy Office for a period determinable at Our pleasure; and by way of salutary penance, We order you, during the next three years, to recite once a week the seven Penitential Psalms." (Concluding with formalities and signatures.)

Following is the essential portion of Galileo's recantation:
"I Galileo Galilei, . . . swear that I have always believed, and
now believe, and with the help of God will in future believe, every
article which the Holy Catholic and Apostolic Church of Rome
holds, teaches, and preaches. But because I had been enjoined by
this Holy Office altogether to abandon the false opinion which
maintains that the sun is the center and immovable, and forbidden
to hold, defend, or teach the said false doctrine in any manner, and
after it had been signified to me that the said doctrine is repugnant
with the Holy Scripture, I have written and printed a book, in
which I retract of the same doctrine now condemned, and adduce
reasons with great force in support of the same, without giving any
solution, and therefore, have been judged greviously suspected of
heresy; that is to say, that I have held and believed that the sun
is the center of the world and immovable, and that the earth is not
the center and movable.

Wishing, therefore, to remove from the mind of Your Emi-
nence, and of every Catholic Christian, this vehement suspicion
rightfully entertained toward me, with a sincere heart and unfeigned
faith, I abjure, curse, and detest the said errors and heresies, and
generally every other error and sect contrary to the said Holy
Church; and I swear that I will nevermore say or assert anything
verbally, or in writing, which may give rise to a similar suspicion
of me; but if I shall know any heretic, or anyone suspected of
heresy, that I will denounce him to this Holy Office, or to the
Inquisitor and Ordinary of the place in which I may be.

I swear, moreover, and promise, that I will fulfill, and observe
fully, all the penances which have been or shall be laid to me by
this Holy Office. But if it shall happen that I violate any of the
said promises, oaths, and protestations (which God avert!) I
subject myself to all the pains and punishments which have been
decreed and promulgated by the sacred canons, and other general
and particular constitutions, against delinquents of this description.
So may God help me, and His Holy Gospels, which I touch with
my own hands.

I, the above-named Galileo Galilei, have abjured, sworn,
promised, and bound myself, as above, and in witness thereof with
my own hand have subscribed this present writing of this abjura-
tion, which I have recited word for word."

Sedgwick and Tyler continue: "We have no record of Galileo's
subsequent feelings, and it is questionable whether he uttered the
words 'and still it moves' attributed to him, but he must have suf-

fered more from having recanted than he would have from any punishment that might have been inflicted upon him. . . . One of his biographers says: 'If, then, once, and only once, when faced with the terrors of the Inquisition, he, like Peter, denied his master, no honest man, knowing all the circumstances, will be in a hurry to blame him.' "

The Inquisition tribunal committed the supreme blasphemy of calling their poorly formed judgments the unalterable truth of God. The tribunal was, of course, Roman Catholic, but Galileo and his predecessors and many of his followers received no support from Protestants. In fact the Protestant Church was hardly less energetic against the new astronomy than the mother Church. Arguments against the heliocentric theory included the standing still of the sun for Joshua, and the backward movement of the shadow on the sundial for Hezekiah. In 1833 books on the Copernican system were removed from the Index Expurgatorius, but as late as 1873 a book by a president of a Lutheran Teacher's Seminary attacked the Copernican system.

This much can be said in defense of the Inquisition, according to Hesse: [12]"In (Galileo's) dealings with the Church, however, he was overbearing and tactless, often putting forward his ideas dogmatically without sufficient evidence to support them, and at this time the Church was understandably concerned about the implications of the new cosmology, which in destroying the uniqueness of the earth, also tended in the popular mind to destroy the uniqueness of man himself." On the other hand, the overall picture is thus summarized by White: [13]"It is most suggestive to see in this crisis of the Church, at the tomb of the prince of the apostles, on the eve of one of the greatest errors in church policy the world has known, in all the intrigues and deliberations of the consecrated leaders, no more of the guidance or presence of the Holy Spirit than in a caucus of New York politicians at Tammany Hall."

Scientists have been misunderstood, maligned, and persecuted in many ways, but only a few have died for their beliefs at the hands of their fellow men. Giordano Bruno (1550-1600) was the one who has received most attention. He was a Dominican monk who was arrested by the Inquisition in 1592, imprisoned for seven years at Rome, and then burned at the stake. He had accepted the Copernican theory of astronomy but also maintained a pantheistic view of the universe. He was not strictly a martyr to the scientific revolution, because he was condemned largely on the ground of his theological heresies. Also, as in the case of

Galileo, more tact on his part might have lightened the punishment. Even with these extenuating circumstances, the martyrdom of Bruno and the near-martyrdom of Galileo mark a low in the treatment of scientists by the Church, and never again were scientific heretics so harshly treated by either the Catholic or Protestant denominations. On the other hand the epithets "infidel" and "atheist" as White continues, [13]"have been used against almost every man who has done anything new for his fellow-men. The list of those who have been so labeled includes almost all great men of science, general scholars, inventors, and philanthropists. The purest Christian life, the noblest Christian character, have not availed to shield combatants. . . . These epithets can hardly be classed with civilized weapons. They are flaming arrows; they set fire to masses of popular prejudice, always obscuring the real question, sometimes destroying the attacking party. They pierce the hearts of loving women; they alienate dear children; they injure a man after life is ended, for they leave poisoned wounds in the hearts of those who loved him best—fears for his eternal salvation, dread of the divine wrath upon him." These words have lost most of their truth at the present day; science is respected for what it can do materially and most theologians have abandoned anti-scientific views.

The seventeenth century marked a turning point in the history of science. In addition to the progress in astronomy, other important events included the discovery of the circulation of the blood, the invention of the barometer, the transition from alchemy to chemistry, and the erection of the foundations of nineteenth-century physics. The outstanding trend in that century, however, was the recognition and development of the experimental-inductive method. In so far as medicine is a science it is necessarily largely experimental, and it was the only experimental science among the Greeks. There are various methods of experimentation. At one end is that of Thomas Edison, who was, strictly speaking, not a scientist. When he was looking for a material for the conductor in the incandescent lamp, he simply tried everything that came to hand, without reference to its resemblance to anything else he had tried, until he finally found the best material. At the other extreme were the Greeks, who disdained any practical experimentation, but depended on logic alone. Roger Bacon, in the thirteenth century, made some experiments, although in his works the experimental is mixed with the mystical. The greatest experimentalist of that period was Leonardo da Vinci (1452-1519). But they were candles in the dark.

Sir Francis Bacon, (1561-1626) not a scientist himself, laid down a procedure for inductive experimental science which is almost as valid today, embracing these steps: (1) collection of reliable tested information, especially by means of experiments; (2) classification of this material through "tables of invention" so that all the instances of the phenomenon could be compared; (3) by these tables arriving at minor generalizations which we would call theorems or rules, the compilation of which would give rise to general scientific laws; and (4) confirmation of these laws by pointing out new instances of the phenomenon studied. The modern method differs from this suggested procedure merely in that we use our judgment in selecting the questions we ask of nature, instead of collecting every possible fact that may possibly bear on the subject; moreover, we endeavor to collect numerical data and handle them by mathematical reasoning.

According to Taylor, [14]"On the continent, Réné Descartes (1596-1650) did work similar to that of Bacon. His *Discourse on Method* also purports to be an account of a new way of finding out the principles of nature. But while Bacon was a lawyer and relied on evidence, Descartes was a mathematician and relied on reasoning. Descartes believed that, just as Euclid seemed to have got his axioms out of his head, and to have evolved from them the vast structure of geometry so the scientist, merely by thinking with only a minimum of observation of phenomena, would be able to arrive at axioms or principles from which long trains of reasoning would lead to an understanding of the whole course of nature. He was wrong, of course, erring far more in one direction than Bacon in the other. Bacon gave too much attention to gathering facts and little or none to mathematical reasoning about them; Descartes made precisely the opposite error. The practical scientists of the subsequent decades found out the happy mean; and such men as Boyle and Newton were able to treat Bacon's observations and experiments by Descartes' reasoning, with the greatest success."

Recognition of the experimental method as an important tool of science opened floodgates which have permitted an ever-growing stream of new facts discovered, new correlations drawn between them, and creation of new sciences as branches of those then existing. On the background established by Kepler and his predecessors, Newton formulated the law of gravitation. Newton also made a beginning in the field of optics, which developed further by Young and others, enlarging our understanding of the nature of light and color. The growth of the knowledge of electricity began with the researches of Davy and Faraday early in the nineteenth century. Natural philosophy, embracing knowledge of mechanics, light, sound, and electricity, later became known as physics.

The science of chemistry was retarded about 100 years in the eighteenth century by the phlogiston theory. According to this theory, combustible substances, including metals, contained an element or principle called phlogiston. When they were burned or otherwise oxidized they lost their phlogiston. The reverse process, such as production of metals from their ores, was a process of adding phlogiston. The difficulty with this simple explanation, as scientists gradually became aware, was that when metals and some other solids are burned, or as we now say, oxidized, they gain weight while phlogiston is supposedly being lost; and when metals are formed from their ores weight is lost as the phlogiston is supposed to accumulate. The advocates of phlogiston accounted for these phenomena by assuming that phlogiston is "the principle of levity" and has negative weight. To most chemists this explanation did not seem sensible, and the final blow to the theory was given late in the century by Lavoisier, who laid the foundations of modern chemistry. As every student now knows, metallic ores lose oxygen when they are reduced to metals, and substances add oxygen when they are burned. Once a sound theory was established, the knowledge of elements and compounds and the mechanisms of their reactions have progressed to the point where new compounds are discovered every day.

Progress in the biological sciences before the middle of the nineteenth century was not as spectacular as in the physical sciences. Both botany and zoology consisted mostly of what is now called taxonomy, which is merely the classification of plants and animals, respectively, on an arbitrary basis, with no thought of the reasons for the variations observed. So far as we know Aristotle made the first systematic classification both of plants and of animals, and some of his descriptions are remarkably accurate. Other classifications followed through the centuries. That of Linnaeus (1707-1778) far surpassed all the others in clarity, but still it was classification and description. In the seventeenth century biologists began to study the structure and physiological functions of both plants and animals; but it was not until the early nineteenth century that the importance of the cell as the unit of living things was fully realized and progress was made in cell theory and comparative anatomy. The importance of biology in its relation to medicine was still unknown.

From very early times there were some philosophers who held that all life had a common origin. A broad idea of evolution first appeared in Chaldeo-Babylonian thinking. A more definite conception of evolution was held by two Greek philosophers, Anaximander and Anaximenes, in the sixth century B. C. Aristotle but not Plato maintained a belief in evolution. Hints of evolutionary theory appeared in the writings of many subsequent philosophers, but thought favoring evolution was restrained by belief in the fixity of the species.

The early and middle nineteenth century saw the development of evolution from a philosophical speculation into a well-substantiated theory, by the work of Lamarck and Darwin. Although Lamarck (whose works were published 1809-1822) is regarded as the founder of the theory, it was Darwin, by his *Origin of Species,* published in 1859, who converted the scientific world to its acceptance. The essence of Darwinian theory is: (1) that chance variations occur in inheritance; (2) that there is a continual struggle for existence on the part of all living beings; (3) that some of these variations increase the probability of survival of the individual; and (4) that these variations that have made for the survival of the most individuals are perpetuated to the greatest extent. The principal deviation of Lamarck's theory from this picture is that it assumes also that characteristics which the individual has developed as the result of its exposure to its environment are also inherited. The theory in that form has been almost universally rejected by scientists; but some of Lamarck's ideas have been accepted as modifications of those of Darwin.

Darwin's *Descent of Man,* published in 1871, did still more to upset previous conceptions, especially of the importance of man in the universe. The disputes between Darwin and his opponents is sometimes represented as a phase of "the conflict between science and religion". Testifying to that viewpoint are thousands of sermons that have been preached against evolution, often with a misunderstanding of its meaning; moreover, not long after the *Descent of Man* appeared, Darwin engaged in a celebrated debate with Bishop Wilberforce of Oxford, who tried to prove that Darwin's beliefs were false. The truth is, however, that the theory was not universally accepted by scientists; Agassiz, Youmans, and

Owen were Darwins' best known opponents. Moreover, the theory was accepted from the beginning by a number of religious leaders. As Alfred Noyes points out, [15]"the real warfare was between men like Owen, the exponent of the older scheme, and Darwin (or Huxley), the exponent of the new. When Bishop Wilberforce went to the famous Oxford debate, foolish as he may have been, he went escorted by Owen. He was primed with his 'facts' by Owen, and he spoke as the universally accepted 'science' of his generation and two centuries of scientific dogma had taught him to speak."

One basis of opposition to Darwinism was the "fixity of the species". Orthodox theologians and most lay Christians believed that the pairs of animals who were preserved in the Ark were the ancestors of all animals now living, without any changes. According to Noyes, however, the doctrine of the fixity of the species had a scientific, not a theological origin. It is to be found first in the writings of John Ray (1628-1705), who is called the father of modern zoology. "The growth of the idea in England during the seventeenth and eighteenth centuries was due far more to the influence of Milton's account of the creation in *Paradise Lost* than to Genesis. The reading of Genesis did not prevent St. Augustine from entertaining evolutionary notions about those creatures which 'being removed by degrees in time and space, make or undergo beautiful variations.' On the other hand, Darwin asserted that in his intercourse with the scientific naturalists of the nineteenth century 'he never came across a single one who seemed to doubt the permanence of species'."

Another point is that Darwin is not responsible for the pagan or atheistic interpretation of evolution that has often been accepted. Noyes continues: [16]"The situation was complicated, moreover, by the fact that the truth was not entirely on one side; and that, as in almost every other case in history, those who were eagerly grasping at new truths were almost indifferently dropping certain older truths. This is the constant Nemesis of what we call 'progress'. Any new or rediscovered truth is, for the moment, more important to us than what we already possess. Men will die to make a very small discovery; but, when it is made, and securely our own, it falls into its proper place, and is seen to be far less important than some of our former knowledge. The followers of Darwin were right on most of the facts; but, in a vivid American phrase, they tried to 'empty out the baby with the bathwater', and if you remarked upon the value of the baby, they triumphantly pointed to the dirtiness of the soap-suds. Then both sides grew angry, and the defenders of the baby denied that the soap-suds were dirty, and their opponents replied that the baby was nothing but a soap-sud, and that probably the whole race of babies originated in a bubble.

"Our admiration for Darwin should not make us forget that his opponent, Owen, was really a great naturalist, and our acceptance of what was really true in Darwin's theory should not be allowed to cancel out the really deeper, though older, truth at the back of Owen's mind when he said that 'organic changes take place in accordance with the laws fixed beforehand by the All-seeing and Almighty Being who has conferred upon the organisms their tendency to transformation.' There was nothing in this that was really inconsistent with Darwin's own repudiation of 'blind chance', though it might have been stated more subtly, on both sides. Owen, however, made the deadly mistake of denying the undeniable. He was defeated and Bishop Wilberforce went down with him."

There may or may not be full agreement with the views of Noyes that have been just stated; but Darwin's own statement follows: [17]"I am aware that the conclusions arrived at in this chapter" (the final chapter of *Descent of Man*) "will be denounced by some as highly irreligious; but he who denounces them is bound to show why it is more irreligious to explain the origin of man as a distinct species by descent from some lower form through the laws of variation than to explain the birth of the individual through the laws of ordinary reproduction. The births both of the species and of the individual are equally parts of a grand sequence of events, which our minds refuse to accept as the result of blind chance. The understanding revolts from such a conclusion, whether or not we are able to believe that every slight variation of a structure,—the union of each pair in marriage,—the dissemination of each seed,—and other such events, have all been ordained for some special purpose."

Notwithstanding the evidence given that Darwin's views were not as anti-religious as is sometimes supposed, the theory of evolution had a profound influence. White says: [18]"As the great dogmatic barrier between the old and new views of the universe was broken down, the flood of thought pouring over the world stimulated and nourished strong growths in every field of research and reasoning; edition after edition of the book was called for; it was translated into Japanese and Hindustani; the stagnation of scientific thought . . . gave place to a widespread and fruitful activity; masses of accumulated observations, which had seemed stale and unprofitable, were made alive; facts formerly without meaning

now found their interpretation." In spite of the subtle agreements
of evolution with religion mentioned above, the theory encountered
violent opposition on the part of theologians. Their general
response was that if evolution is true the Bible is false. The natural
reaction of non-theologians was, "all right, then, the Bible is not
true". At first the religious proponents of evolution were too small
a minority to be vocal. But in 1892 the Archdeacon of Man-
chester accepted evolution. In 1893 the first of Henry Drummond's
books, in which he shows that evolution does not necessarily conflict with Christianity, was published.

The two general courses of evolution of science in the nineteenth century were the extension and multiplication of the sciences,
and the industrial revolution. These trends had been evident in
the preceding centuries but now they progressed at a much accel-
erated pace. The science of physics which already embraced the
study of mechanics, sound, light, and heat, now included the rapidly growing knowledge of electricity. A "principle" that proved
to be erroneous in the light of present knowledge was developed
—that of the luminiferous ether, with practically no weight or
density but more rigid than steel; but it did not interfere with the
progress of physics as the phlogiston theory retarded chemistry in
the preceding century. Chemistry grew by the discovery of new
compounds and the role of electricity. Geology was beginning to
be a science late in the eighteenth century, and made rapid progress
when it had once escaped from the shackles of the brief period of
the earth's existence imposed by a literal understanding of Genesis.
Evolution gave a clue to the closely related science, paleontology.
The biological sciences progressed from being merely catalogues of
living creatures to a study of their life processes.

In reading the histories of scientific developments and biographies of scientists one is struck by the wide variations in the
time required for acceptance and application of new ideas. Discoveries have often lain buried for years before their worth was
realized. Mendel's work on heredity is an example. Mendel was
a monk and later abbot of a monastery and had as part of his work
the care of the garden. He experimented with the breeding of
certain plants and found certain relations which have become
known as Mendel's law. He was the first to use the terms gene,
dominant, and recessive, which have become standard words in
biology. His book was published in 1865. Darwin would have
been glad to know about it, but apparently he did not; the book
attracted no attention until 1900, when it was brought to light

simultaneously by several biologists who were conducting genetic experiments. Darwin, on the other hand, found the scientific world awaiting evolutionary theory.

Psychology and the social sciences became studied extensively in the last half of the nineteenth century and the first half of the twentieth. The physical sciences called for new developments in mathematics. The interrelation of the sciences led to "hybrid" sciences connecting two or more of the older ones; for instance physical chemistry, chemical physics, geophysics, geochemistry, biochemistry, bionomics, paleobotany, thermodynamics, and social psychology.

The most important scientific feature of the twentieth century, to date, has been the advent of nuclear physics and its applications. Nineteenth century physics pictured a tight little world, almost as tight as that of the earlier theological conception. The building blocks of the universe were the atoms, of which there were eighty-some kinds, unchangeable through the course of time, although a new variety was occasionally discovered. They were held together by gravitational and molecular forces and consumed or produced energy when they combined to form molecules or exchanged molecules. The picture was fairly consistent, although there were disturbing features in the background. One of these was the assumed existence of the mysterious ether which was believed essential for the transmission of light and electricity. Late in the century, however, some discoveries were made that upset the picture.

Experiments by Michelson and Morley in the 1880's demonstrated that the velocity of light is the same in all directions and thereby exploded the theory of the ether through which it was supposed to travel. The experiments were repeated again and again to meet objections and their results were finally accepted as conclusive in 1929.

Even more startling were the results of another series of experiments. In 1895 Roentgen discovered that radiation of a type previously unknown was produced when electricity was passed through highly rarefied gases. He gave it the name x-rays. The next year Becquerel found that radiation of the same type is given off spontaneously from uranium salts. In 1898 the Curies isolated two new elements, radium and polonium, which emit similar radiations but a thousand times as strongly as uranium. Moreover, these experimenters learned that these radioactive elements change into other elements in the process of emission of these rays, with the release of great amounts of energy. At first

all these phenomena were considered the material for just another
chapter in a physics textbook; but it was soon realized that a
revolution of the whole science of physics was in progress. The
atom lost its status as a fundamental unit, and became known as a
complex organization. In 1956 the recognized "ultimate particles"
included protons, deuterons, tritons, antiprotons, electrons, posi-
trons, neutrons, neutrinos, photons, several kinds of mesons, and
three types of hyperons. According to Pollard in 1961, there are
two sequences of particles: those [19]"called *fermions,* which in order
of ascending mass are called the neutrino, electron, muon, proton,
neutron, lambda-particle, sigma-particles, and cascades," and "the
corresponding sequence of so-called *bosons* which in the same order
are called the photon, pions, and K-mesons." Other types of particles have been suggested but their existence has not been substantiated. None of these particles possess the "primary" qualities,
as formerly considered, of size, shape and position; but they have
the basic substantive properties of mass, electric charge, and
nuclearity together with the dynamical and symmetrical properties
of spin, lifetime, and parity. It is evident that there are simple,
undiscovered relations of entities which may account for the multi-
plicity of these particles and their properties. Pollard says:
"Whether it will prove possible to find an answer to these questions
we, of course, cannot know. If and when it is found, the answer
will certainly constitute the next great fundamental advance in
physics."

The logical consequence of the indifference of the velocity
of light to its environment was the theory of relativity, first developed by Einstein in 1905 and later elaborated by Einstein and
others. The principal features of the theory are: the finitude of the
material universe; the non-objectivity of time and space; the
meaninglessness of absolute motion; the effect of gravitational
fields on light and other radiant energy; the equivalence of mass
and energy; the acceptance of time as a fourth coordinate or dimension; and the introduction of the relativity effect of the finite velocity of light into physical equations. Several of Einstein's assumptions have been verified by experiment and observation. Another
development was the quantum theory, according to which energy
is not continuous but comes in definite small packages just as
matter does. Newton was convinced that light consists of "corpuscles;" his opponents, who conceived of light as waves, were
apparently victorious; but the relativity view is that it is both

particles and waves; that is, for some purpose the wave concept gives the correct mathematical correspondence, while the particle theory is consistent with other facts. Most curious of all these developments is the Heisenberg indeterminancy principle, which says that the position and the velocity of a given sufficiently small particle can never be exactly determined at the same time. Series of waves are now known, with frequencies ranging from 10^4 to 10^{24} vibrations per second, and having different effects at different frequency ranges; the longest are the radio waves, then light, then ultraviolet, then x-rays, gamma rays and finally cosmic rays.

All these developments amounted to a revolution in physics. The principles of Newtonian physics and its accompanying mathematics are still sufficient for dealing with ordinary large-scale materials; but for particles as small as the constituents of the atom new principles and new kinds of mathematics are necessary. The theological attitude toward scientific developments has changed. The advances made in the sixteenth to nineteenth centuries were bitterly fought by some theologians; but those of the twentieth involved no further contradiction of scriptural accounts or of human understanding of them. Some theologians even found a divergence from the materialistic views of the nineteenth century and possible means of harmonizing religious and scientific beliefs. That viewpoint will be discussed in Chapter IX.

In all the other sciences the present century has seen steady progress in many directions although the results have not been as spectacular as in physics. In astronomy much is being learned about the stars and nebulae. It is evident from the spectra that distant nebulae are receding at speeds which increase with their distance. This fact has led to two theories, the first of which is that all the material of the universe was created, or at least appeared, all at once and in a very small space, and has been expanding ever since. The other theory is that as the universe expands more matter is created to fill in the vacant spaces. Astronomers hope at some not too distant time to have evidence that will decide between these theories.

In biochemistry more and more is becoming known about the large molecules which are the building blocks of living material, and it is hoped that they will provide a key to the understanding of life itself. Geologists are learning more about the interior of the earth, at least of the portions just below the "crust," if there is a crust. In psychology and the social sciences not so much prog-

ress is noticeable to the outsider, because changes are less spectacular than in physics and astronomy, but steady progress is
being made in various aspects of these sciences.

Applied Science

The industrial revolution may be said to have begun with the
invention of the steam engine about 1769. In this case invention
and application followed on the heels of science; Black's investigation of the properties of steam was followed almost immediately
by the invention of the modern steam engine by Watt, who was in
constant touch with Black. Although invention and science were
not always so closely related, the revolution proceeded from that
time with ever-increasing speed. It was not until well into the
twentieth century, however, that science was intentionally and
directly applied to industry to any great extent. In 1911 there
were three chemists employed in the steel mills of Pittsburgh. It is
said that at the beginning of World War I the American Chemical
Society offered the War Department its services as required. The
reply was that the Department already had a chemist. Some industrial companies employed chemists, but their duties consisted of
necessary analysis of a few materials and products. Other sciences
were applied to a still smaller extent than was chemistry.

Robert Kennedy Duncan was a pioneer in the systematic
application of science, especially chemistry, to industry. In the
face of considerable opposition, he founded an industrial fellowship system at the University of Kansas, and later Mellon Institute
which began as a department of the University of Pittsburgh. On
a relatively small scale this experiment showed what could be
accomplished. One of the largest chemical manufacturing companies in America had its beginning in the work conducted there,
and some other companies profited by research conducted at the
Institute. Several other industrial research institutions were founded
and a few large companies formed research departments of their
own; but on the whole little industrial research was accomplished.
The pure researcher was regarded as a rather queer bird, and the
industrial scientist. or engineer did not entirely escape the classification.

Such was the situation up to World War II. Experience in
that war taught the value of applied science. It was responsible
for the acceleration of the application of science to industry and
a new prestige was given to science and scientists. The invention
of synthetic fabrics, plastics, and other new materials brought

the scientist out of a dark, smelly, laboratory into public notice. The development of nuclear science led to the invention of radio for entertainment and communication, television, and most spectacular of all, the atom bomb and its successors. The desire for speed has resulted in faster and faster means of travel and communication. For many purposes wood, glass, metals, and other products have been replaced by synthetic materials. Hand production is giving way to automatic production. New medicines are constantly appearing on the market. Foods that were once considered exotic are in common use. Each of us has experiences of which our grandfathers knew nothing.

To the scientist it is evident that we are only at the beginning of knowledge. We can still say with Newton (as quoted in an earlier chapter): "I seem to have been only like a little boy playing on the seashore, and diverting myself in now and then finding a smoother pebble or a prettier shell than ordinary, whilst the great ocean of truth lay undiscovered before me." The present sciences will probably undergo great expansion; but in our undifferentiated experience lies the germs of sciences yet unborn. We simply cannot contemplate life in 196,100 A. D. or even 19,610 A. D. On the other hand, there are many factors which may retard or even stop the recent rapid progress of science. They include, for instance: (1) the destruction of a large part of the world by a nuclear bomb or other weapon; (2) animosity toward science caused by the application of scientific methods to the detriment of a part of the human race; (3) exhaustion of human resources to a point where science cannot be supported; (4) conquest of the civilized world by barbarian hordes, such as occurred at the beginning of the Dark Ages; and (5) natural forces such as the next ice age, or collision with a large meteor or space body. On the other hand, the survival of the race may at some time depend upon the success of scientific endeavor against a new course of nature or society. For example, assuming the validity of the ice-age theory of Ewing and Dunn, it may be necessary to construct a huge barrier under the connecting channel between the Arctic and Atlantic Oceans between Greenland and Scandinavia. On the other hand, the problem may be that of survival under intense heat. Another phase of the question of survival is the depletion of natural resources. There may be a period, or periods, when there will be a race between man's ingenuity and the supply of food or other necessities. The supply of petroleum, for instance, will eventually be exhausted, and it is a question whether atomic energy or some other form of energy will be ready in time to replace it.

Discussion of the more immediate effects of science on man raises a number of questions which will be considered in Chapter VIII.

Just when the struggle of science for existence terminated and science became generally accepted is difficult to determine. One is tempted to call the present situation the "triumph of science," but that term has limits of meaning. Science has not triumphed in the sense that most people are science-minded; it has triumphed in the sense that it is an important factor in life, and in the sense that its progress is no longer limited by theology or pseudotheology.

Chapter V

The Effect Of Science
On Protestant Theology

IN THE PRECEDING chapter we have seen how science gradually freed itself from the shackles of conservatism under the guise of religion or theology. In doing so, science strongly affected religious thinking, because theologians had to take some account of the new scientific ideas, whether they liked them or not. Theological literature from the time of Copernicus to the present offers all possible variations on the theme of science versus theology, from condemnation of the scientific viewpoint to partial agreement and attempts at reconciliation. The change in religious thinking was gradual, but the two events which had most impact upon it were the Copernican-Galilean revolution in the sixteenth and seventeenth centuries, contemporaneous with but independent of the Protestant Reformation, and the advent of organic evolution in the nineteenth century.

The Reformation was, strictly speaking, not one movement but four, conducted respectively by Lutheran, Calvinist, Anglican, and independent groups. It was in the ranks of the Lutherans and Calvinists that the most important battles were fought. It is not within the scope of this book to describe the sometimes abstruse differences between the Calvinist and Lutheran theologies; they are given in detail in several books. In all Protestant organizations the authority of the Bible was substituted for that of the Church. That does not mean, as it has sometimes been understood to mean, that both groups had a mechanical, literal view of the inspiration of the Bible. That is an oversimplification. In both Calvinist and Lutheran beliefs there were variations in the relative importance of the word of the Bible and the "inner light" of the believer. For the Calvinists the disagreement was officially terminated by the Helvetic Confession, adopted in 1556, which asserted that the Bible was revelation because it was "written under the spirit." That interpretation included literal acceptance of miracles and predestination. Although Lutherans agreed neither with the doctrine of predestination nor with the Calvinistic idea of Grace, the word of God was as important to them as to the Calvinists.

Anglicanism began with the dispute of Henry VIII with the Roman Catholic Church. No new doctrines were introduced; the English Catholic Church, with the king at its head, was substituted for the Roman Catholic. In America after the Revolution, the Protestant Episcopal Church retained a similar hierachy without the king. There was nothing in this movement to make the conclusions of science more acceptable.

Among the independent groups, Congregationalists asserted the independence of the local church, but remained Calvinistic in doctrine. The Anabaptists and Baptists rejected the idea of infant baptism, but in other respects were Calvinists. The Friends or Quakers had no creed but depended on "inner light". They were apparently more sympathetic toward the new scientific views, but they constituted a small minority,

Calvinists and Lutherans, then, contributed most to the debates about science and religion in this period. Dillenberger and Welch summarize the attitude of these denominations: [1]"In spite of the Ptolemaic assumptions of Luther and Calvin, they did not defend the old astronomy in the light of a developed conception of the inerrancy of the Scriptures. Rather, the new science was not yet widely accepted. In so far as they knew of it, it exhibited a spirit which would prove difficult to harmonize with a Biblical understanding. But Biblical passages were not yet used in and of themselves as proof texts in the defense of astronomical theories. That was a later development. . . . The spirit of this approach is reflected in the term 'Protestant scholasticism.' This differed from medieval scholasticism in that it had to argue with the new scientific theory of the world, which stood in striking contrast to the Biblical scheme, and a philosophical trend which was almost exclusively rationalistic. But in this encounter, Protestantism did not escape the spirit of rationalism itself. It was, in fact, akin to the new rationalistic currents both in temper and in method. It was no wonder that the dissatisfaction with philosophical rationalism should also bring dissatisfaction with this type of theology. This orthodoxy was part of Puritanism, ancestor of Presbyterianism and Congregationalism. This dissatisfaction also expressed itself in Pietism, from which Methodism also developed."

Whatever were the official attitudes toward science, Christians

soon found that they had to live with the new views, and that their
acceptance would not really make much difference in their personal
beliefs. Milton, writing a century after Copernicus and fifty years
after Galileo and reflecting the general opinion of his time, considered the view of the universe as a matter of individual choice,
as the following quotation indicates:

> [2]"And Raphael now, to Adam's doubt proposed,
> Benevolent and facile, thus replied:
> 'To ask or search, I blame thee not; for heaven
> Is as the book of God before thee set,
> Wherein to read his wondrous works, and learn
> His seasons, hours, or months or years;
> This to attain, whether heaven move or earth,
> Imports not, if thou reckon right; the rest
> From man or angel, the great Architect
> Did wisely to conceal, and not divulge
> His secrets to be scanned by them who ought
> Rather admire; or, if they list to try
> Conjecture, he his fabric of the heavens
> Hath left to their disputes, perhaps to move
> His laughter at their quaint opinions wide
> Hereafter; when they come to model heaven
> And calculate the stars, how they will yield
> The mighty frame! how build, unbuild, contrive
> To save appearances; how gird the sphere
> With centric and eccentric scribbled o'er
> Cycle and epicycle, orb in orb;
> Already by thy reasoning this I guess,
> Who are to lead thy offspring, and supposest
> That bodies bright and greater should serve
> The less not bright, nor heaven such journeys run,
> Earth not sitting still, when she alone receives
> The benefit. Consider first, that great
> Or bright infers not excellence; the earth
> Though in comparison of heaven, so small,
> Nor glistering, may of solid good contain
> More plenty than the sun that barren shines;
> Whose virtue on itself works no effect,
> But in the fruitful earth; there first received,
> His beams, unactive else, their vigor find,
> Yet not to earth are those bright luminaries
> Officious; but to thee earth's habitant."

Most theologians were less tolerant of the new ideas than was Milton. The teachings of Aristotle held sway in a large section of the Protestant world as well as in the Catholic. The philosophy known as Protestant scholasticism was shattered by Sir Isaac Newton, who confirmed and united the work of his predecessors by his discovery of the law of gravitation. Francis Bacon and Robert Boyle had undermined the authority of Aristotle by their emphasis on the method of inductive reasoning, but Newton showed that terrestrial and celestial objects were subject to the same law, which gave a much simpler view of the material universe than all the suppositions of men from Aristotle on. Newton disavowed metaphysics and did not try to make a philosophy of his scientific reasoning. He accepted the traditional arguments for the existence of God, but he affirmed that God was also actively related to the world of nature. His rational but somewhat inconsistent conception of Christianity was considered heretical by orthodox churchmen. The new scientific ideas, however, were more acceptable to the Puritans. Although Newton was not a philosopher, systems of philosophy based on his discoveries began to appear. Others sprang to the defense of conservative philosophy. More and more natural theology came to be considered, sometimes as a prelude to revealed theology, but also without reference to Biblical tradition.

Denials of the accuracy of the Scriptures, based on these new philosophies did not lead to atheism or agnosticism. At least there is no record of atheists or agnostics in this period. The position farthest from orthodox Christianity was Deism. It appeared in America about the middle of the seventeenth century and later in Europe. Its underlying principle was that a rational religion must be independent of any special revelation; therefore it involved disbelief in miracles, including the Resurrection, and in the inerrancy of the Scriptures. The God of the Deists was a Being whose existence can be proved, who made the universe and the laws to govern it and then left the universe to be subject to those laws; in other words he was, as he has frequently been called, a watchmaker God.

Hordern says: [3] "Deism never got down to the common man; it was a religion for intellectuals only. Its power among the intellectuals is attested by the influence it had upon the writing of the Declaration of Independence." The Deists had neither churches nor organization. Many Deists remained members of established churches, but in the last decade of the seventeenth century fewer than 10% of the population of America belonged to any church. In 1773 the ratio in Virginia was about five per cent.

Unitarianism in the eighteenth and early nineteenth centuries constituted a relatively minor break with orthodox Christianity. Among the Unitarians the Trinity, inherited guilt, eternal punishment, and vicarious atonement were abandoned or regarded nonessential, but miracles were accepted. Creeds were rejected, not as incredible but as nonbiblical. Unlike the Deists, they did not depend upon a logical proof of the existence of God. Thomas Jefferson was essentially a Deist. He considered religion a private matter; he was intensely opposed to Calvinism, but he refused to join the Unitarians as firmly as he refused to join other churches. He wrote however, to James Smith in 1822: [4] "The present generation will see Unitarianism become the general religion of the United States;" and in a letter to Benjamin Waterhouse in the same year: "I trust that there is not a young man now living in the United States who will not die a Unitarian." Like most predictions about religion, Jefferson's was wrong. The Adams family were Unitarians. Although Emerson was too radical for the Unitarians of his time, the sect became more and more rationalistic and ready to welcome the new scientific views as they appeared; but numerically they have remained a minor denomination.

Two factors contributed to the fall of Deism, one philosophical and one religious. In the late eighteenth century the philosopher Kant demolished the proofs of God's existence which had been accepted as logical. Hordern says: [5] "The critique which Kant made of the proofs of God was a more serious blow to the Deists than it was to the orthodox, for rational proof of God was far more central to the former than to the latter." The other factor was the "Great Awakening", the first of the great revival movements. It began about 1730 with a few ministers who preached the necessity of conversion and a new life. The Great Awakening was not confined to any one denomination. One of the best known and most successful revivalists was Jonathan Edwards, a highly intelligent Congregational minister. Edwards and the other revivalists depended upon an emotional appeal rather than reasoning to win converts. Edwards said that while he rejected extremism in the form of overheated imagination, he thought it reasonable to frighten people from hell. His mission was to make hell a vivid concept and to prove that 'good works' and respectable living did not assure salvation. In one well-remembered sermon, he said: [6] "The God that holds you over the pit of hell, much as one holds a spider, or some loathsome insect over the fire, abhors you, and is dreadfully provoked; his wrath toward you burns like fire; he looks upon you as worthy of nothing else, but to be cast into the fire. . . . O sinner . . . You hang by a slender thread, with the flame of divine wrath flashing about it." Loetscher says: [7]"In such sermons he had to pause for quiet, for all over the building men and women were crying aloud in their distress, feeling that they were slipping into hell."

Other revivalists such as George Whitfield and James Davenport preached sermons equally emotion-provoking. During the first year more than 300 in Edwards' community professed conversion. The revivalist movement spread throughout New England. In a two-year period between 25,000 and 30,000 members were added to the New England churches out of a total population of only about 300,000. Naturally such methods, which would now be called "brain washing," were condemned by the less emotional churchmen. There is nothing in any of the prevalent theologies that says that God abhors or is wrathful toward man. A reaction of the "Old Light" faction, who were opposed to these sensational methods, set in, and Edwards was dismissed from his post. Later, however, he became president of Princeton Seminary.

This revivalist movement has been called a reaction against Deism. This does not mean that many Deists were converted; they were only a small portion even of the religious minority, and intellectuals are repelled rather than attracted by such appeals. The preaching had most effect upon the less intellectual and less educated and greatly increased the number of Christians among them. Even today estimates of the value of the Great Awakening vary. A favorable review is provided by Loetscher: [8]"In spite of its emotional excesses, the Great Awakening was a permanent blessing to America. Hitherto Christianity in the colonies had been a rather austere enterprise for the spiritually select; now the gospel came home to the common man with overpowering effectiveness. The Great Awakening decided that America should be, not a pagan, but a Christian land. It stimulated moral earnestness, missionary zeal, philanthropy, cooperation across denominational lines, and the founding of educational institutions. It gave new value and confidence to the average man and so contributed to the development of democracy in America. It strengthened the nonestablished churches more than the established, and so helped to prepare for religious freedom. But later revivalism's emphasis on emotion often undermined sober religious thinking, and its almost exclusive interest in individuals greatly weakened the idea of the church." On the other side of the question, Wish says: [9] "In morals and customs, the revivals produced a narrow 'Puritanism', condemning as sinful 'wanton' tunes, dancing, horseracing, and other popular recreations." One might add, it also encouraged resistance to intellectual progress. Whatever its vices and virtues, the Great Awakening was part of the Romantic reaction to the intellectualism of the period following the scientific discoveries of the seventeenth century.

Just after the Revolution, the percentage of church members in the country was not much higher than in the early part of the century. The second Great Awakening, about 1830, was similarly a reaction to the eighteenth century Age of Reason. It depended upon emotionalism just as the first did. It was one of several factors contributing to the gradual increase in church membership which has occurred since that time, and has tended to keep religious thought conservative. The people affected by these revivals are likely to be unstable, and the effect is very often temporary, but it must be admitted that some have been led to more useful lives. There have been many revivals since these Great Awakenings. Their methods have been similar, although there has been a tendency toward saner methods and greater appeal to reason, as a comparison of Billy Graham with Jonathan Edwards will demonstrate. In some local revivals excessive emotionalism is conspicuously absent, and in all of them it is much less evident.

The effect on religion of the scientific developments from Copernicus to Galileo were all based on changes in the literal acceptance of the first two chapters of Genesis and other passages in the Bible implying the old cosmogony, and the reduction of man almost to insignificance in the universe. Newton's conception of gravitation did away with the necessity for God to keep the universe going. But all through these changes man remained in a unique position as the direct creation of God, and next to Him, master of the universe, or of this earth at least, although it was frequently questioned whether other planets were inhabited. We shall pass over the theological literature of the period, which consists of attacks on and defenses of the new scientific system and attempts to harmonize it with the Word of God. Natural theology was the cornerstone of Deist belief; it was of very little importance in orthodox theology; and there were many intermediate positions. The occurrence of miracles was accepted, but opinion varied as to the extent to which they could be accounted for by natural causes. The line between conservative and liberal thinkers became more sharply drawn.

One consequence of this continuous dispute was the development of Pietism in Germany and Methodism in England. The thought of their founders was that whatever the truth of the rival doctrines, the essential feature of Christianity is the awakening of the emotions which support the good moral life.

In the nineteenth century the effects of astronomical discoveries on Christian theology were overshadowed by those of the theory of evolution and of higher criticism. Although Darwin's theory applied only to the organic world, the broadest form of the idea of evolution includes the inorganic world also. The fundamental idea dates back to the Chaldeans. In fact the first chapters of Genesis describe a form of evolution in the broad sense. Even this view of evolution was disputed by some of the early theologians. The question between them was whether the world was created all at once or in six days. As a compromise, [9]"Thomas Aquinas drew from Augustine a subtle distinction. 'God created the substance of things in a moment, but gave to the work of separating, shaping, and adorning this creation six.days.' " Calvin insisted on a six-day period, and this was incorporated into the Westminster catechism. In the seventeenth century, Dr. John Lightfoot, Vice Chancellor of the University of Cambridge, declared: [10]"Heaven and earth, center and circumference, were created in the same instant, the clouds full of water, and this took place and man was created by the Trinity on October 23, 4004 B.C., at 9 o'clock in the morning." This date was calculated by accepting Biblical records literally, and using the most prob able suppositions in cases of contradiction. It was a question even to early thinkers, however, how the creation of light (on the earth) took place before that of the sun. Within two centuries it was established that highly developed civilizations existed long before the reckoned date of creation.

The history of evolutionary theory has been related briefly in the preceding chapter. Its violent shock to the beliefs of the time lay in a great reduction in the importance of man in the universe. Instead of a special creation at the head, man was relegated to one of a number of end-points of evolution. Some fundamentalists save the position of man by believing that evolution may account for all beings except man, and by accepting the meaning of "day" in the first chapter of Genesis to mean a very long period. They still insist that man was a special creation. The conflict over the theory was not entirely between science and theology; there were scientists who opposed evolution and there were churchmen who accepted purposeful evolution, usually with these modifications, from the first. Later in the century it was accepted by an increasing number of theologians.

Historical criticism had an even greater impact on religious thought than did evolution. The application of science to history was a consequence of the rise of the scientific method. In its nature history cannot be an experimental science, and can be a science at all only to the extent that scientific methods can be applied to it. At every point in every historical account the question arises, "Is this true?" The ideal solution of the problem would be to invent a "history machine" which would give by a sort of photographic method an objective account of everything that took place. But it would be too late now to set up such a machine, if one existed, for events already past. Another objection is that such an objective account would provide only a part of the material of history. The motives, the desires, the ideals of people would not be recorded or transmitted by the machine, unless its design could be more greatly complicated by having it connected to the nervous system of every individual; and it is a serious question whether it would work even then.

If there were a history machine, the first interest of most historians and theologians would be in the period 4000 B.C. to perhaps 100 A.D., or more especially 2000 to 1000 B.C. and about 4 B.C., to 35 A.D.; that is, the dates corresponding to the periods of the patriarchs, the Exodus, and the life of Christ. But since no such machine is possible, we must be contented with the results of other methods. There are three such methods practicable; radiocarbon dating, language studies, and archeology. Radiocarbon dating tells with considerable accuracy the time which has elapsed since the transformation of the nitrogen of the upper air into the carbon of plants, which are used in paper, burned in fires, or enter into various materials. There are no cases in which radiocarbon dating has been applied directly in the study of the Bible; the books of the Bible found in the Dead Sea caves were not the original writings.

The language method, that is the comparison of the language used in a document with that of a known date, has been used ever since its discovery. A number of fairly ancient copies of the Old Testament exist in Hebrew, Greek, and other languages. Every translation of the Bible has been aided by a careful comparison of such documents. There are inconsistencies which must be

explained in each of these texts. A brief attentive reading of the
Bible will reveal a number of such passages.

Archeology has proven very useful in the critical study of the
Bible. Archealogical studies showed that as far back as the date
assigned to creation a great civilization was flourishing in Mesopotamia; that 2,000 years before the date given for the migration
of Abraham Chaldean civilization was advanced in art, science,
and literature; and that many stories resembling those in the Bible,
especially in Genesis, appeared much earlier in other countries.
The story of Moses in the bullrushes was told of King Sargon and
of other great personalities; there are chronological inconsistencies
in the book of Ezra and many exaggerations and improbabilities
in the book of Daniel. The value of archeological studies is summarized by White: [11] "But Egyptology, while thus aiding to sweep
away the former conception of our sacred books, has aided Biblical
criticism in making them far more precious; for it has shown them
to be a part of that living growth of sacred literature whose roots
are in all the great civilizations of the past, and through whose
trunk and branches are flowing the currents which are to infuse a
higher religious and ethical life into the civilizations of the future."
Higher criticism has been dependent upon both archeology and
language study.

It should be emphasized that "criticism" in the sense used
here does not mean opposition, as the word is sometimes interpreted. Textual or "lower" criticism has long been accepted by
the churches and is taught in the seminaries of all denominations.
It consists of study of all available ancient manuscripts for the purpose of determining as nearly as possible the original texts of
Biblical writings, thereby eliminating possible errors that have
occurred in copying and translation. So far as textual criticism is
concerned, it may be accepted that the Scriptures were verbally
inspired and hence absolutely authoritative. Higher or historical
criticism, however, has an aim far beyond the words of the original
texts. [12]"The critics now sought to answer such questions as the
following: What is the relation of the Biblical books to each other?
How were they written? By whom? When? What did the writers
intend to say? Were there historical causes which might account
for the recorded developments in the Scriptures? And what is the
relation of the Biblical records to other records of ancient times?"

Higher criticism made no progress during the first fourteen
centuries of Christianity. One complication and deterrent to its
study was that late in the pre-Christian era the Jewish theologians

had developed a system of interpretation of the Old Testament which was not only literal but also allegorical; different schools gave different allegorical interpretations. The Jewish philosopher and theologian Philo [13] "spoke reverently of the Jewish Scriptures as 'oracles'. Oracles they became; as oracles they appeared in the early history of the Christian church; and oracles they remained for centuries; eternal life or death, infinite happiness or agony, as well as ordinary justice in the world, were to depend on shifting interpretation of a long series of dark and doubtful utterances—interpretations frequently given by men who might have been prophets and apostles, but who had become simply oracle-mongers." The same methods of interpretation passed over into the Christian church, and were applied at times to the New Testament. In almost every instance in which a number is mentioned, it had some sort of mystic significance. Fantastic interpretations were given the simplest statements. Although there was some opposition, Origen in the third century, St. Augustine in the fifth, and others continued this method of interpretation, which prevailed for ten centuries. There were occasional efforts to present the claims of reason against these fantastic interpretations, but the evolution of unreason continued, and opponents were placed under the ban. Even Savonarola, who powerfully preached the gospel of righteousness, was under the spell of the allegorical method of exposition. There are still survivals of this method among minor sects.

In the fifteenth century, however, Lorenzo Valla used modern critical methods to prove that certain accepted documents were forgeries, and that the "Apostles' Creed" post-dated the apostles by several centuries. He also initiated the critical study of the New Testament. Fortunately the ruling Pope was not interested in orthodoxy, and so Valla escaped the penalties he would have incurred in earlier or later times. Later Erasmus attempted to purify the New Testament text and found an interpolation in the First Epistle of John referring to the Trinity. The passage, however, remained in the text until the recent revision, although Luther did not accept it. Erasmus also stated that some of the epistles attributed to the Apostle Paul were not his work.

[14]According to White, "On the coming in of the Reformation the great structure of belief in the literal and historical correctness of every statement of the Scriptures, in the profound allegorical meaning of the simplest texts, and even in the divine origin of the vowel pronunciation, towered more loftily and grew more rapidly than ever before. The Reformers, having cast off the authority

of the Pope and of the Universal Church, fell back all the more
upon the infallibility of the sacred books." Luther mildly repudiated some of the extreme views, and although Calvin went much
further in this repudiation, Luther's ideas finally prevailed. At
about this time the divine inspiration of the Vulgate (the Latin
translation of the Bible made in the fourth century), even when it
conflicted with Hebrew texts, came to be believed by the Catholic
Church. About the middle of the seventeenth century, Nikon,
Patriarch of the Russian Greek Church, attempted to correct the
Slavonic Scriptures, but was unsuccessful on account of strong
opposition. There are persons today who believe that only the
King James version is inspired.

Sir Isaac Newton was the first to apply scientific methods to
the study of the Scriptures, although some of his results had been
anticipated by Ibn Ezra in the twelfth century and by Spinoza in
1670, shortly before Newton's work. [15]"From internal evidence
he (Newton) not only discarded the text of the Three Witnesses
(in the passage in 1 John), but he also decided that the Pentateuch
must have been made up from several books; that Genesis was not
written until the reign of Saul; and that the books of Kings and
Chronicles were probably collected by Ezra; . . . and that the book
of Psalms and the prophecies of Isaiah and Daniel were each
written by various authors at different dates." On the other hand,
he also made an exposition of the Apocalypse, the book of
Revelation, making it a prediction of the entire future of mankind.

From this time on, there were critical scholars both within
and outside the Church; some were ecclesiastics and some were
not; but they all endeavored to find out the truth as nearly as possible. As Hordern says: [16]"Albert Schweitzer points out that some
of the first critics to contribute to our knowledge of the New
Testament were enemies of Christ, men who looked at the Bible
critically because they hoped to destroy the religion based upon it.
But the Church quickly took Bible criticism unto itself, and in
time the seminaries became the centers of critical research. This
was not achieved without a battle; but the critics slowly won their
case, although many a scholar lost his position in the process."
There is no modern critic whose aim is to ridicule the Bible. It
is true that some, like Robert Ingersoll, have used the results of the
critics to cast aspersions on the whole Bible and on Christianity;
but they contributed nothing to the study. One of Spinoza's conclusions was that to [17]"look for exact knowledge of natural and
spiritual phenomena in the sacred books is an utter mistake, and

that the narratives of the Old and New Testaments, while they surpass those of profane history, differ among themselves not only in literary merit, but in the value of the doctrines they inculcate." Two principles that he derived are: (1) Sacred Scripture *contains* the word of God, and is therefore incorruptible; and (2) that error in speculative doctrine is not impious.

Kuehnen published *The Religion of Israel* in 1869. He showed that the true starting point for research into the history and literature of Israel is to be found in the utterances of the great prophets of the eighth century before our era. He showed also that Old Testament history is largely mingled with myth and legend; that the laws of Moses were a late development and that much of their historical setting was an afterthought; also that Old Testament prophecy was never supernaturally predictive. Wellhausen was one of the most thorough and best known of the critics. White says: [18]"Every revelation of new knowledge encountered outcry, opposition, and repression; and, what was worse, the ill-judged declarations of some unwise workers in this critical field were seized upon and used to discredit all fruitful research. Wellhausen met all this opposition successfully. Reverently, but honestly and courageously, with clearness, fulness, and convincing force, he summed up the conquests of scientific criticism as bearing on Hebrew history and literature." The science of Biblical criticism met the least opposition in Germany and Holland. In England, in addition to conservatism, the evangelical movement was still alive. [19]"Orthodoxy was the vaunt of the University of Oxford. A riot ensued when Edward Everett, a minister from the United States, spoke at the receipt of an honorary degree at that institution, because he was thought to have been in his early life, and to be possibly at the time, below what was then the Oxford fashion in belief, or rather feeling, regarding the mystery of the Trinity." Pusey at the center of biblical teaching at Oxford had ventured to defend Holy Writ with the argument that there were fishes actually existing which could have swallowed the prophet Jonah. He was attacked on the scriptural ground that the fish was created for the express purpose of swallowing Jonah.

A number of other critics expressed views similar to those just cited; they all met opposition and ridicule. In America Theodore Parker pioneered in the new ideas. White says: [20]"Beautiful and noble as were his life and his life work, he was widely abhorred. On one occasion of public worship in one of the more orthodox churches, news having been received that he was dangerously ill, a prayer was openly made that this arch-enemy might be removed from earth. He was even driven out from the Unitarian body." In 1862 *The Pentateuch and the Book of Joshua Critically Examined,* by Bishop Colenso of Natal appeared, again expressing liberal views, and it encountered the usual amount of opposition. But finally a fairer spirit prevailed. In 1893 Sanday gave at Oxford some lectures on Inspiration, in which concessions to the newer criticism were made. The views were accepted. Benson, Archbishop of Canterbury, instead of prosecuting authors of some liberal essays, asked the famous question, "May not the Holy Spirit make use of myth and legend?"

At about this period the methods which had been applied to the Bible were also followed in studying other ancient writings. In that field as in the Biblical, myth was distinguished from fact by the critical methods. Even here authors did not escape persecution, especially when their field was Jewish history. As in the case of Biblical study, however, a liberal spirit finally prevailed.

"Critical writings were suppressed in Catholic countries. [20a]*The Study of Sacred Scripture* by Pope Leo XIII took pains to insist that there can be no error of any sort in the sacred books; it even defended those parts which Protestants consider apocryphal as thoroughly as the remainder of Scripture, and declared that the book of Tobit was not compiled by man, but written by God. He condemned higher criticism, but dwelt on the necessity of the most thorough study of the Sacred Scriptures, and especially of adjusting scriptural statements to scientific facts. According to the Jesuit Father Clarke, the Pope had no thought of denying the variety of documents in the Pentateuch, the plurality of sources of the books of Samuel, the twofold authorship of Isaiah, or the spuriousness of the final portion of the last chapter of Mark beginning with the ninth verse; he dwelt significantly on the power of the papacy at any time to define out of existence any decisions which may be found inconvenient. He declared that there is a human element in in the Bible pre-calculated for by the Divine. These utterances may prove a better bridge between the old and the new than could have been framed by engineers more learned but less astute."

The following are results of higher criticism that are generally, although not unanimously accepted by scholars.

(1) The book of Genesis and some of the other historical books are the work of more than one author, whose writings have been blended so as to retain as much as possible of each text. The result is sometimes a confusing and contradictory account;

examples may be found in the story of the Flood and in the account of the selection of Saul as king.

(2) The Pentateuch was not the work of Moses but was written at a much later date.

(3) Therefore, the literal accuracy of the Scriptures is denied. Such persons as Adam, Methuselah, and Noah are probably allegorical. Abraham, Isaac, Jacob, and others are legendary and their actual existence is uncertain.

(4) Authorities differ about the sojourn in Egypt and the Exodus. Some authorities have concluded that the events recorded are not at all historical; others believe that only a small number of Hebrews went to Egypt and they or their descendants returned.

(5) The Ten Commandments were not given full-fledged by God at Mount Sinai, but represent a gradual development over the years, and were not written in their final form until the captivity or later. At one time they may have been in competition with another set of commandments (Exodus 24) that were formal rather than ethical.

(6) The greater part of the book of Isaiah was written by two persons who lived about two centuries apart, one at the time originally accepted, and the other, whose actual name will probably be forever unknown, who lived during the captivity.

(7) Some of the miracles are fictitious and others have a rational explanation.

(8) King David wrote few of the Psalms, if any. Solomon did not write the Proverbs, Ecclesiastes, or the Song of Solomon.

(9) The books of Job, Jonah, Esther, and Daniel are largely fiction.

(10) The Gospel of Mark was the first gospel to be written, and was one of the sources used by the authors of the Gospels of Matthew and Luke.

(11) The Gospel of John was written later than the other gospels, and probably not by the Disciple John. It is a theological interpretation, rather than a direct report, of Jesus' life and teachings.

(12) Paul did not write the Epistle to the Hebrews or the Epistle to the Ephesians. This conclusion about the book of Hebrews has been almost universally accepted for some time.

(13) The non-Pauline epistles were not written by the Apostles whose names they bear.

(14) The Book of Revelation was not written by the same author as the Gospel and Epistles of John.

In saying that these conclusions have been accepted I do not
mean to imply that they have been proved. They are the results
of the application of scientific methods; but it must be remembered
that the further one goes from physical science the less accurate
the method can be and the less conclusive are the results. J. H.
Jauncey says: "The author is grateful that he commenced this
study" (of higher criticism) "after considerable training in science.
After the rigorous methods of science, the procedures were often
appalling. At times the weightiest decisions were found to have
been made on the slightest and most trivial grounds. The whole
study was littered with assumptions without any substantiation in
fact. This, of course, is not true of all scholars, but this subjectiv-
ity is so prevalent that you cannot assume the reliability of histories
and "introductions" on the Bible. It will take some years before
facts and conjectures in this field can be separated."

The conclusions given above are among those that have
received the greatest approach to substantiation; but probably they
represent the maximum that is likely to be said against the complete accuracy of the Bible. Much of the most recent investigation
has tended to substantiate the accuracy of the Bible; many of the
negative conclusions had been reached because study seemed to
indicate that certain events could not have happened as long ago
as they were reputed to have occurred. Archeological or other
study that proved the *possibility* of that occurrence at the time
assumed would tend to corroborate the Biblical account. Examples
are: the presence of camels in Egypt in the patriarchal times; the
archeological accuracy of the description of the environment in the
Gospel of Luke and in the Acts; the discovery that houses were
built on the walls of Jericho; and that Belshazzar was acting as
king of Babylonia at the time of the Persian conquest. It remains
to be seen just how much this will affect the main question.

Besides the comparatively minor subjects just mentioned, the
following conclusions on the positive side of Biblical accuracy are
well established:

(1) The chronological records of the Old Testament are
fairly accurate, that is, within about twenty years, at least back to
the time of the reign of Solomon, but not as accurate as Assyrian
and Babylonian records.

(2) The writings of the prophets are mostly authentic, and
the dates of most of them have been established. The dual or
plural authorship of Isaiah has been mentioned. There may have
been additions to some of the others, but such additions are minor.

Themes running through all the prophetic writings are: protest against a materialistic idea of religion; belief that the Hebrews were God's chosen people; condemnation of injustice in their social and economic life; and belief that their continued existence and prosperity depended upon national righteousness.

(3) Jesus lived at about the time recorded and taught ideals which are fairly accurately presented. In contrast to belief about fifty years ago it is now generally concluded that he regarded himself as the Messiah and believed in the early coming of the Kingdom of God. There is no question that he was crucified or punished by a similar method.

(4) The teachings of Paul were founded more upon those of Jesus than on Greek philosophy, although they may have been to some extent influenced by the latter.

(5) By the time of the writings or final revision of the Gospels of Matthew and Luke, Christians believed in the Virgin Birth of Jesus at Bethlehem, although there was disagreement on some details, as shown by the divergent accounts in Matthew and Luke.

Soon after the beginning of the present century Albert Schweitzer entered the field of New Testament criticism. Some of his conclusions will be discussed in Chapter 7. Since his time no great critical works have appeared. The general tendency of the writings of this period has been toward conservatism, at least to the extent of withdrawal from some extremely liberal views.

Liberalism

The new conceptions of religious authority which led to historical criticism and the results of the critical method resulted in basic reorientations of Protestant thought. The principal effect was the rise of liberal theology. One of the first liberals, if not the first, was Schleiermacher (1768-1834). Dillenberger, who has presented the history of Christianity and its relation to science in considerable detail, thus summarizes his account of Schleiermacher: [21]"He brought the Newtonian world and the religious dimensions together without obscuring or mixing them. It was axiomatic that for Schleiermacher it could never be 'in the interest of religion so to interpret a fact that its dependence on God absolutely excludes its being conditioned by the system of nature.' And conversely, natural science was not to be hampered by the 'assumption of the absolutely supernatural.' For Schleiermacher, everything depended upon the apprehension of another order of reality in and through the natural order without conceiving of such an order in the spatial sense. In such matters Schleiermacher was indeed creative. In retrospect, we can easily see that his positive theological views were far too much under the influence of the very Enlightenment he wished to overcome. . . . He was culturally and methodologically significant, even if theologically wrong."

Albert Ritschl (1822-1889) was known as the theologian of practicality. According to him religion is based upon value judgments and is to be sharply separated from science. Hordern thus summarizes Ritschl's principles: [22]"Science tells us the facts, things as they are; but religion weighs the facts and deems some more valuable than others. The great fact about man is that, although he is a product of evolution, he has a sense of values. We can explain this only if we interpret the universe as one which creates not only atoms and molecules, but also values. For Ritschl God is not known intuitively, as for Schleiermacher, nor is God known from a rational inference from the world, as for the Deists. Instead, God is the necessary postulate to explain the sense of worth that man has."

[23]Adolph von Harnack reduces Christianity to three affirmations: belief in God the Father, divine sonship of man, and faith in the infinite value of the human soul. The teachings of Jesus can be summarized under three heads: (1) the kingdom of God and its coming; (2) God the Father and the infinite value of the human soul; and (3) the higher righteousness and the commandment of love.

Horace Bushnell criticized the orthodox doctrine of the atonement and popularized the idea of growing into Christianity. These were extreme views, as can be judged by the doctrines omitted in these statements; and most liberals did not depart as far as Harnack from orthodoxy. The spirit of liberalism meant open-mindedness toward new modes of thought and mutual sympathy and tolerance within Christianity. Four other themes of liberal Protestantism were more definitely derivative from the nineteenth century milieu: (1) respect for science and the scientific method; (2) tentativeness or skepticism as to the possibility of achieving certain knowledge of ultimate reality; (3) emphasis upon the principle of continuity; and (4) confidence in man and his future. Four other aspects were derived from its rooting in Christian tradition: (1) the authority of Christian experience; (2) the centrality of Jesus Christ; (3) criticism of the tradition from within; and (4) social idealism.

Unitarianism remains an extreme form of liberalism or modernism, which takes its stand first with the presuppositions of science and then seeks to reclaim what it can of the traditional faith.

Fundamentalism

A reaction to liberalism was the rise of fundamentalism, at the opposite extreme from modernism and Unitarianism. Both modernism and fundamentalism assume that traditional Christianity is essentially incompatible with modern thought; but modernism gives up the tradition, while fundamentalism seeks to preserve Christian doctrine intact from all attacks of science and modern skepticism. The word fundamentalism is taken from a series of tracts published in 1912-1914 called "The Fundamentals," by Dr. C. C. Laws, but it had appeared as a definite movement in the last quarter of the nineteenth century. Many representatives of this school preferred the name "Conservative Christianity" or just "Christianity." There is no recognizable difference between the doctrines of the fundamentalists and those of the church before the scientific era. The difference is that they were now reasserted in spite of all the evidence that science and liberal thought had brought against them. They included: (1) the verbal inspiration of the Scripture; (2) the Virgin Birth of Christ; (3) the bodily Resurrection; (4) the substitutionary atonement; and (5) the expectation of Christ's visible return. The evidence for the last four of these doctrines rests upon the first. If the higher critics have been successful in discrediting the verbal inspiration of the Bible and hence its absolute accuracy, we are dependent upon the reliabilty of good memory of many individuals. This does not merely apply to the events in the first chapters of Genesis but to the life of Christ. We cannot be sure that He said and did what is recorded in the Gospels, nor can we be sure that Paul's theology has a sound basis. Although allowance can be made for minor errors, Dillenberger and Welch state the Fundamentalists' position thus: [24]"Either the words of the Bible are infallibly the words of God or we have no basis for our faith. It is all or none. Moreover, the fundamentalist sees in the Biblical criticism a denial of the uniqueness of Christianity, for the indisputable proof of Christianity lies in the miracles and the fulfillment of prophecy recorded in the Bible. To deny that the prophets foretold in detail the coming of Christ, or to deny the historicity of the Biblical miracles, is to reject the signs by which God's activity is recognized. If these be not accepted, then Christianity has no claim to final truth."

The views just expressed were not, and are not, confined to uneducated people. John Machen,[25] one of the leading fundamentalists, was one of the most learned Biblical scholars in America. He presented a plausible defense of fundamentalism against every opposing argument. He and other conservatives admitted that many versions of the Bible have existed. Their contention was that the original text was free from error, but that God permitted that text to be lost because He knew that man would worship it. Another prominent fundamentalist was E. J. Carnell. In his *Introduction to Christian Apologetics,* to quote Hordern, [26] "he uses 350 pages in presenting a closely reasoned argument, tested by coherency and ability to explain the facts. He reveals a knowledge of modern philosophy, science, and non-fundamentalist theology. He attacks every effort to shield religion from the responsibility of defending itself rationally. He will not allow it to hide behind the intuitions of mysticism or feeling with Schleiermacher, nor will he allow it to express itself in the contradictory paradoxes of Karl Barth. He has only one reason for accepting conservative Christianity; it explains all the facts of existence more coherently than any alternative philosophy. One may not agree with the arguments of the book, but no one can call it obscurantist or irrational." Carnell proposed a theory which he called "threshold evolution" that attempted to harmonize the Bible and evolutionary theories.

To these arguments the opponents of fundamentalism could reply that no matter what effects the denial of the verbal inspiration and accuracy of the Scripture may have, the denial rests on a thorough scientific study of the Bible; there may be mistakes in some of the conclusions, but altogether so many contradictions have been discovered that one cannot conceive that God would have permitted them, nor based the fundamental philosophy of the universe on an inaccurate collection of statements. One must begin there and develop a philosophy consistent with those facts. The natural antithesis to fundamentalism is atheism, but a comparatively small number of persons have adopted atheism. The others feel that there is a middle ground, not so much from the logical aspect of the controversy as from a compulsive feeling that there is something in Christianity too deep to be ruled out by the failure to accept everything that is implied in fundamentalism. Nonfundamentalists believe that the sense of security presented by fundamentalists is false. If Columbus had a similar sense of security he would never have discovered America, nor, to use a Biblical illustration, would Abram have left his comfortable home at Ur for a life among possibly hostile strangers. Fundamentalism sets definite limits to our religious reasoning; scientific philosophy says that we are at the beginning of the knowledge of the world, and that duty as well as curiosity and adventure call us forward to discover what truths may be in the scientific and philosophical fields, and even in the theological field, and that we should resist the temptation to security based on the assumption that the ideas of any one person, book, or group of persons are absolutely authoritative. Moreover, the scientist or scientific philosopher does not expect a day when there will be nothing left to know. His look is forward; that of the fundamentalist is backward.

During the first quarter of this century the fundamentalists had the upper hand in most Protestant denominations. Liberal professors in seminaries, students who were about to be ordained, and even ordained clergymen were attacked and many lost their positions. It was not long however, before liberals began to win the battles. The first dissension occurred in the Northern Baptist Convention. It began in 1917 with the discovery that the teachings of its foreign missionaries did not correspond to the literal gospel of orthodoxy. The seminaries where the missionaries were trained were investigated and found wanting in this respect. After much heated discussion the investigating committee recommended leaving decisions of such doctrinal matters to the local church bodies. Most of the leaders finally decided that they were Baptists before they were fundamentalists, and although the decision was not agreeable to everyone, it still remains. The doctrines of the churches composing the Southern Baptist Convention were unaffected. The Conservative Baptist Association of America separated from the Northern Baptist Convention in 1947.

The Presbyterian Church of the U.S.A. (the "Northern Presbyterian" Church) was the scene of the most widely publicized disputes. The General Assemblies of 1910, 1916, and 1923 recommended the five doctrines given earlier as essential. Alarmed at the trend toward liberalism in 1927 William Jennings Bryan attempted to have these five doctrines adopted as requirements for all candidates for the ministry. His proposal was rejected by the assembly. Instead the [27]"Auburn Affirmation" was adopted. The essential paragraph of that Affirmation is: "We all believe from our hearts that the writers of the Bible were inspired of God; that Jesus Christ was God manifested in the flesh; that God was in Christ, reconciling the world unto Himself, and that through Him we have our redemption; that having died for our sins He rose

from the dead and is our everliving Saviour; that in His earthly
ministry He wrought many mighty works, and by His vicarious
death and unfailing presence He is able to save to the uttermost."
Although at first sight this statement may seem to uphold fundamentalist doctrine, there are important differences, and what it
omits is significant. Points brought out in the discussions include
the denial that the Scriptures were "kept from error" and the affirmation that there is no authority for the General Assembly to declare
what the church teaches. "The statement that the five doctrines
are essential is not warranted." The Assembly of 1927 ruled that
the Assembly may not, without the joint action of the Presby-
teries, single out particular doctrines as "essential" and binding
upon all ministers. Loetscher says: [28]"Thus the church declined
to adopt the platform of so-called 'fundamentalism'. Though
fundamentalists courageously warned the church of dangers
involved in theological change, the times called for more sympathetic understanding of contemporary thought and for more profound analysis of the essence of Christianity than was offered by
fundamentalism."

These changes did not mean that the Presbyterian church
became liberal. The tone of the Auburn Affirmation, it will be
noted, was permissive, not mandatory. To this day the number of
clergy who deviate from the original doctrines is comparatively
small, and those of the laity very much smaller. In the same year,
1927, Harry Emerson Fosdick was dismissed from a Presbyterian
pastorate on account of his liberal views. [29]Among them, which
he shared with other liberals, were the rejection of the exact
truth of Scripture, the idea of a gradually developing religious consciousness, rejection of miracles as facts, and approach to the scientific spirit. After his dismissal he accepted a pastorate in the
Baptist Church, in which greater variations in doctrine were
permitted.

In 1929 Machen attempted a reorganization of Princeton
Seminary, where he taught, so that the teaching would stress fundamentalism, but he failed. He then resigned and helped to found
Westminster Seminary in Philadelphia. Machen also considered
the teachings of some of the missionaries heretical, and he and
others founded an independent mission board. The Presbyterian
Church was successful in legally dismantling this board in 1936,
and its members were expelled. Machen and others then founded
a new denomination known as the Presbyterian Church of America. Dr. Machen died January 1, 1937, and his leadership was

continued by E. J. Carnell, Carl McIntire, and others. In 1939 the name of the denomination was changed to the Orthodox Presbyterian Church; later the Bible Presbyterian Church seceded from the parent organization on the ground that it had too much of a spirit of compromise toward the liberal branches. When the United Presbyterian Church of the U.S.A. was formed, in 1958, these two factions naturally refrained from joining with the main body. Each of these fundamentalist churches is represented by fewer than one hundred congregations. The position of the Presbyterian Church in the U.S. (the "southern Presbyterian" Church) was generally considered to be fundamentalist, and it did not unite with the other branches of Presbyterians, but in 1962 it passed resolutions similar to the Auburn Affirmation and therefore stands on the same basis regarding fundamentalism as the United Presbyterian Church.

The course of belief in some of the other Protestant denominations was similar to those in the Presbyterian and Baptist churches. A schism arose in the Disciples of Christ, and some branches remain fundamentalist. One branch merged with the Congregational Church. In the latter, called the Congregational Christian Church, as in the Baptist, local congregations are autonomous. There is a division of belief in the Protestant Episcopal Church, but no organizational break. In the Methodist Episcopal Church, in which the emphasis is on life rather than on doctrine, the fundamentalist-modernist dispute took a minor place, and the general tenor of belief is more liberal than in the other groups mentioned. In the Lutheran Church a large group of extreme fundamentalists comprise the Missouri Synod, but most other groups are more liberal. An Independent Fundamentalist Church of America, unconnected with other denominations, was established in 1930, and several small independent fundamentalist groups have been formed. More than ninety per cent of all members of Christian churches in the United States are associated with two dozen religious bodies, including subgroups of the denominations mentioned. The other ten per cent are members of smaller sects, practically all of which are fundamentalist, and some of which have extra-biblical beliefs. It is significant that according to a survey made by the National Council of Churches in 1951, the largest *per centage* membership gains from 1926 to 1949 were made by some of these minor denominations, making their gains in numbers of the same magnitude as those of some of the larger denominations.

It is not to be wondered that fundamentalists were and are

concerned about their differences with liberalism. Fundamentalists have at the basis of their belief the divinity of Christ, the verbal inspiration and therefore accuracy of the Bible, the Virgin Birth, the Resurrection, and eternal life in a place which depends upon acceptance of these beliefs. Liberalism seems to be another religion, which some Fundamentalists denounce as anti-Christian or not Christianity. One cannot strictly speaking call any of its variations true liberalism, but it is fair in general to say that Liberalism consists of the acceptance of the words of Jesus as a guide for life without inquiring into the historical truth of any of the factors of fundamentalist belief that have been mentioned. Liberals could retaliate that they are the true Christians and the fundamentalists are paulinians. They follow [30]"The teachings of Christ rather than the theology of Paul."

A very large proportion of Christians in the United States are fundamentalists. Most of them are passive, simply accepting the doctrine without thought or desire to think. A small number, mostly in the separated denominations, are militant fundamentalists. Fundamentalism is not so much an attitude of thought as an emotional reaction. They charge that the liberals by abandoning the only true way expose themselves to the propaganda of Marxian atheistic Communism. Communism has a fanatical appeal to its zealots; no such devotion exists in the Christian religion, except among the fundamentalists. It must be admitted that so far no kind of liberalism has the emotional appeal of fundamentalism.

It has been frequently stated that fundamentalism is disappearing. It is, apparently, in the seminaries, but it is still fairly strong among laymen who are active in the church. It is stronger in the East than in the West; in the South than in the North; in rural areas than in cities; and among laymen than among the clergy. It is significant that at a recent General Assembly of the Presbyterian Church, a man who did not believe in the Virgin Birth was selected as a regional officer in California, and that the strongest objection to his appointment came from a Pittsburgh layman. The general tone of the literature distributed by the United Presbyterian Church of the U.S.A. (the newly combined Presbyterian church) is cautiously modern orthodox; but in individual churches there are many members who do not know that fundamentalism is not a requirement for membership, or even for ordination, and others who think that non-fundamentalists should be expelled from the church. There are many other members who know nothing of these diverse views and many who are not interested. In the Baptist, Christian, and Congregational Churches, which have no set creeds or general organization, the theological tone of the local church depends upon its members and its pastor. Many individual churches of these denominations are extremely fundamentalist, while some churches in large cities and university towns are noted for liberalism or modern orthodoxy. The situation in the Methodist Episcopal and Protestant Episcopal Churches is much the same as in the Presbyterian, except that in the Methodist church the average tone is somewhat more liberal.

Fundamentalism has not been as strong in Europe as in America. A movement, however, has arisen in Europe which has much in common with American fundamentalism. Dillenberger and Welch say, [31]"In this country some of the most rapidly growing sects (although still quite small) are fundamentalist, some with the addition of an expectation of the early return of Christ, and with the insistence on radical and overt signs of the working of the Holy Spirit, especially in conversion. . . . There are some signs at the present time that the fundamentalist position (except in the denominations just mentioned) is being modified—by less hostility to evolution (and science in general), by reinterpretation of the meaning of miracle (i.e. of the relation of the supernatural and the natural), and by a more liberal social outlook. If this trend continues, fundamentalism in the former sense will cease to exist and will have merged with other conservative patterns of Protestant thought." On the other hand, many false predictions have been made concerning the future of religion, for example that of Jefferson which was related earlier in this chapter.

Later Developments in Liberalism

Whereas there is little difference in the beliefs of different fundamentalists, those of liberals vary widely. The methods of liberalism include the attempt to modernize Christian theology (hence the term "modernism," which is practically synonymous with liberalism) and its refusal to accept religious beliefs on authority alone. Liberalism drew from the idealistic philosophy of Hegel, Lotze, and Royce, but the liberal theologian did not forget the Bible. For the liberal the Virgin Birth is not only unnecessary but also embarrassing, for he finds God at work in the birth of every child. Liberals emphasize immanence, that is, God as part of the universe, but most liberals have retained the belief that God is transcendent as well as immanent. Most liberals have been keenly interested in the search for the historical Jesus. Liberals as a whole have denied the doctrine of original sin, but many liberals insisted that they were taking sin more seriously than the fundamentalists. . . . All liberals emphasize ethics.

Hordern describes four main trends in liberalism, although many theologians cannot be fitted into any one of the four. On the left wing of the liberals there grew up a group known as humanists. In 1933 this group published a manifesto which was clearly naturalistic in philosophy. That is, it denied the existence of God, immortality, and the supernatural in general. For these it substitutes faith in man and his capabilities. Instead of looking beyond himself for help or dreaming of life after death, man is to fulfill and develop his personality. This leads to the necessity of remaking society so that it will minister to the growth of man. All things are to be judged by the effect they have on man and his welfare.

"The humanist claimed to be carrying the ideals of liberalism to their logical conclusion. Liberals had made God immanent; now humanism made Him completely immanent; God is the world; God is man and his dreams. Liberals had appealed to religious experience; now humanists identify religion with experience. Wherever there is the experience of the integration of personality, there is religion. Liberals had emphasized ethics and judged religion by its ethical fruits; now religion is to be identified with ethics. Liberals had humanized the Bible; humanists see that it is a purely human book. Liberals emphasized the humanity of Jesus; humanists see Him as a good man, a good teacher, although hampered by a pre-scientific view of the universe. But He is not to be preferred to other ethical teachers past and present. Liberalism, the humanist charged, had recognized the right of science to enter all fields, but somehow it got cold feet when it was suggested that science could solve all problems. Liberalism, in short, is condemned for being a halfway reform; its supporters have seen the promised land from afar but have been afraid to enter it." Most humanists are not members of any church, and they have no organization.

Charles Hartshorne thus characterizes humanism: [32]"In general, humanists hold that, so far as we know, man is the highest type of individual in existence, and that therefore if there is any proper subject of religious devotion, any real 'God', it can only be humanity considered in its noblest aspirations and capacities together with nature so far as expressed in and serviceable to humanity. . . . Humanism is not so much atheism as a reinterpretation of God, not so much irreligion as an attempt to separate the human kernel of religion from its supernatural husks."

Tillich defines humanism thus: [33]"Humanism is the attitude which makes man the measure of his own spiritual life, in art and philosophy, in science and politics, in social relations and personal ethics. For humanism the divine is manifest in the human; the ultimate concern of man is man. All this, of course, refers to man in his essence; the true man, the man of the idea, not the actual man, nor the man in estrangement from his true nature."

A second form of liberalism was known as "The Empirical Philosophy of Religion." Its advocates sought a religion that could be based squarely upon the scientific method. One of its leading advocates, A. N. Wieman, states among other things that the time has come to quit arguing about the existence of God; God is to be defined so that His existence cannot be denied. One of his definitions of God is [34]"that character of events to which man must adjust himself in order to attain the highest good and avoid the greatest evils." Another wing of the empirical school is associated with personalist philosophy. One of its leading exponents is E. S. Brightman and for him, religion is to be based primarily on experience, but experience consists of all conscious life. The most unique aspect of Brightman's theory is that God is limited. A third group of liberals is represented by Leroy Waterman in his book *The Religion of Jesus*. Waterman finds two religions in the Old Testament, so sharply distinguished from each other that they cannot possibly be interpreted as variations of one faith. First is the popular religion of the Jews which is nationalistic, and the other is that of the prophets. The latter renounces all nationalism and proclaims that God is for all men. It emphasizes ethical living. This religion would have been lost except that Jesus taught it again, broadening it with greater emphasis upon the love, mercy, and universality of God. Only recently has attention begun to be given which, it is believed, could sweep even greater areas than Communist philosophy in less time if only it were liberated from the entanglements of theology and church life.

The Evangelical Liberals, the fourth group, constitute the majority of liberal churchmen, including Harry Emerson Fosdick, W. A. Brown, Rufus Jones, and Henry Sloane Coffin. These men were alike in dedication to reason, openness of mind, and modern thought, but at the same time they were grounded in the Bible and the Christian tradition. Jones, typical of this school, feels that the arguments over whether Jesus was divine or human rests upon a mistaken conception of man. If we believe that man is essentially related to God, created in His image, the problem becomes simple. In Jesus we find one in whom the divine possibilities of man have come to full growth. Each of the first three groups of liberals have beliefs which represent a radical break away from orthodox Christianity. [35]"The Biblical God has disappeared completely from the humanists and he is hardly to be recognized in the concept of God used by the others. The uniqueness of Christianity is completely lost in all of them, and revelation is mostly denied or ignored. The idea of the divinity of Jesus is either abandoned or given a completely new meaning. The fourth type of liberalism disagreed with the first three on each score."

The disintegration of liberalism began as early as 1934. An implication of liberal theology, though many liberals would deny it, was that man was approaching perfection, at least that he was throwing off the yoke of his brute ancestry, and that sin is something that can easily be eliminated by reason and education. Never was a belief so thoroughly disproved by the course of events, including World War I and the depression of the thirties. Higher criticism and archeological research tended more to substantiate orthodox positions than had been supposed. The quest for the Jesus of history turned out to be a chase of the will-of-the-wisp. It was concluded that Paul's gospel about Jesus is not radically different from Jesus' gospel about Himself. The Gospel of John provided evidence that it was written earlier and is more reliable than had been supposed. In 1935 Fosdick surprised the entire church by a sermon "The Church must Go beyond Modernism", in which he abandoned some of the extreme views that he had maintained.

The most modern form of liberalism is called neo-liberalism. Potthoff thus summarizes its deviations from the earlier liberalism: (1) a larger idea of God; (2) a deepened view of man; (3) a profounder view of salvation (this will be discussed under the heading of salvation); and (4) a more vital view of the church. Neo-liberalism recognizes sin and the impossibility of remaking man by education and science. As yet there is no agreement on what is meant by the divinity of Jesus, but there is an increasing awareness that it must be taken seriously. Hordern says: [36]"Neo-liberals were forced to doubt that the real problem is to tell man how he ought to live. On the whole, man seems to know that. Is not the real problem how to remake man so that he can do as he ought?" Neo-liberals are ready to admit a need for some kind of mediator between God and man; they have a new sense of the importance of the church. Neo-liberals are not in complete agreement upon any set of beliefs. As Hordern says: "They are on the march, seeking for a camping ground."

Neo-Orthodoxy

Another factor that hastened the decline of the liberalism of the early century was the rise of neo-orthodoxy. The essence of this movement was a return to orthodoxy, but it was a changed orthodoxy. Certain aspects of liberal thought were retained. Fundamentalism was repudiated as completely by the neo-orthodox as by the liberal. Biblical criticism was accepted, sometimes in its most radical forms; but there were also reactions against liberal concepts, such as the supremacy of reason and the use of natural theology.

In Europe, according to Hordern, its most prominent advocates were Kierkegaard, Barth, and Brunner. Potthoff, however, puts existentialists in a separate class, and considers Kierkegaard as the first of the existentialists. It is difficult to separate the two groups, because all the neo-orthodox, modern orthodox, and neo-liberals have been more or less influenced by existentialism. Potthoff says about Kierkegaard [37]"Kierkegaard interpreted the human situation in terms of despair, indecision, vanity, and anxiety. He taught that each individual must do more than reflect on life in general; he must realize the reality of his own existence as a person threatened by death and destruction. It is not enough to say, 'All men must die.' One must face the fact, 'I shall die.' It is not enough to be a spectator of life—one must be a participant in the dreadful pain and splendor of being human. This is what it is to face the fact of one's own unique existence." . . . The vital question is not 'What is Christianity?' but 'What is it for me to be a Christian?' For Kierkegaard, being Christian involves a radical 'leap of faith'—a complete commitment of self without regard to the cost. In this radical leap of faith one exercises his freedom, becomes a true self, is confronted by God in Jesus Christ, and comes to know the certainty of divine grace and forgiveness of sins. Kierkegaard was certain that God is love—but one comes to know that love only out of the background of despair and in the radical leap of faith." In Kierkegaard's lifetime (1813-1855) he was scarcely known outside Denmark, but through the influence of Karl Barth, he has become one of the best known Protestant theologians.

Niebuhr is the foremost American neo-orthodox thinker. He regards his theology as simply a rediscovery of the lost wisdom of Christian orthodoxy. Theology, according to him, is the attempt to express the dimensions of depth in life. Niebuhr applies the term "myth" to this form of thinking. By "myth" he means [38]"that, which, although it deceives, none the less points to a truth that cannot be adequately expressed in any other form. It is deceitful and yet true, just as is the deception of depth which is attained by the artist." This is in contrast to fundamentalism, which "takes the myths literally and thus enters into conflict with science over evolution. But such an interpretation is not only absurd science, it is also false religion. It over-simplifies the relation of God to the world. Liberalism saw in these myths only simple folk tales and prescientific speculation." Niebuhr, however, insists that we must take such myths seriously but not literally. So interpreted, they reveal true insights into the God-man relationship. For example, the story of Adam and Eve does not describe the first man and woman historically, but it is a mythical statement of the situation of every man and woman."

Kierkegaard and Barth put Christianity over and above reason. Modern liberalism stresses reason, as did Origen and Aquinas in the early days. [39]"The mistake of this school, believes Niebuhr," is that it prematurely grasps some principle of rationality to which all life must conform. It interprets all reality in terms of nature or mind, or in terms of nature or supernature. It knows clearly where reason ends and faith begins. In short, it pretends to know too much. Niebuhr may be said to have applied the Christian virtue of humility to thought." He feels that anti-rationalism is dangerous because it destroys the meaning of the gospel; this mode of thought lacks any standard by which we distinguish true from false revelation. Niebuhr's most characteristic concept is that of original sin. Sin arises from the fact that man is a finite creature, an animal, who is capable of spirituality. The only cure for man's sin lies in the Christian doctrine of salvation by grace. Sin arises from man's attempt to escape anxiety. One of the prevalent sins is self-righteousness. Niebuhr believes that it is impossible to identify Christianity with any social achievement. The tragedy of social life is that one must choose the lesser of two evils rather than an abstract absolute good. [40]"Niebuhr has, more than any other, raised America above the impasse of the fundamentalist-modernist controversy by daring to see values and errors on both sides. . . . Hardly a book on theology appears today which does

not take Niebuhr into serious consideration, even if it comes ultimately to an anti-Niebuhrian point of view."

Naturally there are shades of opinion in all these schools. The
theology of Paul Tillich is considered the boundary line between
liberalism and neo-orthodoxy. Tillich is a complex thinker, and
his theology cannot be easily summarized; but one example of his
thought may be of interest: [41]"For Tillich religion is not a matter
of certain beliefs or practices; it cannot be identified with the
traditional religions. A man is religious at the point where he is
ultimately concerned, and he is ultimately concerned when he
experiences the unconditional. . . . Ethical obligation, the striving
for truth, and beauty, all have elements of the unconditional in
them. An ultimate concern is one that takes precedence over all
the other concerns of life. . . . When one understands religion in
these terms, it is evident that religion is often found among the
so-called 'irreligious'. The atheist usually has an ultimate concern
for truth or for some other reality. In fact, says Tillich, we must
realize that the atheist may be saved by faith. His atheism may
arise from a commitment to, and ultimate concern with, truth.
Loyalty to truth will not allow him to believe in the God pictured
by a religion. But his loyalty to truth itself is a relationship to
God, although the atheist does not recognize it as such."

Modern Orthodoxy

A number of theologians are seeking a way between the
extremes of fundamentalism, liberalism, and neo-orthodoxy. There
is no definite name for this school, but Hordern suggest "modern
orthodoxy". "One of the most significant things about modern
orthodoxy is the appeal it has for laymen. Our age is witnessing
the rebirth of theology written by laymen, men and women whose
work and fame lie in other fields. The most prominent of these
are C. S. Lewis, [42]Dorothy Sayers, Herbert Butterfield, and Chad
Walsh. In each case these lay writers have found their way to a
modern orthodox position, repudiating fundamentalism and
liberalism as twin perversions of the faith and showing a bewilderment about neo-orthodoxy. But they have found spiritual enlightenment in a reinterpretation of the orthodox position."

The Social Gospel

Reference has been made earlier in the chapter to the movement known as the Social Gospel. A somewhat fuller exposition
follows.

Quotations are from the book, "The Decline and Revival of the Social Gospel" by Paul Carter.

Webster defines the Social Gospel as [43]"A movement in American Protestant Christianity initiated at the end of the nineteenth century and reaching its zenith in the first part of the twentieth century and dedicated to the purpose of bringing the social order into conformity with the teachings of Christ."

"Love one another" was one of Christianity's primary injunctions, but material aid to others was confined to care for the poor, with the exception of the brief experiment with communism. There is no evidence of interest in the welfare of non-Christians. This was true up to the time of the industrial revolution. The status quo was accepted in the economic sphere as in other fields. The industrial revolution of the sixteenth and seventeenth centuries, however, accentuated the difference between the favored and the unfavored. People worked at starvation wages; child labor even at tender ages was common; the twelve hour day was the general practice. Dickens and other authors dramatically called attention to these conditions. The Great Awakening of the eighteenth and nineteenth centuries aroused the consciences of many people to the existence of these evils as well as to those of slavery, drunkenness, war, and injustice to women.

All religious programs previous to the Great Awakenings had been based upon individual approach. Fundamentalists and others considered the winning of souls to the Faith to be the primary task of the Church. There was little reference to material welfare; it was believed that the financial status of the individual was ordained by God. This was a current belief in spite of the fact that the Old Testament prophets, as early as the seventh century B.C., decried social injustice, the oppression of the poor by the rich. Some reforms were accomplished by the passage of laws which greatly ameliorated prevailing conditions. For some reformers, however, that was insufficient and to them the only solution was to change the system by compulsion if necessary.

Looking back to the beginning of the Social Gospel we see three schools of thought, each of which offered a solution for social problems. The conservatives assumed that society was in need of reform, but went only to the extent of asking employers to raise wages rather than to found philanthropies. In general their approach was through individual action. At the opposite pole were the radicals who considered such measures worse than useless. They believed that the Christian should renounce his stake in existing society and work for a completely different type of social order. Their aim was the same as that of the Marxists except that the latter considered religion a deterrent to the revolution, while these radicals accepted communism as the goal of Christianity. Many even interpreted the teachings of Christ as communism. Did not Jesus advise the rich young ruler to sell all he had and give the proceeds to the poor?

In their short-sightedness they did not realize that Jesus was dealing with an individual case and not enunciating a general principle. The idea, "from each according to his ability, to each according to his need" is alluring. Social reformers have at many times envisioned such a state; the only conclusive argument against it is that it does not work.

The progressive school adopted a position intermediate between those of the conservatives and the radicals. They affirmed that the institutions of society should not be scrapped for others that might be no better; but institutional as well as personal changes would be required. Communism versus socialism is not to be considered a sharp dividing line between the radical and progressive groups but in general the goals of the progressive groups can be regarded as socialistic. Rauschenbusch, one of the chief advocates of the progressive position maintains that salvation is impossible so long as capitalism remains untouched.

The progressives also placed emphasis on the personality of Jesus and on his ethical teachings as they understood them as distinguished from the abstractions drawn from them by the Church. The ethical teachings were taken to include social reform. This progressive view was the surviving form of the Social Gospel. Some of the objectives of the conservative group had been accomplished by regulatory laws; the ideals of the radicals were too revolutionary to have broad appeal. It is more difficult to refute socialism than to refute communism on the same ground; several nations have experimented with socialism in varying degrees and with more or less questionable success. In this country State participation has for many years been confined to the postal system and the schools; its present actual and threatened inroads into other fields is being debated. One positive statement is that human freedom is curtailed to some extent by any socialistic advance.

The Welfare State assumes the form of a specter which haunts conservatives. [44]Webster defines "Welfare State" as "A social system based upon the assumption of a political state of primary responsibility for the individual and social welfare of its citizens, usually by the enactment of specific public policies (as health and unemployment insurance, minimum wages and prices, and subsidies to agriculture, housing and other segments of the economy) and their implementation directly by government agencies."

Advocates of the Social Gospel have not been unanimous in supporting socialism; moreover there have been other causes that have received their attention and support. The activities of the Social Gospel have included: temperance and prohibition; pacifism; sympathy with labor unions; ecumenicalism and internationalism.

It has been said that the Federal Council of Churches was formed to implement the Social Gospel. The active movements were sponsored by that body which was later succeeded by the National Council of Churches.

Carter writes "Labor was the area of the Social Gospel's earliest concern. In 1928 the 12-hour day in steel was abolished. The dry crusade had profounded kinship with the Social Gospel. The Federal Council of Churches spent $150,000 to put Prohibition across. The better index of the post-War (I) Social Gospel was the issue of the entering of international affairs directly into American domestic politics. Denominational weeklies stood against isolationism, prepared by the enormous expansion of foreign missions. Religious sentiment was readily transferred to a Wilsonian secular internationalism. Cruder varieties of American Firstism did not appeal to the missionary minded. The churches, especially the Methodist worked for the "League of Nations."

"The general trend of Fundamentalism was a strong dissent from the Social Gospel." The Late John Machen and his successor Carl McIntire, leading Fundamentalists, who founded the American Council of Churches in 1941 accused the Federal Council of Churches of Modernism, Liberalism and fellow traveling with the Pope.

The course of the Social Gospel was not continuous progress; the unprecedented prosperity of the late twenties caused a shifting of thought toward conservatism; people thought this must be a pretty good world after all, even though the capitalists were at the head of it. The great depression of 1929 furnished the terrible lesson which was required to break the mold of the churchmen's minds." Eventually the nature of the Social Gospel changed somewhat. Its aims were no longer considered absolute; it would not mean that the Kingdom of God had come, but it would mean that the Kingdom was a little nearer.

Carter again says: "The ministerial generation of the 50's and 60's, the product of this Niebuhriam atmosphere, will determine whether these ideas can be made to take root in American cultural soil, and whether the Church has succeeded in changing *with* the times without adapting itself *to* the times. In an age which makes a fetish of adjustment to a norm and powerfully facilitates that adjustment through the pressure of the mass media of communication, such a success would be a contribution of incalculable importance to American Society in addition to saving the soul of the American Church."

The part of the Unions in achieving some of the aims of the Social Gospel movement cannot be ignored. The contributions of the unions were incalculable, and if the various organizations have come to wield undue influence we must not forget that in the struggle between Management and Labor, Management was the first offender.

In the early days of the Social Gospel conservatives were as much interested in some of its goals as the liberals; later, fundamentalists have strongly opposed it, on both religious and patriotic grounds. They are conservative politically as well as theologically; they are among the strongest supporters of free enterprise and capitalism. They do not believe that Jesus advocated changes in the social order; some have gone so far as to say that he taught capitalism.

The advocates of the Social Gospel, therefore, are in general the liberals.

Chapter VI

Some Concepts In Religion

A MONG A NUMBER of concepts which are essential features of most religions, the first is the definition of religion itself. The word is of doubtful etymology. Cicero connected it with *relegere*, to read again; later authors, trace it to *religare*, to bind, in the sense of taboo which meaning has been generally accepted. In *Religion without Revelation,* Julian Huxley presents and discusses critically the definitions of religion given by a number of authors. He points out that belief in a god or gods is not an indispensable feature; Buddhism, for instance, does not involve such a belief. He says: [1]"There have been many attempts to define religion and the number of definitions produced is almost as great as the number of men who have attempted definition. What is more, many of the definitions are mutually contradictory." Examples are: "Morality tinged with emotion," by Matthew Arnold; "The perception of the infinite under such manifestations as are able to influence the moral character of man," by Max Muller; "A propitiation or conciliation of powers superior to man which are believed to direct and control the course of nature and of human life," by Sir James Frazer. Huxley quotes four definitions by Whitehead: [2](1) "Religion is force of belief cleansing the inward parts. . . . A religion, on its doctrinal side, can thus be described as a system of general truths which have the effect of transforming character when they are sincerely held and vividly apprehended;" (2) "Religion is what the individual does with his own solitariness;" (Huxley points out that the social character of religion is totally neglected in this definition); (3) "Religion is the art and theory of the internal life of man, so far as it depends on the man himself, and what is permanent in the nature of things; and (4) "Religion runs through three stages, if it evolves to its final satisfaction. It is the translation from God the Void to God the Enemy, and from God the Enemy to God the Companion." Huxley criticizes these definitions because they apply only to developed religions. He quotes the statement about religion in the Epistle of James: "Pure religion and undefiled before God is this, to visit the fatherless and the widows in their affliction, and to keep himself unspotted from the world," and points out that it is incomplete and does not claim to be a general definition. Another incomplete definition is the statement by T. H. Huxley [3] "Together with the awe and reverence, which have no kinship with base fear, but arise whenever one tries to pierce below the surface of things, whether they be material or spiritual, constitute all that has any unchangeable reality in religion."

The statement that religion is "betting your life that there is a God" is credited to Donald Hantry. Professor Wallace defines religion as "a belief in the ultimate meaning of the universe." These definitions are examples of many expressing approximately the same idea. Huxley says: [4] "This indeed is and always has been one of the two besetting vices of religious systems, to over-exalt the purely rational and therefore communicable elements of religion at the expense of the non-rational but deeper intuitions and felt experiences which are unique and personal, difficult or impossible of easy communication to others, and yet the true material of religion. It has led to the setting-up of creeds and dogmas as the supreme standard of religion, and to the belief that salvation may be assured by adherence to an intellectual statement of belief." Perhaps the most generally acceptable definition of religion, expressed by the Oxford Dictionary (definition 5), is "recognition on the part of men of some higher unseen power as having some control of his destiny, and as being entitled to obedience, reverence, and worship; the great mental and moral attitude resulting from this belief with reference to its effect upon the individual and the community; personal acceptance of this feeling as a standard of spiritual and practical life."

Gatland and Dempster make this comment: (Religion is) [5] "the recognition of God as an object of love and obedience. . . . Is it belonging to a religious sect, repeating prayer, or reading the sacred books? Orthodox religion is all these things. It reveres, it idolizes, and it expounds dogma. But if purpose exists in the universe, can one really imagine that man's entire function is to acknowledge his Creator passively as an act of faith? Does it not also imply a search for Truth at all levels of human consciousness? Indeed, by indulging in traditional stereotyped prayers, without understanding, we are carrying out a routine that must inevitably destroy our powers of thought and reasoning. The mind, which stands at the head of evolution, instead of being used creatively, is dulled and restricted."

God

The first approach to the idea of God to be considered is that of natural theology. One of the best approaches is the argument from design, which was first advanced early in the Christian era and has appeared in many forms since. The argument is: examine, for instance, a watch. Its intricate parts did not come into being of themselves. It is evident that someone must have designed and made the watch. Now consider the human body, or even one of the much simpler forms of life. Even in its mechanical aspects it is enormously more complicated than the watch; and the combination of electrical and chemical forces that are also evident adds greatly to the complexity. Does not this point to the existence of a designer, much more learned and greatly more skilled than any human being? Many theologians and philosophers have considered this argument a proof of the existence of God. As late as 1950 a book was written expounding this argument. But suppose we pursue the question a little further. How does one go about making a watch? One either copies another watch after finding just how it has been made or devising a way in which it can be made, or he follows the general design of another watch while making some improvements in it. If the history of watches is traced back, it is found that there was once a crude instrument which could barely be called a watch, an adaptation of an instrument used for a different purpose. Each subsequent maker or inventor had a previously constructed model before him, and had to learn some fundamental principles of the action of watches.

Briefly, then, each watchmaker had to learn something. God, then, in making an animal, had to learn at each step how to proceed; there was a fund of knowledge that God did not possess but had to acquire. God, then, is the Great Experimenter. Such a view has occasionally been advanced; but it has encountered the objection that if God is thus limited, the knowledge must have been in the possession of some other power. This conception is called demonism. On the other hand, this knowledge can be that of a material world, just existing without being in anyone's mind, from which God had to learn by experience. This view assumes that God is neither omnipotent nor omniscient. To rule out these possibilities we must return to the concept of God as the Creator, not the designer; and creation is vastly different from manufacture or design. Again, this idea that God gradually proceeded with creation as He learned is not far from that of evolution.

Suppose we disregard the objections to this conception, and suppose the existence of God were proved by this argument; what would be the nature of such a God? What would be His relation to man? Let us consider two animals which according to this conception God has made, for instance the fox and the rabbit, and suppose for simplicity that the rabbit is the principal prey and food of the fox. The fox is made in such a way that he is wonderfully adapted to catching and eating rabbits. He can outrun them; his teeth are adapted in the highest degree to masticating them; his stomach secretions are admirably adapted to digesting and assimilating rabbit meat. The rabbit, on the other hand, is well equipped for defense against the fox; it has protective coloration; it can easily hide from the fox; it cannot usually outrun the fox, but it can double back and elude him. Similar situations exist between many pairs of animals one of which is the prey of the other. For any particular kind of animal, this is called "a wise provision of nature." How do the "wise provisions of nature" apply to individual animals? In the encounter between a fox and a rabbit, the rabbit may perish or escape, depending upon the fox's ingenuity and strength, the rabbit's power and readiness to escape, and many accidental factors. Finally the rabbit is killed by a fox or dies from some other cause. The fox may catch enough rabbits so that he does not starve, but finally dies as the prey of some other animal, or of a disease-causing germ, or by accidental injury. The sum of these deaths and escapes may contribute to the survival or death of the species, but the species may die out on account of adverse physical conditions.

Man is no exception to this struggle between races of animals. Man finds most of his prey by subduing and domesticating it. Man has found the way to conquer wild animals that might cause him harm. He is wonderfully equipped to destroy microorganisms within his own body; but sometimes they are victorious and destroy him. The conclusion is that God may create but is not interested in the survival of an individual or of a race, including man. Such a God has little resemblance to the Christian God, although this idea may involve an incomprehensible purpose beyond the existence of species, even the human.

This leads us to the conception of man "made in God's image," or as it is sometimes reversed without complete contradiction, "God made in man's image." Study of and experience with outer space has led to the magnificent conception (unsupported of course) that there may be intelligent beings at many distant places in the universe, and probably many of them may excel us in culture and knowledge. Some of them may be very different from earthly beings; they may have other senses than ours; for instance, they may have organs sensitive to a different part of the radiation spectrum than our eyes are. They may exist in different dimensions than ours; they may be conscious of us and even of our inmost thoughts. Such beings may have a belief that they are made in the image of God. We cannot say that we are right and they are wrong; if creatures are made in the image of God, it must be a very partial image. As man is enormously more complex than the amoeba, so must God be very much more complex and powerful than we are, or even than we can imagine. That idea is not inconsistent with modern belief.

The British theologian Maude Royden has this to say about a personal God: ⁶"Man makes God in his own image. It is indeed because he is part divine that he knows there is a God at all. To know it is to know something that is true and therefore it is rightly said that there is 'truth in all religions' . . . To say that God is 'a person' is no doubt an error; to say that His Being includes that our thoughts are adequate. This is the tragic error that has in God certain human qualities. We err only when we imagine personality must be true. . . . We do not think wrongly if we find hampered progress and taught mankind the vices of intolerance and cruelty. This is what has made believers persecute those whose beliefs are unlike their own, claiming for themselves the possession of the truth. . . . Egypt gave to us the idea of God as scientific truth, Persia as light or purity, Greece as beauty, Rome as law, India as spirit, Islam as transcendence, Judaism as righteousness. . . . Christianity centers its teaching—and to us Christians consummates all—in the conception of a God Who is love. . . . So short a space as 2,000 years may well find us very primitive Christians still. 'The Spirit of truth will guide us into all truth!' "

Another approach to the idea of God is that of the existentialist. Strictly speaking, each transcendentalist has had his own approach. The somber conceptions of Kierkegaard were discussed very briefly in the preceding chapter. Tillich and Bultmann have been influenced by transcendentalism; but a continuation of the exposition of the views of Heim and Buber should be illuminating. Heim's metaphor of the prisoners in cells has been described in Chapter 3. He extends this metaphor by assuming that the cells are all open at the top. [7]"The chief warden can look into all the cells from above, while the prisoners are unable to see each other because they are separated by the cell walls. In the same way God can look down directly into the inside of us, while we are unable to look into one another." Naturally in such a picture the relations are oversimplified; many theologies conforming to this metaphor are possible.

From this picture Heim goes on to his formal philosophy. To bring the I-thou relation into thinkable terms, he has assumed the existence of a space independent of ordinary three-dimensional space; but God cannot be fitted into this space. According to Heim, both the "I-thou" spaces are "polar"; that is, the poles that establish the space are in the first case I and it, in the second, I and thou. The space in which we encounter God, however, is suprapolar; the I is the only fixed point, but God cannot be localized. Thus if the I-thou space has some dimensions which are not in the world of which we are conscious, still more dimensions are required in order to conceive our relation to God. Heim summarizes this rather difficult conception as follows: [8]"There is a suprapolar space in which we all stand together with all the rest of reality. From this there follow four inescapable consequences: (1) there is a personal God, who rules all things and in whose omnipresence all things stand; (2) each one receives his personal existence, and the position in which he is placed in the world, directly from God; (3) there is a sanction for our action, a commission from God, in which I can rest effectively, and supported by which I can defy the world; and (4) behind the whole world and the processes of nature, despite all appearances to the contrary and in spite of everything which seems to us meaningless and incomprehensible, there must be a plan which we view from a universal mind or spirit. The course of the world must be directed toward a final goal, which is now concealed from us."

Heim's is the boldest attempt to picture God and religion in terms approaching those of science. He does not, however, advance his philosophy as proof of the existence of God. He reviews some of the attempts to prove the existence of God and concludes as many others have concluded, that no such proof is possible. He warns theologians and laymen in the field of science against drawing over-hasty inferences which are father to the thought, from deductions from scientific facts. He does not believe that the relations between his "spaces" nor the conclusions derived will be understood until all the evidence from science is in.

As Heim admits, the secularist, the materialist, or the humanist will not be impressed by his arguments. On the other side, the theologian will not see the necessity for the assumption of additional spaces to support religious beliefs; but if we substitute the word "world" for "space" he will be on familiar ground. Otherworldliness has always been a characteristic of Christanity; in fact, of almost all religions. I cannot claim to accept all of Heim's conclusions without a deeper study of his work, but points which seem very pertinent are: that if God exists, He must be of the same nature as the human soul, the I; and that additional dimensions, in the broadest sense, are necessary to give an adequate picture of: (1) me; (2) you; and (3) God. Also, if the crowning degree of the I-thou relationship is love in the Biblical sense, it follows that love is an attribute of God.

Buber antedated Heim in his conception of the I-thou relationship; but Buber does not advance the idea in two stages, as does Heim, and his ideas are therefore somewhat more difficult to follow. Buber's background and theology are Jewish, but that fact does not introduce any conflict with Christianity.

The concepts of the I-hypothesis and the you-hypothesis were suggested in Chapter 3. The existentialist conception as just outlined is equivalent to the introduction of a third, the God-hypothesis. Just as the you-hypothesis can be valid only if the I-hypothesis is valid, the God-hypothesis depends upon the other two. The you- and I-hypotheses are accepted because they "work"; that is, they agree with all our experience; there can be disagreement as to the validity of the God-hypothesis because it cannot be demonstrated that it is fully in accord with experience. To each of us all other persons are both "its and thous", but God is the supreme "Thou", that is, pure spirit. We can think only of "its"; therefore God can be thought of, symbolically, as an "it". The human mind cannot long retain the idea of God as spirit; hence representations of God and ritual follow. In the course of time the symbols of God come to be worshiped; in other words man falls into idolatry, and a reformation is necessary to revive the original attitude of Thou-ness. This happens again and again. Protestants sometimes accuse Roman Catholics of idolatry because of their use of statues and other representations of Bible characters; but if their allegations are true, Protestants are not guiltless. It is understood that Catholics are now taking steps to minimize the use of such representations.

Naturally it would require much space to give an adequate idea of the Christian God as presented in the Bible. The differences between the fundamentalist and orthodox conceptions are not great. God is both cosmic and personal. That is, God existed from the beginning and created the universe, which came to its full fruition in man, whom He made a responsible agent. God, as a person, sustains the universe but is a person with whom each one of His followers can be in contact through prayer. According to the fundamentalist view, God talked to Adam and Eve in the form of a visible man, and to a number of other persons in the form of an invisible voice; He also interfered in events as a powerful person might. According to the liberal and most orthodox views such stories are allegories; this humanization of God is called anthropomorphism. The idea of God is an extension of that of a father; God is the Father of mankind. According to all fundamentalists and many of the orthodox school He became the Father of Jesus Christ through a miracle. No proof or disproof of this idea of God's existence is possible.

The acceptance of scientific discoveries and thought necessarily changes one's ideas about God, especially in the direction of greater complexity. If the principles of evolution are true, and if God exists, instead of creating species with a word, He has directed the survival of the fittest in such a way as to bring about the present state of the living world, including that of man. He does not perform miracles which violate the "laws of nature". He is present in those laws. If we go beyond the facts of science to a radical philosophy suggested by science, and assume that time is in reality a dimension like the other three that we experience, we must say that God is independent of time. We can extend the idea, "to God a thousand years are as a yesterday when it is past", and say, "to God eternity is as an instant"; if that is true, creation in the ordinarily understood sense cannot be conceived. What is created is the dependence of man (and other creatures) upon that dimension. In that sense He created the universe, for the universe as we understand it is inseparably connected with, and fully dependent upon, the time sequence. Thus we are led beyond the depth of our thinking.

This idea is not far from that of Tillich when he speaks of the "God above theism" (and therefore above the God of theology), the object of absolute faith, and the source of the courage to be. [9]"The courage to be is rooted in the God who appears when God has disappeared in the anxiety of doubt." The highest conception of the Christian God was given in the Gospel of John: "God is love." Of course that is not a complete definition: but it is con-

sistent with the views of Tillich as well as those of the fundamentalist. The key to the solution of the problem lies in faith, not
in thought.

Life of Jesus Christ

Jesus is the central figure in the history of the middle-eastern
and western world, and more has been written about Him than
about any other person. Unfortunately for the exact understanding
of His words and deeds there were no reporters or stenographers
on the scene; He wrote nothing; most or all of the accounts that
we have were written some time after His death by persons who
had never seen Him, although some had been in contact with His
associates. His teachings were ethical and eschatological. Eschatology is defined as "the doctrine of the last or final things, as
death, resurrection, immortality, the end of the age, the second
advent of Christ, Judgment, and the future state". His basic
ethical teachings are embodied in the Sermon on the Mount and
in other passages in the Gospels. Some of His discourse was in
the form of parables which are unequaled in literature. The central
feature of His ethical teaching was that men should love God and
each other. Some of His sayings have instant appeal, but some
others are not accepted literally even by the most devoted Christians, such as "turning the other cheek" when struck.

Many persons disagree with the idea that we have little exact
information about Jesus. The belief became crystallized in the
Church about the third or fourth century that the Bible is literally
inspired and that therefore the history of Jesus as given in the
Gospels is entirely true. It is still the belief of fundamentalists
and of some other orthodox bodies. According to that belief,
Jesus was born within a few years of the date selected as the
beginning of the Christian Era, in Bethlehem, the Divine Son of
the Virgin Mary. He performed many miracles, mostly of physical
and mental healing, and several of resurrection. He taught that
He was the Messiah and the Son of God. After about three years
of His ministry, His eschatological teaching and His opposition to
some of the religious leaders, adroitly turned by His enemies into
the semblance of rebellion against the Roman Empire, led to His
arrest, trial, crucifixion and death. On the third day He rose to
life, and during the next forty days was seen alive by many persons.
Finally He ascended into heaven with the promise that He would
return to judge the world. This view remained official in the
Church throughout its early and medieval history and well into the

period of enlightenment. Conflicting views were denied and suppressed.

At the beginning of the scientific age, in the eighteenth century, the doubts expressed by non-orthodox writers and teachers became more open. Since then hundreds of biographies of Jesus have been written from different viewpoints. Many of them are simple paraphrases of the Scriptural accounts. Reimarus (1694-1768) was the first to write an unorthodox biography. His writing was polemical rather than scientifically historical. He contradicted most of the ideas of Jesus which were held earlier. According to Reimarus, Jesus believed in Himself as the Messiah Who was to be an earthly ruler. The Kingdom of God was nowhere explained; therefore the people must have understood just what it meant. He did not break at all with the Jewish tradition. He did not baptize. The Lord's Supper was simply an episode in the observance of the Passover. After His burial, the disciples stole and hid His body, and the Second Coming was foremost in their thoughts. Reimarus' work was not all published in his lifetime but was brought to life later by Lessing.

Reimarus was followed by a number of theologians who wrote lives of Jesus which are characterized by compromises between orthodoxy and rationalism. Hess, for instance, accepts the Virgin Birth and the Resurrection but rationalizes the miracles. Then followed other rationalistic lives of Jesus. Schweitzer says of Paulus, who is typical of these authors: "The method is doomed to failure because the author saves his own sincerity at the expense of his characters." A few authors argued that Jesus did not live at all, and the idea seemed plausible considering the meager information that we have outside New Testament sources; but the consensus of opinion has always been that there must be some historical ground for the accounts that we have.

Strauss, in his *Life of Jesus*,[10] was the first to affirm that the Gospels were not written by eye-witnesses. This book was first published in 1835-36. Strauss was also the first to dispute the accuracy of the Gospel of John. The Marcan hypothesis, that is, the theory that Mark was the first and most factual of the Gospel writers, was first advanced by Weisse in 1838. Bruno Bauer, in 1840, published the first skeptical life of Jesus, and it was followed by a number of imaginative lives. Renan's, published in 1863, was the most popular of these biographies, possibly because it was romantic and did not claim to be scientific.

The *Quest of the Historical Jesus*,[11] by Albert Schweitzer, was first published in 1910. It was not intended to be a complete biography, but a criticism of other books and a statement of a new theory. Schweitzer shows that we cannot reconstruct the life of Jesus from the material available. He rejects the theme of those lives which picture Him as a moralist with no conception of Himself as a divine being or prophet; but at the same time, he finds no evidence that Jesus claimed to be the Messiah. In another book Schweitzer[12] refutes the idea that Jesus was to any degree insane, which had been suggested by Strauss, Holtzmann,[13] Baumann,[14] and others. The most important contribution made by Schweitzer was the theory that Jesus at first believed that He would bring about the Kingdom of God in His lifetime and that later He realized that the idea was wrong and that His death was necessary to pave the way for the Kingdom. This idea, of course, was radical; if true, Christians are called upon to believe in a Savior who was mistaken and changed his mind. In defense of Schweitzer's views, it can be said that no matter what the conception of Jesus' divinity may be, His humanity may have prevented Him from being omniscient. That is, His knowledge of the physical universe and of history was limited by His senses. His eschatology as a prediction of what was later historical fact was no more accurate than that of Daniel, John, or other prophets. Without having made a thorough search of Schweitzer's works, I am inclined to believe that the above is what he meant. At any rate, Schweitzer's contemporaries found his ideas unacceptable, and he adbandoned theology for medicine and practical Christianity.

Probably the most thorough recent summary of the atheistic or non-Christian viewpoint was made by Homer W. Smith in *Man and His Gods,* published in 1952. It is not primarily a life of Jesus but rather a history of religion. He points out that the only records of Jesus' life that we have are the Gospels, all of which were written in the second century, and none by eyewitnesses. The first mention of Jesus outside the New Testament is a passage supposedly written by Josephus in 94 A. D. but it has generally been judged spurious. The next mentions of Christtians were made by Pliny about 111 and by Suetonius about 117-138. The comments of both these authors show that they knew little about Christians. Smith shows that Jesus shared with gods and mythical heroes in the stories of virgin birth, in the rite of Baptism, in the sacrificial meal, and in resurrection and ascension. All these alleged miraculous occurrences made the stories more credible to readers of the time, instead of making them more difficult as they do in modern times. In the second century there were more than fifty gospels, only four of which were accepted and have survived. The conventionally accepted dates for the writing of the gospels are: Mark, 66-68; Luke, 80-95; Matthew, 100; and John, 110. Smith suggests the dates: Mark 135; Matthew 140; John before 145; and Luke (with Clement as author) about 142. Some interpolations were made in the second and third centuries. Smith denies that Christ's teachings were original; he finds them all in earlier Hebrew literature. The novel features of the morality advocated by Jesus were based upon the apocalyptic expectation that the world would soon be destroyed and that a new world would arise; as Jesus said: "This generation shall not pass away, till all be fulfilled."

Smith has presented one of the most complete summaries of the arguments against the reliability of the account of the life of Jesus as given in the Gospels. His implied conclusion is that Jesus did not live at all, an idea which is held by a minority of rationalistic critics. The scope of this work does not permit detailed treatment of the extensive discussion. There are a few points on which it must be admitted that the historical facts are in Smith's favor. Instances are that the census of Quirinius, which compelled Joseph and Mary to go to Bethlehem, did not occur until after the death of Herod, and that there was no eclipse or any recorded period of darkness at the time of the Crucifixion. Aside from a few such discrepancies, which affect minor parts of the history, there is no conclusive evidence for or against the truth of the story. All statements on both sides of the question are speculative. Smith quotes the common argument that if the "Christ-myth" theory is true, and if Jesus never lived, the whole civilized world has been deceived for almost two thousand years, and the greatest power for good that the world has even known originated in a delusion. He points out that Plutarch made a similar statement about the worship of Osiris, which everyone now knows was based upon myth.

Smith says in conclusion: [15]"The ultimate answer to the question of historicity will not be found in sentiment or prejudice, or on the apologetic grounds which Plutarch states, but through the careful and dispassionate evaluation of the social and ideological forces of the first century, as opposed to the obscurely complex Biblical texts. The answer will continue to be sought by all historians, Christian and otherwise, who are anxious to guard against an error that would be contrary to the first principles of their task." No honest searcher for historical truth will disagree with that statement, but the extreme difficulty of obtaining all the facts must be recognized.

At first sight it appears that if Smith is even partly right, Christian belief is founded on falsehood. To a number of Christian thinkers, however, there is a side of the question that Smith and the authors he quotes have not considered at all: Does Christianity as it exists today depend upon the accuracy of the Biblical account? [16]*The Religion of a Mature Mind,* written by G. A. Coe in 1902, remains one of the best expressions of the idea that experience is all-important and dogma and history are secondary. Coe's final chapter, entitled *The Christ of Personal Experience,* is devoted to the idea that "the Christ of experience must take precedence of the Christ of dogma." It is difficult to summarize his ideas in a few words, but the following quotations may assist in presenting them. "A first step in discipleship is taken . . . whenever, convinced of the soundness of the moral ideal expressed in Christ, one accepts the Christ-ideal as one's own. This movement away from mere negations and mere questionings is based upon experience as distinguished from doctrine." Having made this acceptance, the Christian can come to his own conclusion regarding the historical life of Jesus. Reasoning from his experience, he may feel compelled to accept the entire story, in spite of all that has been said against its historicity; on the other hand, if he largely rejects it, his acceptance of the ideal Christ is not affected. "Whoever finds the Christ-ideal a supreme one, has firm standing-ground on the positive side, whatever be his state of mind with respect to all else. Granting nothing but the fact of his own approval of the Christ, whether the Christ be merely ideal or also historical, he faces the immediate duty of becoming a worker for the Christian ideal." Naturally this view has little, if any, more appeal to fundamentalists than do those presented by Smith.

Coe wrote before the time of the existentialists Buber and Heim, but their views would have given him support. The ideal Christ, or the "living Christ", is a Thou with whom I can "come in contact", as with other living persons; it makes no difference whether we think the "living Christ" exists because He lived on earth, died, and was resurrected or whether we accept Him as an ideal through the thought-world. To me Christ is speaking directly to a greater extent than any other person of the past who is not in the flesh. That may be because I have come to think so through religious training and thinking; but to me it is an argument that

Christ lived and said many of the things attributed to Him. "speaking with authority and not as the scribes."

If Christian belief is belief directed toward the ideal Christ instead of the historical Christ, the arguments presented by Smith lose their force. It is not true that the civilized world has been deceived for two thousand years, because fundamentally it has been guided by ideals rather than by questionable facts. If the same reasoning is applied to Plutarch's statement about the worship of Osiris, it is evident that the ideal of Osiris had some effect on the daily life of his worshippers. The same is true of every god. Smith and other historians of religion are likely to confine their discussion to the external side of human nature. They do not fully emphasize the personal need for religion which men have felt throughout history. To our modern ideas, Christianity is the climax of such beliefs.

It may be objected, that this belief in the ideal Christ is very close to humanism. The difference is that to the humanist all ideas of God are extensions of the self, while to the religious person they are founded on "something" outside the self, no matter how indefinite that "something" may be. The difficult question is, however, whether belief in the ideal Christ, with the knowledge that it is only an ideal Christ, is as effective as a belief on a positive historical basis. Our thinking and beliefs are geared to objects. The test of these beliefs is in the lives of the believers.

Early Christianity

Although the key to some of the problems raised in the preceding section depends upon the discussion of the third person of the Trinity, that will be postponed until the history of early Christianity is reviewed. According to accounts generally considered reliable, within two months after Jesus' death His followers were convinced of His resurrection. Immediatey a campaign of preaching began with the aim of converting as many people as possible to Christianity. At first only Jews were admitted to the new sect, but its followers soon realized that its teachings must be preached to the entire known world, and that Gentiles should be welcomed without imposing the rites and customs of the Jews. The word "Christian" was first used in a sense of opprobrium, but it was soon accepted by the Christians themselves. They did not immediately become saints; a reading of almost any of the Epistles easily dispels any idea that they did. There were many good and pious persons among them, but there were others who saw the promise of a future life and the early return of the Messiah as a deliverance from the extremely harsh conditions of their time, without much consideration of the ethical teachings. Such persons, however, were somewhat deterred by persecutions of Christians by the Roman government.

Suetonius mentions persecutions by the Emperors Claudius (41-54) and Nero (54-68) and describes the Christians as "a sect of men who held a new and maleficent superstition." It is easy to see why the early Christians were looked upon as trouble makers. While the advocates of the various other religions were tolerant toward each other, the Christians believed in the one and only God, and refused to join in any ceremony which had any suggestion of recognizing the pagan gods. They refused to go to war. They were at first mostly members of the lower classes, who perhaps expressed their differences with the prevailing religions in rather crude ways; but perhaps above all, they strongly expressed their disgust with the public and private vices that were common. On the whole, the rulers showed much forbearance toward the new sect; but often the excessive zeal of individual Christians and groups aroused the clamor of the populace and ire of the rulers. The anti-Christian feeling was stronger under some of the emperors than under others; so there were periods of persecution and periods of peace. This situation continued until the early fourth century.

Gibbon, in *The Decline and Fall of the Roman Empire,* gives five cause of the growth of Christianity: (1) the inflexible zeal of Christians; (2) the doctrine of a future life; (3) the miraculous powers ascribed to the primitive Church; (4) the pure and austere morals of the Christians; and (5) the union and discipline of the "Christian republic", which gradually formed an independent and increasing state in the heart of the Roman empire. As time went on, Christianity penetrated more into the upper classes. One reason was that the sobriety and industry of the Christians naturally increased their wealth and social esteem. In the second century Celsus wrote a book opposing Christianity. Smith, in discussing this book at length, says: [17]"The fact that Celsus bothered to write a book refuting Christianity showed merely that it was making its way upward through society and gaining a hold among those of wealth and education. Admittedly many who joined the movement were social outcasts, and many others were attracted by its ascetic doctrines, either because they esteemed self-immolation, were possessed by a sense of sin or were, on more moderate grounds, opposed to idols and bloody sacrifices, the theater, the circus, indulgence, and promiscuity in general. On a higher plane the new creed offered a future life which was posited on an attractive but spurious pretense to Hellenic rationalism; it described the human body as base, doomed to decay and death, the human soul as naturally simple, incorruptible and everlasting; it permitted willful freedom to replace the fatalism of the Orient, and an eternal democratic kingdom of heaven to replace the despotism of an empire which was so unstable as to be always on the verge of collapse."

The period of most severe persecution occurred at about the beginning of the fourth century during the reign of Diocletian. The emperor himself, favored the Christians, but the persecution was due largely to the instigation of two associates, Galerius and Maximian. Gibbon estimates that about two thousand Christians lost their lives during this period. With the rise to power of Constantius, and even to a greater extent with the accession of Constantine, a more tolerant spirit toward Christians prevailed, and the persecutions of Christians by Romans ended.

An important event early in the fourth century was the conversion of the Emperor Constantine. According to legend he saw a cross in the sky, accompanied by the words, "By this sign shalt thou conquer." Whatever truth there is in the legend, it fully indicates Constantine's philosophy; the cross was a sign by which to conquer, not a symbol of a life of dedication. He later murdered some of his relatives; he let himself be known as a worshipper of other gods; and like many others, he postponed Baptism until near the end of his life in order to enjoy pagan practices and then be forgiven. His conversion accentuated the profound change in the position of the Christians, from a persecuted minority to a powerful majority. What centuries of persecution had failed to do was now accomplished by acceptance; politics had triumphed over Christianity. Loetscher thus describes the change: [18]"But the Church's new and unaccustomed position of privilege was not an unmixed blessing. Christianity was no longer something to suffer for, but something to profit by. Following the example of their emperor, unconverted heathen flocked to the Church, bringing with them many of their heathen immoralities and religious beliefs. Even the clergy became secularized and worldly. Church affairs now hopelessly entangled with court politics. Christian leaders, from their new vantage points, could use the government's authority to prosecute heretics. Some of the more spiritual churchmen looked away wistfully from the newly acquired wealth and honor to the time, now past, when to be a Christian had sometimes involved making the supreme sacrifices of life itself."

Constantine was followed on the throne by his son Constantius II, whose Christianity was no better than his father's. In the new city of Constantinople all organized pagan worship was prohibited on pain of death. Under his successor Julian the apostate paganism and toleration were revived, but his successor Theodosius the Great restored Christianity to power with the renewal of persecution of pagans and heretics. Numerous heresies were propagated during the early Christian period; among the most successful were Gnosticism, Arianism, and Manicheanism. Gnosticism, an adaptation of Oriental mythology, had died out before the fourth century. Arians believed that Christ was not the Son of God and was therefore inferior to God. Manicheanism originated in Persia and emphasized the perpetual conflict between light or goodness and darkness or evil. Minor heresies and variations of those mentioned were also held. There is no record that anyone in announcing a heretical opinion said, "I know little about these difficult matters, but in my thinking I have come to this conclusion." Instead, both the heretical and the orthodox regarded their own opinions as God-given, and so came into serious conflict with each other. Those who did not accept the reigning theology were persecuted, stripped of power, and in many cases put to death; but when a new ruler favored a different theology, the former orthodox became the heretics and were persecuted to the fullest extent. Sometimes under Constantius whole troops of "heretics" were massacred and many towns and provinces were destroyed.

After the fall of Rome when the Church was forced to fend for itself its aim was to convert all barbarians. Moslems frankly supported their founder in putting to the sword all who would not accept their religion; but Christians were equally ruthless in the name of the Prince of Peace. Under the pagan emperors thousands of Christians had been martyred; but for over a thousand years, to quote Smith, [19]"The cost of Christianizing the whole of Europe is estimated at eight to ten million lives, while the necessarily late introduction of Christianity into the New World was to cost twelve million native lives, and utterly destroy the civilization of the Aztecs, and the Incas." Thus pseudoreligious zeal became an excuse for plain physical conquest, and Christianity was a thin veneer over savage cruelty; the triumph of Christianity, was an important goal although secondary to that of conquest. The

Founder and the disciples would have been filled with horror at such a sequence of Christ's teachings; there must have been very many people at the time who were horrified by the course of events; but they were not influential. It must be remembered that Rome was at the time under the authority of the barbarians who were officially but actually very superficially Christian, and that many of the Church officials also came from the barbarians. Persecutions continued, however, for many centuries.

The Reformation did not immediately change this situation; it led indirectly to wars, and some "heretics" were put to death under Protestant rulers. In the history of the United States there were no deaths of heretics, except those accused of being witches, in the colonial days, but many minor persecutions have occurred. In a way the war with the Mormons could be called a religious persecution, but the chief reason leading to that war was the espousal of polygamy, which was extremely irritating to the general idea of morality. Toleration is now the purported order of the day, and we believe that in being more tolerant we are more nearly Christian. It is safe to say that in the last one hundred years very few persons have met death at the hands of any *religious* body for religious belief or lack of belief. The number of Jews and some others martyred during the second world war has approached the figure given by Smith for earlier centuries; but the persecutors made no pretense to religion; in fact their tone was anti-Christian. Similarly, in atheistic Soviet Russia there has been persecution of many religionists of various denominations. To some extent science has been a factor in the trend toward tolerance, by showing how mistaken individuals or groups may be. On the other hand, pseudo-science had a role in the excuses for the murder of the Jews and others.

The history of Protestant theology as modified and developed by the Reformation, the Renaissance, and the development of science has been discussed in Chapter 4.

The Holy Spirit; The Trinity

Both the Holy Spirit and the Trinity have always been difficult subjects for the layman. One reason is that almost entirely throughout Church history the members of the Trinity have been regarded as independent Persons in the customary sense, whereas, as many theologians have repeatedly pointed out, the Greek word corresponding to the Latin word persona means characters in a play rather than individuals. One of the original sources of the doctrine of the Trinity was the verse in the King James version: (1 John 5, 7) "For there are three that bear record in heaven, the Father, the Word, and the Holy Ghost: and these three are one." This verse did not appear in the earliest New Testament manuscripts, and its genuineness was challenged. It has been omitted in the Revised Standard and subsequent versions. There are other verses, however, referring to the Holy Spirit.

Another difficulty lies in the definition of spirit. Webster gives twenty-two definitions, many of which naturally would not be pertinent but there are still enough to cause confusion. The word "ghost", which appears in the King James version and has been often used, adds to the confusion. In its present use it conveys the idea of a mysterious indefinite creature, somewhat transparent and somehow floating through the air; even the word "spirit" has to some the same connotation. As one of the broadest definitions, spirit could mean the motivation to act in a definite manner; we speak of a spirit of pride, a spirit of restfulness, and so on. Aldous Huxley has postulated five or six non-egos that we carry about with us, [20]"and finally, beyond the rest, but immanent in every mental or material event, is that universal not-self, which men have called the Holy Spirit, the Atman-Brahman, the Clear Light, Suchness."

In a solitary individual, this spirit would evidently have a physical entity associated with it, that is, a state of the molecules of the nervous system; but the word "universal" indicates that it is something broader. In fact, the examples of its use seem to imply that. A "spirit of restlessness," for instance, is more applicable to a group of persons than to a single person. According to Pollard, any spirit is an attribute or possession of a community. He uses as an illustration the spirit of the Marine Corps. The Holy Spirit can only be embodied in the Church. Pollard believes that the widespread individualism which Christianity has approached during the past century is in the wrong direction. [21]"For the Holy Spirit belongs to that community of the faithful in Christ which is the holy Catholic Church just as the Marine spirit belongs to the Marine Corps." Whether or not one agrees with Pollard on the necessity for church union (he is an Episcopalian), it must be admitted that the Spirit is a unifying principle. As science is the underlying reality of the scientific spirit, so is God the underlying reality of the Holy Spirit.

Many spirits, such as that scientific spirit and that of the Marine Corps can coexist in the same person with the Holy Spirit; but there are other spirits that directly oppose it. Pollard says:

[22]"Every spirit, by the very nature of spirit in community itself, has a power over human lives and a capacity to mold and transform human persons which is similar to the power of the Holy Spirit in the Church to seize, transform, redeem, and save. Consider, for example, some of the exceedingly powerful spirits which have scourged humanity in the last few decades: the spirits of Italian Fascism, German Nazism, and Marxist Communism. The terrible fascination which these demonic communities have for many persons and their consequent capacity to grow powerfully has been noted by all of us. Once incorporated into such a community, the experience of the individual is often strikingly similar to that of religious conversion. Communist literature from Russia, Poland, China, and elsewhere today gives many moving testimonials to this fact. Those who really believe in Communism with their whole hearts have a faith in it and a loyalty and devotion to it so total and complete as to be baffling to many free world readers. There is a sense of the unquenchable power and certain victory of the spirit and movement which they serve, which is remarkably parallel to that found in Saint Luke's Acts of the Apostles. The individual feels himself lifted, empowered, and redeemed by the spirit of the Party in a way entirely similar to the corresponding experience in the Church. There is the same sense of newness of life, of having been rescued from bondage to a worthless and perishing self, of enjoying for the first time a sense of the grandness of freedom in the service of that which is great and noble and true—a genuine experience, in other words, of real redemption and personal salvation. Fascism and Nazism produced essentially the same effect on those who were captivated by them, especially on the youth of the interwar period.

"There is nothing more terrible than the agony of the soul of one who, having given himself totally and without reservation to such a movement, is forced slowly to the dawning realization that the spirit which has given him so much and acquired so much power over him is in actuality demonic and not at all the divine power he so confidently believed it to be when he first gave himself over to it."

Although Pollard uses the term "demonic" for such communities and spirits, there is no evidence that he implies that demons are persons; he means merely that they are the opposite of divine. How can one know that the spirit he is following is a good spirit? Naturally there is no scientific test. Observation of its effect on others is too slow for any decision. Pollard quotes the test given by the writer of the First Epistle of John: [23]"By this you know the Spirit of God: every spirit which confesses that Jesus Christ has come in the flesh is of God, and every spirit which does not confess Jesus is not of God." The quotation from Huxley implies, however, that the equivalent or near-equivalent of the Holy Spirit exists in other religions. The humanist could say that there is no sure test except that of experience.

[24]Arthur H. Compton presents a view of the Trinity acceptable to modern understanding. According to this view God has three aspects: (1) as ruler of the universe; (2) as a hero to be admired and emulated; and (3) as the spirit of the highest good which serves as the guiding principle. Julian Huxley has a closely corresponding idea: [25]"As I see it broadly, 'God the Father' is a personification of the force of non-human nature; 'God the Holy Ghost' represents all ideals; and 'God the Son' personifies human nature at its highest, as actually incarnate in bodies and organized in minds, bridging the gulf between the other two, and between each of them and everyday life. And the unity of the three persons as 'One God' represents the fact that all these aspects of reality are inextricably interconnected." A more intimate and existential view can be added. God is an incomprehensible and indefinite but encounterable being, as Tillich says, a God beyond theism. Jesus Christ is a person who speaks to me through the ages, providing ideals toward which I strive. The Holy Spirit is something in me but beyond me, leading me to those ideals.

In some theologies the Second and Third members of the Trinity are sharply distinguished; the Holy Spirit and the indwelling Christ are separate entities; but if the word "persons" is not considered in the modern sense, the two can be the same. That is, the meaning conveyed by "I am the vine, ye are the branches" and "My Comforter I leave with you" refer to the same entity. In support of this idea, the question may be asked, could a course of conduct recommended by one be any different from one recommended by the other? "The still small voice that spoke to Elijah is the Old Testament equivalent of the Holy Spirit. Aldous Huxley's quotation above shows that this idea exists in other religions. Also, the distinction between the Holy Spirit as present in the individual, and conscience, is not clear.

An important distinction between fundamentalism and all other religious beliefs concerns the role of the Holy Spirit in the writing of the Scriptures. The keystone of fundamentalism is that the Bible was written "under" the influence of the Holy Spirit; that is, the pens or thoughts of the writers were guided by the Spirit, independently of what their conscious thoughts might have been. To all other Christians, from the modern orthodox to the extreme liberal, the writers of Biblical history took what materials they had, and copied and combined them, conscientiously and perhaps more critically than is generally realized, but they were not in a position to guarantee the accuracy of what they wrote. Of course, there were probably a few who wrote from firsthand observation. The point is, that to the non-fundamentalist the Holy Spirit was not and could not be a source of fact. Facts are discoverable only by observation; and judgment must be applied to all written records. This applies both to the writers of Genesis and those of the Gospels. The advent of science has resulted in new criteria for accuracy, and it is now judged that fact has been mixed with legend. The role of the Holy Spirit remains in the spiritual realm; it is in the guiding of the reader toward the ideals that are set forth.

The nature and role of the conception of the Trinity is admittedly difficult from any standpoint. Hordern says: [26] "After considerable reflection, I have decided that it is impossible for me to make this doctrine clear to the reader in the space that I can devote to it. The best minds in Christendom debated for centuries before they came to any conclusion, and that debate, presupposing a full knowledge of the philosophies of the time, cannot be explained briefly." If any apparent progress has been made by modern authorities it is by ignoring some of the questions that troubled the early thinkers. To the medieval Christian and the fundamentalist, the Holy Spirit provided the authors of the Bible with facts; to the more modern Christians, it said rather, "seek and you will find." The role of the Holy Spirit indicates an important difference between Christianity and humanism. To the humanist each person has his own holy spirit (not capitalized); to even the most liberal Christian, the Holy Spirit is universal.

Prayer

In discussing the metaphor of the prison cells, Heim continues: [27]"God alone transcends the opposition between the many possible positions in space and time in which by a fatal necessity we have been irrevocably situated since the time of our birth. . . . Here we have an entirely new and unique I-thou relationship, one which is fundamentally different from the onlooker and scientific observer, from the mystical immersion of myself in myself, and from the thou encounter which in polytheistic religions is extended to include intercourse with the gods. This new and unique relation is prayer. Prayer stills the incessant movement of my quest for a thou to whom I can devote myself wholly. God is the omnipresent Thou of every I, the Being who is immediately close to us, before whom we all stand always, before whom we do all our deeds, and before whom we think our most secret thoughts. It is He who listens to our most secret conversations with ourselves, and who never misunderstands us. . . . When I come before God in prayer, all other ego-beings are, in a mysterious manner, also present. By way of God I am linked with all the beings the universe contains. When I stand before God they are all my brothers, even though within the polar space I am divided from them by insurmountable walls."

Prayer has two aspects: submission to the will of God and asking something for one's self. The purest form of prayer may be the former; yet it is considered entirely within proper attitudes to include the latter. One may pray for health and strength and all the qualities that will make one a good Christian. Many people pray at the time of a great danger who do not at other times. The implication is that God will intervene in the course of nature, and will upset its forces to accommodate them. Almost all scientists and science-minded people and many modern theologians reject this idea. On the other hand, some missionaries and other religious workers who have prayed for support have received that support from unexpected gifts or some other means. In these cases a human agency is involved. The conclusion could be drawn that God does not upset the order of nature for anybody, but does work through human agencies. Skeptics interpret such occurrences as coincidences, and naturally no proof is possible for either opinion.

The lines of demarcation between this subject and those of faith and miracles are thin, but the matter of healing by prayer maybe considered at this point. Experiments were conducted at the University of Redlands (California) with forty-five persons, whose condition can best be described in the words of Parker and St. Johns, who report the experiment: [28] "Obviously, whether they were suffering visible psychosomatic symptoms, which include migraine headache, arthritis, tuberculosis, functional heart trouble, acne, allergies, or were simply fast becoming nervous wrecks, these forty-five individuals were moving farther and farther away from that 'victorious life' which some unquenchable inner instinct keeps

assuring man is his birthright." These subjects were carefully
divided into three equal groups which were treated as follows: the
first group practised prayer without any special guidance; the second were treated and advised according to the best method of
psychotherapy; and the third were given the same treatment and
also practised systematic prayer. In nine months in the first group
there had been no average improvement in the various ailments
which had afflicted them; the improvement in the second group,
as measured by standard medical and psychological tests, was
65%; in the third group it was 72%. The skeptical psychologist
will not accept 72% as being more statistically significant than
65%, and will take the negative results on the first group to show
the futility of prayer. The prayer therapy continued, but no further
comparisons with larger groups are reported, so nothing more definite can be said regarding the experiments.

According to the humanist view people actually pray to them-
sleves, that is, to the subconscious portion of their personality, but
naturally do not realize that it is to themselves. But again, not all
prayer is petition. Genuinely religious persons pray for strength
to become better morally; humanists do not. Of course these attitudes could be subjected to critical analysis; but the difficulties
involved would be extreme. Also, what at first is a sincere prayer
may by repetition become merely a form of words resembling
ancient charms.

Faith

There is much confusion on the subject of faith on account of
the various meanings of the word. It is often taken to be synono-
mous with "belief" or "confidence". Sometimes the scientist is said
to have faith in his sciences. Bridgman writes [29]"It is often said that
the scientist can operate on the assumption that nature obeys laws,
so the mere fact that he is a scientist means that he 'believes' or
'has faith' that there are laws of nature. This it seems to me is a
false position. . . . He may follow a program assuming there are
natural laws in the spirit that that is the best bet, but only in the
spirit of the best bet." We need not take the implied teleology in
the word "obey" seriously. In science it means simply that nature
is uniform. A few theologians have given religious faith a corresponding meaning; faith means that you can bet on the existence
of God.

An important factor in scientific "faith" is belief in persons.
No scientist can take time to verify experimentally all the work that

has been done even in his own narrow field. He must have "faith" in scientists, and this faith will increase with the extent to which a finding has been confirmed. This faith can never be absolute, because he knows that scientists have been mistaken in the past. Is this not also true in religion? Does not our faith increase as we learn from those with the highest religious experience?

The answer of most theologians to these questions is definitely "No". Tillich may be taken as an example of a modern religious thinker. The first sentence of his book *Dynamics of Faith* reads: [30]"Faith is the state of being ultimately concerned." It may be a little difficult to grasp the full meaning of this statement, but the entire book is an elucidation of it. "Man, in contrast to other living beings, has spiritual concerns—cognitive, aesthetic, social, political. Some of them are urgent, often extremely urgent, and each of them as well as the vital concerns can claim ultimacy for a human life or the life of a social group. If it claims ultimacy it demands the total surrender of him who accepts this claim, and it promises total fulfillment even if all other claims have to be subjected to it or rejected in its name." In some countries the nation is a matter of ultimate concern; it is "a god who certainly proves to be a demon, but who shows clearly the unconditional character of an ultimate concern." . . . Another example—almost a counter-example, yet nevertheless equally revealing—is the ultimate concern with 'success' and with social standing and economic power." In the Old Testament the concern was not with the nation, but with the God of justice. In a large portion of his book, Tillich shows that religion—and especially Christianity—is the only genuinely rewarding ultimate concern.

One of the most important applications of faith is demonstrated in the healing of disease. The importance of faith in recovery is recognized by nearly all physicians. It is used by reputable physicians and by quacks. As Tillich says: [31]"Linguistically (and materially) one must distinguish the integrating power of faith from what has been called 'faith healing'. Faith healing, as the term is actually used, is the attempt to heal others or oneself by concentration on the healing power in others or oneself. There is such healing power in nature and man, and it can be strengthened by mental acts. In a non-depreciating sense one could speak of the use of magic power; and certainly there is healing magic in human relationships as well as in relation to oneself. It is a daily experience and sometimes one that is astonishing in its intensity and success. But one should not use the word 'faith' for it, and one should not confuse it with the integrating power of an ultimate concern." A large percentage of all cases of illness are psychosomatic. It is difficult to judge whether a particular case is psychosomatic, purely psychological, or purely physical (if the word "purely" can be used in this connection at all). Often apparently organic diseases are cured by placebos, and there are records of established organic improvement resulting from faith alone. Many of the cures at the Fountain of Lourdes are evidently cures of psychological conditions; yet a reading of the history of the Lourdes miracles indicates that they cannot all be explained on a scientific basis. Some Protestant churches are interested in the healing ministry, and cooperation between churches and psychiatrists is growing.

One of the most enigmatical reported sayings of Jesus is: [32]"Truly I say unto you, whoever says to this mountain, Be taken up and cast into the sea, and does not doubt in his heart, but believes that what he says will come to pass, it will be done for him." It is almost unanimously believed that the mountain mentioned is a psychological mountain; one reason is that if a physical mountain were moved by faith there would be legal complications. Probably a sufficient application is the knowledge that in science as in other fields, the person who does not know that the difficulties of a particular project are insurmountable is the one who goes ahead and accomplishes it. Thousands of such cases are recorded in our books and magazines.

The present cold war is a conflict between faiths, and if at present the Communists are winning it is because their faith is stronger. They have supreme faith in the non-existence of God, in the power of duplicity, and in the success of brute force. We believe in the reasonable way of doing things, the soft answer, and most of us believe in God. I sometimes think that, just as the captivity was the making of the Jewish community, so fifty or a hundred years of enforced subservience to the Communists, followed by a century of agonizing recovery, would be the making of our nation, if it survived at all. On the other hand, in my saner moments I believe that the principles of the Communists will be self-defeating before that time.

Miracles

"Miracle" is another word whose many shades of meaning cause confusion. Originally, before anyone had an idea of laws of nature, the word simply meant a wonder; but both in Hebrew and pagan thought, it usually implied divine causation. It is still used in the sense of a wonder; thus we speak of the miracle of life. The word is often employed to signify the happening of the improbable; thus when we say "he was miraculously saved" we mean that the probability that the person involved would escape a calamity was very low, but he did escape. The conception of laws of nature has added another factor to the meaning. A very common meaning of miracles is an occurrence which violates a law of nature. An explanation is that God is the Author of the laws of nature and is free to violate or change those laws as He sees fit. With better understanding of the meaning of laws of nature, that conception is slowly disappearing. Apparent exceptions to those laws may occur, because we never know the outer boundaries of limits of a law. Of course we constantly interfere with the workings of nature even when we are determining and testing its laws; for instance we have greatly increased the number of organic chemicals in our restricted part of the universe; but such results are not miracles because we still see the laws that have helped us to increase them. In the degree of acceptance of Biblical miracles, a fairly close distinction can be made between the three branches of Protestant belief: fundamentalist, (modern) orthodox, and liberal. The fundamentalist will insist that Jesus really turned water into wine; that He actually fed five thousand people with five loaves and two fishes; that He actually raised Lazarus from the dead; and so on through the list of miracles in the Old and New Testaments. The liberal will not necessarily accept any of these reported happenings as facts, and believes that someone has exaggerated stories of actual happenings. To illustrate modern orthodox beliefs, three authors who would probably be quoted will be included in this class.

The position of M. Holmes Hartshorne is that many of the miracles are subjective. He says: [33]"No scientist would claim that all events *can* be explained, but he would be quite clear that no event *can* be explained by invoking the word 'God'. Scientifically speaking, a miracle is meaningless. . . . The gospel story miracles are marvels; and yet not one bit of 'evidence' would have been visible to a newsreel camera or to the observation of a scientifically trained reporter. A miracle is visible only to the heart it touches. . . . To report a miracle in the visible sense is not therefore to report an objective occurrence; it is to proclaim good tidings of great joy. The Biblical writers were primarily concerned with man's relation to God, not to nature. . . . Christianly speaking, there is only one miracle—God's forgiving love incarnate in Christ.

. . . The early commentators, beginning with Paul, were scientifically in error in discovering references to Jesus throughout the Old Testament, but religiously they were right. . . . In this matter of judgment science and the Christian faith are not dissimilar. The scientist recognizes that theory must stand under the judgment of fact. From a Protestant perspective the scientific view is valid; the Protestant simply insists that its validity is limited to the sphere of man's knowledge of nature. In the dimension of personal meaning it is irrelevant." Here again the word "dimension" shows existentialist influence.

Among the miracles discussed by Hartshorne to illustrate his interpretation of miracles is Christ's calming the waves. According to him the storm is exaggerated in the Biblical account; it was not the physical storm that was calmed, but the fears of the disciples, who had magnified the danger. In other words, the miracle was psychological. Similar interpretations are given to a number of the other miracles. Other theologians of the same school would not agree entirely with Hartshorne; they would insist that most of the miracles of healing were real; that is, an x-ray picture or a bacterial examination, if not a newsreel camera, would have shown a difference in the patient's condition before and after the miracle. Such miracles sometimes occur today.

Rudolph Otto has this to say about miracles of healing: [34]"The narratives of these acts of healing stand out with such an assured and plain simplicity, with a clarity so well-nigh disconcerting, that they cannot be the fabrications of legend. We have only to read the sober account—it is almost like an official report—of the healing of Peter's wife's mother (Mark 1: 29-31) or that of the healing of the man with the palsy (Mark 2: 1-12), with its concreteness of detail. And it is the same with many other cases." (He cites that of the centurion and of the woman of Canaan.) "Moreover, there is the fact that we encounter exactly similar occurrences among the early Christian communities. . . . It is quite evident that both Paul and the first Christian communities were convinced that they had . . . the 'gifts' among them. No doubt he says (1 Cor. 13) that something is higher and more precious than all 'gifts', namely, the simple Christian virtues of faith, hope, and love, and love 'the greatest of all these'. But it is implied thereby that those other gifts, too, are a reality and a present possession. . . . Will this mysterious region one day be clearly revealed to us? We can at any rate say this: that our procedure is very uncritical if we propose to rule it out as non-existent simply because it does not square with our current conceptions of 'agreement with the natural order'."

Otto says further that this power need not be regarded as 'supernatural'; that it is merely an extension of our present capabilities, shown in our regular acts of will, and more highly in telepathy, clairvoyance, and such phenomena. "All these suppositions may be accepted without misgiving, only with this addition, that what Jesus did passed far beyond anything known to us and moreover, that Jesus's whole power grew out of His consciousness of His mission; and His will, unusually strong as it was, drew its strength only from His religious and moral consciousness, from the fact that He was rooted and grounded in God." If this is admitted, it heightens our pity for the afflicted ones of a few hundred years later, when the Church seems to have lost this power altogether, but did not recognize the advance of science which would have relieved much of the sickness, pain and death.

On the other hand, Otto rejects other miracles of Jesus: the changing of water into wine and the raising of Lazarus, for instance. These two miracles are reported only in John's gospel. They have a dramatic flavor and an aura of publicity not shown in the accounts of the healing miracles. Also, some miracles in the synoptic gospels, including the walking on the sea, the feeding of the five thousand, and the driving of demons into the Gadarene swine, are similarly rejected. Otto admits the possibility of two of the resurrections—the daughter of Jairus and the young man of Nain, in which apparent death occurred shortly before the miracle. Otto says about these contrasting miracles: "Jairus's daughter had not lain three days in the grave, like Lazarus; she had only lost consciousness a short time before the miracle. Where is the margin that divides complete death from the last faint glow of the spark of life, very likely already passed into unconsciousness? May not he who by his will had power to restore a consciousness confused by madness have had also the power to arrest a consciousness just vanishing over the borders of life, and even awaken in the body one that has just vanished? Here the account is strikingly concrete. Even the words Jesus uses to awaken the girl as uttered in Aramic—'talitha cumi'—are still given in the Aramaic form by the Greek narrator. There is nothing grandiose or theatrical, as is customarily the case with a miracle designed for display. Jesus only admits the most intimate even of His disciples, and the whole incident closes with the soberly practical injunction to give the newly restored child food, and with the direct prohibition to talk further about the event. We have only to compare with this the raising of Lazarus; here is the exact opposite, a genuine miracle of display. The wonder-worker designedly delays His arrival, so that a miracle becomes necessary; the whole proceeding, with its solemn mise-en-scene, takes place in public, and is accompanied by a prayer, which is at the same time a sort of address to the surrounding spectators. The act is to be performed expressly 'because of the people which stand by'. This is how a miraculous narrative looks when it is the offspring of literary art. The raisings from the dead given in St. Mark are quite other than this, and consequently a circumspect criticism may perhaps in their case suspend judgment." The accounts of these miracles which Otto doubts contribute greatly to the skeptical attitude of many non-Christians. Some theologians consider the stories of those miracles as allegories and give them a purely spiritual meaning.

Another interesting although difficult viewpoint is that of William G. Pollard, who is both a scientist and a theologian. It is difficult to express Pollard's views on miracles without discussing his entire philosophy, but a few quotations such as the following may serve to elucidate them. [35]"The majority of the biblical miracles are, like that in the Exodus, the result of an extraordinary and extremely improbable combination of chance and accident. They do not, on close analysis, involve, as is so frequently supposed, a violation of the laws of nature. . . . Even within the Biblical context, however, there is a strong tendency to give the miraculous happening an objective validity independent of the response of the worshipping community to the presence and action of God in their life and history. This can be done by modifying the account of it so as to make its occurrence, objectively considered, not merely extraordinarily improbable as an event in the natural order," as in the later revisions of the Exodus account. "A singular event may or may not be miraculous depending upon whether it does or does not reveal the presence and action of God within the community to whom God is known. Such, for example, are the miracles of the Creation, the Incarnation, and the Resurrection. These are singular events which were also charged with tremendous revelatory power. With them it is meaningless to speak of chance or accident. . . . It is an error to think of miracle as being 'unnatural'. Chance and the singular enter into and make up history just as much as do scientific, economic, and sociological laws. The miraculous is just as much a part of the nature of history as the coherent. If a miraculous event could only happen outside the natural order of things, then it would necessarily imply that it would be unnatural for God to exercise providence over His creation. Such an idea is, however, clearly un-Biblical and contrary to everything which has been revealed of God in either Israel or Christ. . . . There is an insistent and recurring demand for some way of objectively establishing the fact of God and the reality apart from His self-revelation through Israel, Christ, and the Church. This, however, is a futile hope and the end of such a quest can only be frustration. It is analogous to a demand for acquiring scientific knowledge independently of observation and experiment and in a state of alienation from the spirit, discipline, and traditions of science."

Here again is an approach to the existentialist view. Scientific reasoning is only a part of human mental activity, and its concepts are, as Pollard in his later book expresses, like the raisins in a plum pudding, while the non-conceptual part of thinking corresponds to the rest of the pudding. Anything outside the scientific portion could be called miraculous. That is, if I say "I am", I am expressing something that cannot be conceived by science and is therefore miraculous by the broadest definition. Even if that standpoint is an exaggeration of the meaning of the miraculous, we can say that without admitting the historicity of the recorded miracles, we leave the spiritual field open to incomplete coverage by natural law.

We cannot prove the non-existence of any recorded miracle; but the science-minded person can say that he has more faith in the uniform natural law than he has in the occurrence of anything that is not in accordance with the law. For instance, he has more faith in the principles of chemistry which say that water cannot be turned into wine than he has in the accuracy of an account of a man turning water into wine, no matter how great the divine power he is assumed to have.

It may be added here that one should always make a reservation in denying a miracle. The questionable miracle of today may be the fact of tomorrow. In other words, a natural law may be discovered tomorrow that explains a heretofore miraculous and questionable phenomenon. In the shady areas of extrasensory perception, telepathy, and related subjects, a future discovery may clarify many mystifying occurrences.

This discussion leads to the most important miracle of all, the Resurrection.

Eternal Life; the Resurrection

Another essential doctrine of Christianity and most other religions is immortality or eternal life. Immortality is sometimes taken to mean continued personal existence and eternal life to mean existence in the presence of God. The Bible says little about details; and speculation on the subject is almost unlimited. If there is a life without our present bodies, what is its chemistry and physics, or has it any? Are there possible relations between molecules and their constituents other than in human life as we know it, which may permit consciousness, and may continue the relations of a particular human life? Is it possible that another body may continue the consciousness associated with the present one, in either the Christian sense or that of reincarnation?

The concept of additional dimensions or spaces in which the entities of religion exist has been mentioned several times. Now the question arises whether eternal life may be lived in a different dimension than that of time as we experience it. That has been definitely suggested by Gatland and Dempster in *The Inhabited Universe*. [36]The statement frequently made, "eternal life is here and now" hints at that possibility. The idea appeals to some philosophers. But would it have a popular appeal? How many converts would an evangelist gain who offered existence in an additional dimension or space as a reward for the faithful? One can point out in replying to that question that a dimension is a mere skeleton framework of reality. It is possible that the delights of eternal life as pictured are but a shadowy indication of a reality far beyond our comprehension. The question is thus raised whether the future life as generally understood is a real tenet of Christianity? The fundamentalist would say yes; other groups would say no or give this additional dimension explanation. Popular theology is based on the idea of a future reward for goodness; the message of Christianity is that the reward is for faith, not for deeds; but emphasis is placed on the thought that faith should be held and good deeds should be performed without the expectancy of reward. That is part of the apparent Christian paradox. The subject of the Resurrection is closely connected with that of immortality.

Since I first became acquainted with the ideas of eternal life existing in an additional dimension I have become more and more impressed with it, but my feeling is far from a complete faith. On the other hand I do not have great faith in eternal life in its conventional meaning of a contiunance in time as we experience it.

Without my present senses, which depend upon my body, experience would be so greatly different that it is hard to imagine it.

The validity of the Resurrection of Jesus is one of the most difficult and controversial questions in theology. All but a very few people hold one of two beliefs; first, that the Biblical account is essentially correct and that the Resurrection was physical and historical; or, that the account is founded on imagination and illusion. The literal view is held by fundamentalists and a large proportion of the orthodox; they insist that if the Resurrection did not actually occur Christianity is based on a false hope. There is little doubt that the disciples had unanimously accepted the Resurrection as a fact. On the other hand, humanists, Unitarians, and other liberal Christians argue that any or all of the appearances of Jesus could have been illusions, especially since they were not recorded until many years afterward. Many modern orthodox authorities have little to say on the subject; naturally they hesitate to express themselves on this most difficult problem, of those who do many have somewhat conflicting opinions. One of the few who discuss the question thoroughly is Otto, who has been quoted on the subject of miracles. His position is that the experiences of the Risen Christ were "mystical". The prevailing belief about mystical experiences which is discussed elsewhere, is that a mystical experience of God is possible, but that no mystical experience provides facts. Paul thought that he saw the actual Christ at the time of his conversion; Otto and others believe that the mystical experiences of the apostles who "saw" Jesus were similar; other authors have expressed the idea that they saw Jesus in a dimension different from the ordinary mundane ones.

The story of the Ascension involves more difficulty than that of the Resurrection. It was perfectly plausible under the cosmic conceptions of the time. Heaven was just above the sight of people on the earth. A miraculous whirlwind could actually have taken Jesus to His permanent abode. But with our positive knowledge that heaven is not there, and our strong belief that it is not anywhere in the physical universe, the question of just what happened arises. It would have been more reasonable to modern thinking, and no more miraculous in the eyes of the spectators, if a space ship had come to take Jesus to another corner of the universe to begin a mission there.

Without quoting Otto extensively, his concluding paragraph may be revelatory: [37]"As regards the narratives of the 'Empty Tomb', we shall judge of these as of the narratives of a later date which gathered about the birth of Jesus, appraising them as a holy legend, in which the supra-rational relations of the eternal to the temporal is mirrored in the medium of contemporary thought. They have an enduring value to us from the incomparable beauty and power with which they symbolize the essence of the 'mystery'. We would not be without them in our Bible, nor yet in the pictorial art of the churches, nor in the hymns that express our devotion. And we can retain them thus without being false to the obligation of the most rigid honesty if we remain fully conscious of that other obligation, without fulfilling which we neither can nor indeed should have either Biblical instruction or Christian doctrine. And that is the obligation we are under to train ourselves and the mind of our time to a sincere understanding of three things. In the first place we need to realize the fringe of legend that surrounds the entire narrative of the Holy Scripture and recurs as a constant problem from the first page of the Bible to the last. Secondly, we need to appreciate the signal value and beauty and the profound import which distinguish the Biblical narrative, even where it is of the nature of legend; and, finally, the fact that even in the holy saga and legend, shaped and fashioned unconsciously by the spirit of a people or a fellowship, there is present the very same eternal Spirit of God, which Hebrew prophecy and poetry and history also manifest, that Spirit which, in every form of its expression, is the Spirit of revelation and truth."

On the other hand, Jenkins says: [38]"It was out of the conviction that God in Jesus Christ had proved Himself stronger than the cross and the tomb, that the Christian faith was born. . . . It is inevitable, therefore, that the stories of the Resurrection, if they are considered by themselves, should raise difficulties for modern minds. They are credible only as part of the full experience of God in Christ. But it is essential that their difficulty should not be used as a reason for evading their challenge and for trying to make an acceptable version of Christianity without them."

Sin, Salvation, Redemption

The Hebrew and Greek words translated "sin" meant "to miss the mark"; that is still a good definition and attention has been increasingly called to it. In the fundamentalist conception sin is simply disobedience to God's commands. To some humanists sin is an imperfection which man inherited from his brute ancestry and will be eradicated in the course of his further evolution. This view overlooks the fact that no brute would be guilty of many of

the sinful things that members of the human race do. If its origin
is to be found in man's evolution it must be sought farther back.
The survival of the fittest does not call for the perfection of the individual; only enough coordination to survive under the usual conditions is sufficient. An irregularity in a small particle in a molecule
may produce a large irregularity in the developed body, and may
become a source of disease or other disturbance. In everyone there
are many such irregularities, enough to prevent complete coordination; so man is a blunderer and a sinner. "The things he would do
he does not do, and the things he would not do he does." In other
words, these irregularities lead to compulsory courses of action
contrary to any ideal developed by the individual or others,
whether regarded as of divine origin or not.

The above is the "outer" view of sin. To the individual, sin
may be considered as following a course which he wants to follow
because it will enlarge his experience. What makes it sin is that it
does not have that effect. This is the more true in the "positive"
sins such as drink, sexual sins, enmity, and jealousy. I hope to be
happier and more fulfilled if I do certain things in spite of an inner
restraint based on experience, and conscience, which warns that
that hope is an illusion. I fully realize this later, but next time the
same situation presents itself. In the more serious cases, such as
alcoholism, the subject is no longer capable of making the decision.

The meaning of the consequences of sin is controversial.
"The wages of sin is death." What does this mean? Physically we
all die. Does it mean that if we were sinless we would not die?
Another meaning is that the sinner goes to a state of perpetual
punishment, rather than annihilation. A modern picture of death
as a consequence of sin is the withering of the spiritual nature until
it disappears completely.

According to the fundamentalist, the orthodox, and some
liberals man is a sinner. That statement is reasonable, as is the
idea that man is an ignoramus and a blunderer. The doctrine of
total depravity, held by conservatives some time ago, and still not
entirely absent, is as unreasonable as one of total ignorance or
total incapability. To some liberals, insofar as man is a sinner, he
can save himself; that theory is nearly exploded. To the orthodox,
redemption can come only through faith in Christ. Thus we are
brought to the subject of salvation.

There is no more difficult subject in theology than salvation
or redemption. It is at the basis of all fundamentalist and orthodox
theology. The goal of humanism is the perfection of man rather

than personal salvation, and the same is true of some liberal
beliefs. In primitive religions all men somehow or other incurred
the wrath of their gods and retribution was demanded. In some
religions the death of the firstborn son was required. In the
Hebrew religion and possibly some others they were allowed to
substitute the firstborn of the flock and other firstfruits. These sacrifices were required of everyone as a ritual rather than as punishment for particular sins. Similar considerations applied to relations between persons. The principle of "an eye for an eye, a tooth
for a tooth" arose in early Hebrew history, perhaps as a corrective
for an earlier principle of unlimited punishment, and based on
the analogy to monetary reimbursement in case of loss of property.
In relations with the Deity, "the wages of sin is death" was the rule,
whatever may have been meant by death in that connection, but
an expiatory death could be substituted for the death of the responsible individual. With the background of those beliefs, Paul's
preaching that the death of Christ became the expiation of the
sins of all individuals who accept the sacrifice was reasonable.

The concept of retribution has greatly changed since the time
of the Bible. It is only in financial and property grievances that
equilibrium can be restored by payment in the same kind. The
death of one person does not compensate for that of another; nor
is any physical or mental damage equalized by the infliction of the
same trouble on another. The modern ideal of punishment, which
we hope will eventually be reached, includes the protection of
society and the reform of the criminal. Many modern thinkers are
inclined to apply the same idea to sin. They believe that there is
no way to transfer the sin of one to another or accept the punishment inflicted on one as atonement for the sins of another. If a
clergyman or theologian is asked how the death of Christ saves from
sin, he either replies that he does not know or gives the ancient
explanation. Even the definition of salvation is subject to strong
differences of opinion.

A former communicant of the Protestant Episcopal Church
asked for a definition of salvation, through the correspondence
column of a publication of that denomination. He received sur-
prisingly few replies, published or communicated directly. No
replies were given by anyone in high authority in the church; some
were from laywomen. The replies showed great variations. Such
divergence was to be expected. Bridgman's experience with individual understandings of various words like community and morality has been related, and the word "salvation" is still more lacking

in concreteness. On the other hand, it seems reasonable to expect from those whose business is explaining religion a more definite idea of the meaning of salvation. The inquirer then broke the original question into four parts: "Who is saving whom from what and why?" Three personal replies and a number of published ones were received. The personal answers, which are typical of the others, were: "Who?" (1) God; (2) Christ; and (3) You; "Whom?" (1) Yourself; (2) All mankind; and (3) Man; "From what?" (1) From a selfish, useless, egotistical, non-constructive existence; (2) sin, hell, and death; (3) everything that tends to keep man from being what God intended him to be; and "Why?" (1) Otherwise you will lead a hell of a rotten, wasteful, useless existence, here and now; (2) You are a sinner, Mr. _____; and (3) His plan for the universe is incomplete until each of us is saved in this way. Some replicants recommended books, which the inquirer did not find more illuminating than the personal replies. One of his tentative conclusions was that salvation is different for every person; another was that nobody knows what it is.

The subjects of conversion and salvation can be discussed theologically or in terms of their measurable consequences. Although religion, like personality, is beyond the screen that bounds the scientific method, its results may be a subject for investigation. When the sins of an individual are noticeable in his conduct and he becomes converted and reforms, we can with justification call him saved. One definition that has been given for salvation is "integration of personality". Although the persons who seem to have the best integrated personalities are not necessarily the most religious ones, the change in an individual is often obvious. Lives of torment and confusion have been changed into happy, organized lives, even though they represent only a small minority of those who are converted by an evangelist or otherwise.

H. H. Potthoff writes of the meaning of salvation: "Profound religion offers to man a way of life which lifts him above the changing fortunes of the external world. He lives within the world and yet above it. Salvation means inner freedom from external things at least in the sense that one may find serenity and creativity in changing circumstances. Salvation means the power to seek and do the good, even though there is the persistent pull of the lower. Salvation means the transformation of evil and suffering into some emergent good. Salvation means the vision of God which cleanses the inner life and releases nobler aspirations. Salvation means a living communion with God.

Whether or not we use theological language, the fact remains that salvation is the deepest concern of man. Many there are who do not know what it is that they are seeking. But in the midst of a world in which we lose our way, in which fear, despair, guilt, and meaninglessness haunt the lives of men, and in which life 'goes to pieces' and we will become estranged from ourselves, our fellow men and God—we need the healing which alone brings health and wholeness. We seek the life which is truly life. We seek the courage, meaning, wholeness which can come only from a trusting and creative relationship with God. This is the meaning of salvation."

William James' book, *Varieties of Religious*[39] *Experience* and other textbooks on the psychology of religion tell of many such cases. Even physical improvement is known to result in many instances. It is true, however, that such transformations have followed conversions to religions other than Christianity, or even to atheism.

The most spectacular cases of conversion and the most amenable to study are conversions from, or cures of, alcoholism. The subject is discussed thoroughly and profoundly in the book *Alcoholism, Its Psychology and Cure,* by Frederick B. Rea.[40] The stages of alcoholism are described. The disease is characterized by a slow and gradual progress of which the victim is unaware. In general he will do nothing about his condition until he comes to a point where he realizes that he can do nothing, then he is a slave to the habit. Many do not change even then, and end in a drunkard's grave. But some realize their condition at that point and surrender. This surrender is the first step to recovery, whether the principal agent in the recovery is Alcoholics Anonymous, medical treatment, or some other means. Rea describes several forms of medical treatment, all of which have the object of creating an aversion to alcohol, but he shows that anyone of those methods is successful only when the alcoholic is psychologically ready for it. He is then amenable to the help of another person, who may be a doctor or a person who has been through a similar experience. This dependence on another person can be transferred to dependence on God. Twelve steps in recovery are listed; the twelfth is especially important. In this step the patient helps others who are in the same condition, just as he has been helped by another. The whole attitude of Alcoholics Anonymous and of modern methods of treatment are based on the recognition of alcoholism as a disease rather than a sin. There is much controversy on this point, but it may be generally agreed that the original cause may be a sin, but that the final condition has all the characteristics of a disease.

Rea discusses the difference between the Alcoholics Anonymous treatment and formal religious conversion. Often pastors do not see why they cannot accomplish what Alcoholics Anonymous does. Rea says: [41]"When the pastor thoroughly understands this aspect of the Christian doctrine of sin, he begins to realize that it is by no means inappropriate to look upon sin as a disease. He ceases to regard his fellow men as free moral agents at liberty in any given situation to choose the right from the wrong. He learns to distinguish between objectively sinful deeds and those that are subjectively sinful. A man's act may be evil and he may be morally responsible for it; yet he himself has done it, seriously believing it was right and without any consciousness of having sinned. Sin has robbed him, not only of the power to act freely, but of the power to think truly. In the light of this distinction, the pastor discovers a new depth of sympathy for the criminal and the addict—in fact for all his fellow men. He begins to understand more fully the words spoken by Jesus from the cross: 'Father, forgive them, for they know not what they do.' They are responsible, they are sinning, and they need forgiveness. Yet 'they know not', nor have they the power to act otherwise. . . . The whole emphasis was upon the addict's helplessness and upon the need for acceptance. He cannot save himself. Salvation must come from without. It depends upon the touch of a loving God and of a sympathetic friend. All this is essentially the Christian way. Alcoholics Anonymous is simply applying to addicts a form of therapy which Our Lord regarded as necessary for all humanity. . . . It may be said of the Alcoholics Anonymous program that its framework is essentially Christian, though, of course, it lacks the full content of the Gospel." Rea considers Freud's psychology as two-dimensional, ignoring the third dimension of the Godward plane of human existence.

Salvation, in so far as alcoholism is concerned, is synonymous with cure, and "conversion" is its outward aspect. In alcoholism there is the added complication of a possible change in the nervous system—but who can prove that there is not a similar change in other sin-diseases? In other such diseases there is the same progression to helplessness, as in ambition in Macbeth. Spectacular cures of these sin-diseases are rare in history and literature. Real-life examples of sinful ambition are those of Hitler and Mussolini. In Hitler's case, at least, it is recognized that physical and psychic disturbances were present. Both these cases terminated fatally.

Other forms of selfishness which could be called pathological are known in literature and real life.

On the other hand the course of sin is often arrested before a crisis ensues. Even in the case of alcoholism, the victim's own efforts against it sometimes effect a cure in the earlier stages. In other words, most people's sins do not progress to the point of possible surrender to them. We are using "sin" here in the everyday empirical sense and not in the sense used by Rea when he says: [42]"The Christian faith is primarily concerned with sin, not with sins. Fundamentally there is only one sin, namely, an act of revolt against God." There are the sins committed after a losing debate of the good against the evil, and there are sins which the committer is totally unaware of as sin. Many such sins are unadmitted, and some are discovered suddenly, especially when another person calls attention to them. In the Roman Catholic Church they are often disclosed by the confessional. But probably the most potent force in causing one to realize the presence of sin in him has been the religious revival, one of the first of which was the "Great Awakening" already described. Such revivals, past and present, can be credited with the reform of many people to greater integrity and more usefulness to society; on the other hand, in many there was induced only a temporary emotional excitement, with a return to the former conditions when it had subsided. Also, one unfortunate effect of revivals has been conversion from sins which do not exist. In my younger days, the mark of a Christian, in some denominations and in rural sections at least, was whether he or she danced or played cards. They were considered more serious sins than self-righteousness or self-deceit. Then also, conversion was to fundamentalism or its equivalent.

How can it be determined what is a sin and what is not? The Ten Commandments may be a guide to some extent. But is not the question whether actions are in accordance with the attitude of love, that is, concern for others and all its consequences, a deciding factor? If by selfishness, ambition, or any other trait we are limiting our love for the soul, the persons, of others we are sinning. Often these sins are controllable by our own effort. In cases such as alcoholism, our defenses are broken down and further help is necessary. It is at this point that the humanist and the theist diverge. The theist says that apart from the help we can get from other people, it must be from God. The humanist says that it is from ourselves; when not consciously, it is from the unconscious or sub-conscious self. It may be from the Holy Spirit as defined by Huxley, a part of our individual personality. Neither science nor common sense is capable of answering this question. *Directly* there is evidence that the help comes from the unconscious self. To prove or even to make acceptable the idea of God's help it would have to be shown that there is a relation between the unconscious selves of different people. That, of course, is not proved, but it is made plausible. The conception of God to be employed here may be as broad as you like.

Let us refer again to the distinction between religions of eros and of agape, as Rea puts it, partially quoting A. W. Watts; such religions as Primitive Buddhism, Neo-Platonism, certain forms of Yoga, and Gnosticism have stressed the ascent of man to the divine state. The agape religions include many forms of Mahayana Buddhism, Hinduism, early Taoism, and of course Christianity. Watts (as quoted by Rea) continues: "The meaning of the Incarnation, therefore, is simply that we do not have to attain union with God. Man does not have to climb to the infinite and become God, because, out of love, the infinite God descends to the finite and becomes man. Despite man's refusal of God, despite his pride, his fear, his helpless and hopeless involvement in the vicious circle of sin, God's nature remains unalterably love,—the agape which consists in giving itself wholly and without reservation to the beloved. . . . All that remains for us to do is to say 'Yes, Amen' to this tremendous fact and this is still within the power of our fallen nature."

The next inquiry that may be made is, what is the relation between salvation and the historical Jesus? The original and conventional fundamentalist answer was discussed at the beginning of this section. A higher conception is that suffering is most intense in those with the greatest capacity to suffer, and Christ's, or God's, suffering in the death of Christ takes on a universal character. The quotation from Watts is probably the nearest approach to a clear expression of this difficult dogma. I am not trying to answer the question. I wish I understood it better. Whereas the object of science is to give ever and ever more precise information consisting of facts, that of theology is not, and it fails when it attempts to be exact. But I can point out, as Rea and others have done, that conversion is not exclusively a Christian experience. Some people, in formally leaving the church, have been converted to higher usefulness and harmony with God; but they are in a small minority.

Rebirth

Although this subject is closely related to salvation, and therefore is classified under the attributes of religion, its implications are broader. Every sensation is a new experience, in a way, a creation. Its scope varies from a sensation that leads to the acquisition of unimportant facts to an almost complete transformation, or what may be called an explosive experience. The most explosive is birth, in which the infant starts from nothing and arrives first into a "bustling, blooming confusion," as William James put it, and though experiences are added gradually, the first moment must be the greatest sensation of all. A more partial, but perhaps more sudden, experience is a case in which a person who is born blind suddenly acquires the sense of sight. A wealth of sensations not imagined before are present all at once, although they need to be identified and classified in relatively long experience. Next in order of scope may be the introduction to a new field of learning. A child, or even an adult, having puzzled over the subject of chemistry, for instance, without having acquired much interest, suddenly finds that it is intensely interesting, and begins to pursue it further with pleasure. A scientist, having pondered a long time about the implications and organization of his results, suddenly finds that they fit together into a probable theory. A writer, in any field, similarly finds a new relation between his ideas. Heim says of the non-objective space in which the I and the thou encountered each other: [43]"This notion cannot have entered men's minds through philosophical reflection. A man whose thinking is conducted in terms of one space cannot be persuaded by logical argument that some other space may exist. . . . The great orientation which led to the awakening in us of the notion that some other existence is possible must have arisen not from theoretical reflection but from a cataclysmic shock, disturbing the vital center of man and thus shaking the walls of the immense prison in which he is confined." Jesus said to Nicodemus: "Except a man be born again, he cannot see the kingdom of God." What I am suggesting here is that the differences between these experiences may be only one of degree. Never or rarely in unimportant matters is the process of learning or of finding anything a simple matter of looking for something and finding only that. Even in searching for a lost physical object, its finding comes as a shock, as if the found object did not correspond exactly to what was sought. Therein, I think, rests the foundation for the idea of the grace of God and even of predestination. Something outside our previous experience enters.

It is not our will that gives answers, although it is concerned in the seeking. Probably philosophers and psychologists have a better way of expressing this idea.

In the case of the scientist, it is evident that the explosive experience does not provide him with truth. He must check his ideas by experiment. In conversion or other spiritual experience, however, the person undergoing the experience may, and often does, consider that he has become aware of new facts. Hocking condenses a great amount of wisdom into four words, the convert is "sure of too much". This being sure of too much is at the heart of many religious differences and problems.

Surrender

"Surrender to God" as an act is considered a requisite of conversion, and as an attitude a part of the Christian life. Just what is meant by "surrender" in this connotation? Surrender of what and to what? Every choice that is made involves a surrender of one possibility to another. It is generally understood, however, that any ethical decision is the surrender of the "lower" to the "higher", and the "lower" can be defined in two ways that do not have quite the same shade of meaning. The first is "independence", in the sense in which Dostoevsky uses it in *Notes from Underground;* the haphazard, spontaneous, and unrestrained action with no regard for consequences. The second is self-centeredness, which may or may not involve cool calculation of the effect on the self. The object of surrender in the first sense is not necessarily altruistic; pursuit of hobby may be sufficient to orient and regulate the life. A hobby, however, may be pursued to excess and become a vice. Self-centeredness and relief from it are thus discussed by Toynbee, the historian:

[44] "The role of self-centeredness in Life on Earth is an ambivalent one. On the one hand, self-centeredness is evidently of the essence of Terrestrial Life. A living creature might, indeed, be defined as a minor and subordinate piece of the Universe which, by a *tour de force,* has partly disengaged itself from the rest and has set itself up as an autonomous power that serves, up to the point of its capacity, to make the rest of the Universe minister to is selfish purposes. In other words, every living creature is striving to make itself into a center of the Universe, and, in fact, is entering into rivalry with every other living creature, with the Universe itself, and with the power that creates and sustains the Universe and is the reality underlying the fleeting phenomena. For every

living creature, this self-centeredness is one of the necessities of life, because it is indispensable for the creature's existence. A complete renunciation of self-centeredness would bring with it, for every living creature, a complete extinction of that particular local and temporary vehicle of life, even though this might not mean an extinction of life itself; and an insight into this psychological truth is the intellectual starting point of Buddhism.

"Self-centeredness is thus a necessity of Life, but this necessity is also a sin. Self-centeredness is an intellectual error, because no living creature is in truth the center of the Universe; and it is also a moral error, because no living creature has a right to act as if it were the center of the Universe. It has no right to treat its fellow-creatures, the Universe, and God or reality as if they existed simply in order to minister to one self-centered creature's demands. To hold this mistaken belief and to act on it is the sin of *hybris* (as it is called in the language of Hellenic psychology); and this hybris is the inordinate, criminal, and suicidal pride which brings Lucifer to his fall (as the tragedy of life is presented in the Christian myth)."

Three attributes of surrender are object, degree, and compensation. By object is meant, to whom or to what the surrender is made. It may be a person or group of persons, an organization, an ideal, an ideology, a state or government, a church, or God. From the preceding quotation it is evident that there are degrees of surrender; it can be neither absent nor complete. Also, it may be voluntary or compulsory. For any voluntary surrender compensation is expected consciously or unconsciously.

One surrenders involuntarily to an armed thief or to a captor in war. The surrender to a political opponent after an election is more complex; it is both compulsory and voluntary. At the extreme of voluntary surrender is the case of a mother who sacrifices ease and comfort to the well-being of her child. A literal interpretation of Jesus' words about non-resistance to evil would mean making compulsory surrender to others voluntary. Disputes about their interpretation center around the degree of surrender that is Christian. Voluntary submission to the State is a question about which the advocates of various ideologies differ. The central theme on which our government was founded was retention of as much freedom as possible without detriment to others. Whether that principle still holds in government practice is a matter of dispute. The principle of Marxian Communism is surrender of individual advantages, such as profits, to the welfare of the State. The theoretical compensation to the individual is greater material benefit, but many are finding to their sorrow that the benefit is not forthcoming. The same is often true of surrender to other groups.

In an earlier chapter Thomas Huxley's idea of the analogy between religious surrender and the scientist's surrender to facts has been noted. Sarton discusses the same relation at greater length. I quote him in part:

[45]"Disinterestedness is the keynote of the best scientific efforts. This disinterestness is due mainly to the feeling of participation,— of conscious participation—in the mysterious activities of the universe. The man of science who has the real *feu sacre* in him feels that though he is but an infinitesimal part of the whole, yet his own endeavor may contribute, however little, to the fulfillment of man's purpose: a deeper understanding of nature, a closer adaptation to it, a better guidance, a more intelligent devotion. And this may be also the fulfillment of a greater purpose. If the essence of religion is an earnest consideration of life, independent of any selfish or personal motive, if it is the clear consciousness of the unity and wholeness of life and of our integration with it, then the pure scientist is intensely relgious." (Here Sarton gives the quotation from Huxley to which reference has been made.)

"You understand, entire surrender of self: that is what I call disinterestedness; nothing less. One cannot help feeling that any such disinterested effort must increase the sum of good will in the world. When life seems a bit hard, the man of science can always preserve his equanimity by concentrating his thoughts upon the truth, far away from all the battles and the futilities of life. In that field no deception will await him. I hasten to add that in such a case his equanimity would be tinged with sadness instead of being, as it should, a source of pure joy. To be truly happy and gay we must be able to pursue the truth, not alone, but among lovable men and women, who are kind to us and to whom we can show our own kindness. Even as the discovery of any particle of truth, whether it be to our advantage or not, pleasant or unpleasant, is a positive gain for the whole world, even so every act of kindness is a creation in the right direction. . . . Science like religion implies disinterestedness, earnestness, austerity."

In this rather idealized account, religion is used in its broadest sense, in which it would include humanism. Humanism as Sarton uses it is opposed to scientism rather than to theism; but nevertheless his conception of religion is humanistic. How does "surrender to God" in the sense ordinarily used in religion differ from surrender as used by Huxley and Sarton? The fundamentalist and orthodox would reply that it means surrender to the will of God as expressed in the Bible, and that faith rather than human judgment should be a guide in deciding a course of conduct in the multitudinous matters that call for action daily. The difficulty with that reply is that there is sometimes no ostensible basis for decision, and equally conscientious persons have made different decisions under the same circumstances. Moreover, the Bible is not always clear; although there may not be definite and absolute contradictions between different passages, theologians as well as laymen have followed different courses of thought and action by concentrating on different statements in the Bible. Therefore individual judgment must often be a factor in making decisions, after making full allowance for the importance of faith.

Many fundamentalists insist that "surrender of the mind" is a necessary part of surrender to God. They mean that independent thinking must be suppressed and surrendered to the words of the Bible as literal and unassailable statements of fact as well as principle. Every science-minded person totally rejects that idea because it is a bar to progress in religion as well as in science; to him it is one of the deadly sins.

Surrender, then, must be tempered with judgment. Christianity does not call for perfect submission in the sense that Buddhism does. There is a mean between total surrender which means self-annihilation and complete self-centeredness. This mean is the dignity of man, or with concessions to theology, the dignity of redeemed man. It implies surrender to the best that one knows; man must admit that he does not know all of God's will, but he must take account of all the factors that he knows and let faith be a guide the rest of the way. The attitude is well expressed in the words of the hymn, "Trust and obey". First we must find that we can trust; and although there are cases in which we are not quite sure what constitutes obedience, we usually know what it means and can act on our knowledge.

Chapter VII

Religious Beliefs of Scientists

W<small>E HAVE SEEN</small> that the bulk of Protestant belief at the present time can be classified into three general categories; liberalism or neo-liberalism, including theistic humanism; neo-orthodoxy or modern orthodoxy; and fundamentalism. Before we attempt additional discussion of these beliefs, it may be well to examine the attitude of present-day scientists toward religion. In a book entitled *Religious Beliefs of American Scientists* Edward Leroy Long has presented the religious views of a selected number of American natural scientists, each of whom has written at least one book in which his views are expressed. Social scientists were excluded because the interest of some of them in religion might be professional. Long's book is the basis of most of the following brief summary.

The two principal classes of attitudes are entitled "Approaches through Science" and "Approaches through Religion". A credo that proceeds from the scientific view is "God as cosmic structure", of which[1] Albert Einstein and David Starr Jordan were the most prominent advocates. Long applies the term mysticism to Einstein's belief but qualifies it as follows. [2]"His is not a religious mysticism signifying a flight into fantasy. . . . It is based upon the idea of a cosmic intelligence comprehended by human intelligence. It seeks no mystical bliss as an escape from the realities of experience. And yet it is mysticism".

Einstein feels a sense of awe before the simplicity and beauty of the cosmic structure as expressed in mathematical form. This awe comes, not simply from our ability to understand the mathematical structure, but in response to our inability to understand finally its utter simplicity. This awe is a response to something we cannot fully comprehend, and yet we know it exists. In this 'not knowing about knowing' we may see an idea to which the religious term 'mysticism' is not inappropriate, especially since Einstein himself uses the term in pointing to the religious and reverent aspect

155

involved in it." Einstein's idea of God is highly abstract and sophisticated. He scrupulously avoids anthropomorphism which means a conception of God as a man. Long points out, however, that Einstein goes to the other extreme and makes God sub-human. [2]"How, then, in his religious philosophy as a whole, does Einstein make a place for purpose—for morality and the historical drives of man? He embraces humanism, placing the moral aspect of religion directly upon the shoulders of man. Whereas God is impersonal, the cultural manifestation of religion depends upon the cultivation of the good life by individuals."

Jordan's view is similar, except that he finds a relation between his metaphysics and morality. He suggests that two elements, rational order and love, emanate from the same source. Thus when man loves, he acts creatively and in keeping with the essential order of the universe. In the universe God is truth, while within the human personality God is love. [3]The philosophy of Arvid Reuterdahl is also included in this category, but it employs artificial concepts and attempts to express religious truths by means of mathematical equations.

There are three types of Christian theism, the basic grounds of which are scientific. [4]The first, "God as first cause", is represented by Arthur H. Compton, Heber D. Curtis, Anthony Standen, and William North Rice. Compton's belief is characterized as a "humanism based, not on man's isolated attempt to construct a system of values in an impartial world, but rather on man's capacity to partake of the whole Purpose that rules the cosmos. . . . The argument from design has never been refuted." Standen's work was a best-seller entitled "Science Is a Sacred Cow", which was quoted frequently in our second chapter. Standen's purpose is to explode a bomb under "scientism", that is, the worship of scientific technique, rather than to develop a religious philosophy; his book, however, contains many statements about religious matters which puts him in the category of Christian theists. [5]"Natural law and Providence," writes Professor Rice, "are not as men have fancied, conceptions contradictory and mutually exclusive. Law and Providence are only two phases of the same truth." Curtis holds beliefs which are quite similar to Compton's. He believes that, just as science makes speculations and uses working hypotheses, religion has the right to do the same.

The second of these types of thought places emphasis upon the idea of growth. Toward the end of the controversy of which the Scopes trial was a feature, and in a way a climax, a committee of thirty-five, mostly clergymen and scientists, issued a *Joint Statement Upon the Relation of Science and Religion*. It said:

[6]"We, the undersigned, deeply regret that in recent controversies there has been a tendency to present science and religion as irreconcilable and antagonistic domains of thought, for in fact they meet distinct human needs, and in the rounding out of human life they supplement rather than displace or oppose each other.

"The purpose of science is to develop, without prejudice or preconceptions of any kind, a knowledge of the facts, the laws, and the processes of nature. The even more important task of religion, on the other hand, is to develop the conscience, the ideals, and the aspirations of mankind. Each of these activities represents a deep and vital function of the soul of man, and both are necessary for the life, the progress, and the happiness of the human race.

"It is a sublime conception of God which is furnished by science, and one wholly consonant with the highest ideals of religion, when it represents Him as revealing Himself through countless ages in the development of the earth as an abode for man and in the age-long inbreathing of life into its constituent matter, culminating in man with his spiritual nature and in all his godlike powers."

Those who emphasize growth may be divided into two classes with slightly differing beliefs. In one, the scientific conception of a changing, growing universe becomes a singular proof of God. The general framework of Christian theism is unaltered; God Himself is unchanging and eternal, the ruler or process. In this group are[7] Henry Fairfield Osborn, Robert Andrews Millikan, Lecomte du Nouy, and Michael Pupin. From the other viewpoint evolution becomes a clue to the nature of God. The classic formulation of this view is[8] Alfred North Whitehead's philosophy of organism. The idea of growth is used as a metaphysical principle for the interpretation of all reality.

The third type of Christian theism may be termed theistic humanism, which places the emphasis on man's role in religion. Theistic humanism accepts belief in God as essential but emphasizes the aspiration and devotion of man. Many of the ideas of the theistic humanists would be accepted by all Christians, but their human emphasis causes them to judge religion in terms of its capacity to serve human needs. Adherents of this philosophy include Kirtley Mather and Carl Wallace Miller. Mather says:[9]

"Knowledge concerning God, therefore, becomes a human experience which includes contact with the physical world of sense perception in which he is the motive power, and also direct, though
mysterious, contact with Him when spirit meets with spirit." Theology is not generally regarded as a science, but according to Long's
interpretation of Mather,[10] "Theology is a science because it
assumes working hypotheses. The religious hypothesis is that we
can interpret the reality of the unseen correctly, and that there are
uniform spiritual laws. Hence religion is a further extension of
science; religion is the science of immeasurable values." This can
be true only if religion is discussed merely on the human plane.
According to Miller,[11] "It was neither an accident nor a consequence of a religious theory that the cross of Christ has become a
symbol of the sacrificial devotion of humankind at its best. . . .
Jesus never gave cause for belief that even his own sacrifice on the
cross could by any process of mental gymnastics serve as a substitute for man's fulfillment of his obligation to society." Miller notes
the [12] "lag between material progress (whose engine is purring
smoothly) and the moral forces of society (which are missing fire
noticeably)."

The line between theistic and nontheistic humanism is very
thin. Some have wondered whether there is a line at all, although
two authors,[13] Edwin Grant Conklin and Donald Dooley, have been
said to stand on the dividing line. Long says:[14] "Nontheistic
humanism need not blurt out, 'The idea of God is the wishful
thinking of a prescientific age'; it need only make the question of
God a purely optional or peripheral one by occupying itself solely
with empirical and human categories. By emphasis upon the
natural and by omission of the divine, even more than by cate-
gorical rejection of theistic doctrines, it can imply that man faces
life alone; that is, without supernatural aid and comfort. Even so,
it constitutes an outlook that is religious in character." The book
Modern Arms and Free Men, by[15] Vannevar Bush, presents this
view. No mention of God is made; the basic category is democratic freedom. Long continues: "Bush is pluralistic. The crucial
line-up of men who favor democracy and freedom and oppose
political totalitarianism and applied materialism (which is Bush's
terminology for Russian political Communism) can include both
adherents of formal religions and men without fixed creeds. The
key mark is belief in freedom." Bush is tolerant toward religion
and is opposed to a positivism that insists that sense perception
encompasses all reality.

Percy W. Bridgman,[16] who has been quoted several times in this work, comes closer to a standard type of nontheistic humanism. Bush left room for traditional religious ideas beyond the view of science, but Bridgman did not. Characteristics of Bridgman's thought include: opposition to supernaturalism; the concept of operational meaning; emphasis upon the individuality of knowledge; and awareness of the limitations of science that leads naturally to logical positivism. Webster defines positivism as [17] "A system of philosophy originated by Auguste Comte. It excludes from philosophy everything but the natural phenomena or properties of knowable things, together with their invariable relations of coexistence and succession, as occurring in time and space. All other types of explanation are repudiated as 'theological' or 'metaphysical'." Long says:[18] "Positivism is not a religious creed, particularly in its own eyes, but it is an attitude toward life and toward the matters commonly dealt with in religious thought that is a live option among competing philosophical allegiances. It is negatively religious, strongly convinced of its task to disavow ontological, metaphysical, and theological speculation." [19]Philipp Frank is representative of a group that carries Bridgman's thought into a more logical denial that there can be truth apart from sense perception.

An unsophisticated counterpart of these sophisticated philosophies that deny the meaning of metaphysical and religious speculation is what Long calls enthusiasm for science and invention.[20] "The activity of research and discovery can become an all-consuming passion. It can become an object of enthusiasm and devotion, even though it may carry with it no specifically religious creed and no philosophical speculation. This enthusiasm may give itself expression in spoken and written discourse, and when it does, it becomes a 'religious' type of thought." Among scientists who concur in this belief[21] are Karl T. Compton and Charles F. Kettering.

Another nontheistic humanist not included by Long is Julian Huxley.[22] He calls his philosophy evolutionary humanism. On the subject of a personal God, Huxley is not merely agnostic, but disbelieves in a personal God in any sense in which that phrase is ordinarily used, including that of a "suprapersonal God." To him, the essential feature of religion is the sense of the sacred or the holy.

In contrast to all these approaches through science are approaches through religion, although the authors are scientists. The second section of Long's book is devoted to those who make that approach. It begins with the extreme opposite to the non-theistic outlook, called creationism or disbelief in evolution. Those who support the doctrine of special creation include E. Ralph Hooper and Frank Lewis Marsh.[23] Both these men have defended a use of Biblical revelation long since rejected by sound Biblical theology. They decry the use of philosophy to support scientific conclusions, but employ philosophical methods to defend their position. Another author in this group is J. W. Klotz,[24] who wrote *Genes, Genesis, and Evolution* after Long's book was published. Klotz says that the difficulties in accepting a literal view of creation as expressed in the Bible are no greater than those involved in accepting the theory of evolution. Midway between creationism and Christian theism with emphasis on the idea of growth stands the position of Louis Trenchard More,[25] who accepts evolution as a biological theory but rejects it as a basis for a metaphysical interpretation of reality.

An interesting position is that of the American· Science Affiliation, a fraternal organization of scientists who hold a conservative view of Scriptural authority and seek to exploit every opportunity to accord the facts of modern science with the literal content of the Biblical record. The organization has two classes of members: associates and fellows. Associates sign the following brief statement:

"I believe[26] in the whole Bible as originally given to be the inspired word of God, the only unerring guide of faith and conduct. Since God is the Author of this Book, as well as the Creator and Sustainer of the physical world around us, I cannot conceive of discrepancies between statements in the Bible and the real facts of science. Accordingly, trusting in the Lord Jesus Christ, I pledge myself as a member of this organization to the furtherance of its task."

Fellows, who may be elected after one year as associates, accept a stronger statement of Biblical inspiration, including faith in the Trinity, the divinity and Virgin Birth of Christ, regeneration by the Holy Spirit, salvation by faith as against works, the inevitable choice between eternal blessedness and eternal punishment, and the Second Coming of Christ. A book published by the Association, *Modern Science and Christian Faith,* and papers read at two meetings of the Association, reveal two temperaments which may foreshadow deeper rifts to come in the broader picture of the religion of scientists. One wonders what will happen if newer scientific conclusions cannot be reconciled with the tenets of the Association.

The conflict just mentioned, which is by no means confined to members of this association can have two consequences. One of these is termed compartmentalism, which consists in constructing two watertight compartments in one's thinking, one for religious matters, the other for scientific knowledge. The books[27] *A Scientific Man and the Bible,* by Howard Atwood Kelly, and *A Chemist and His Bible,* by Charles M. A. Stine, display these mental compartments. Kelly rejects higher criticism and discusses questions from the fundamentalist standpoint without reference to scientific considerations with which he must be thoroughly familiar. Stine attempts to show that many Biblical texts and scientific statements have the same meanings. In a later book, however, he makes no attempt to coordinate the two. Long says: [28] "Compartmentalism comes from an attempt to gloss over the conflict between science and faith. It comes when the issue is made acute by a religious view of Biblical statements that supposes them to carry scientific authority. It becomes dominant when obvious discrepancies between the Biblical phrasing of cosmological concepts conflicts with modern scientific theory. It is one method of handling a perplexing problem, but its cost is high in terms of the unbridged gulf between the two sides." It must be admitted that there is a little compartmentalism in all of us.

Long continues: "Fortunately, however, there is another way of dealing with the problem. It consists of a modification of one's view toward the Scripture. The modification does not reject Scriptural authority, but sees this authority in the spiritual rather than the verbal realm. It sees the Bible as the interpreter of existence, and as a word to human life applicable to every situation, but independent of the scientific facts involved. It can therefore openly face and dialectically resolve the conflict between Biblical statement and scientific fact. It can take a new concept of Biblical authority—that it speaks to the specifically religious situation of man, as much in our day as in the day when its now out-of-date scientific references were written—and can relate this to the world picture of modern science. It can, in short, find a reconciliation between Biblical faith (not Biblical record) and scientific fact."

Variations of this philosophy are presented by [29]Frederick J. Pack, Charles E. de M. Sajous, and William Louis Poteat, all of whom wrote in the 1920's. A succinct statement is that of Poteat, who says to the secularists who believe nothing in the Bible, as well as to the literalists who profess to believe everything, "A plague on both your houses!"[30] "Poteat suggests that Christianity

can be looked at in four ways: (1) as an inward experience where
'deep calleth unto deep'; (2) as a rule of life—that is, a moral
standard; (3) as a body of teaching, subject to contemporary philosophical currents; and (4) as a historic movement, originating
with the life, teachings, and death of Christ. The first two categories are more or less fixed; the second two, progressive and
modified in the light of current situations and demands." A characteristic quotation from Henry Higgins Lane, who holds a somewhat similar view, is: [31]"The salvation of the world depends upon
the discovery of the ground where the imperishable truths of both
science and religion may be found to dovetail into a complete and
harmonious whole. . . . The ideas of creation by divine will without natural process is just as contrary to the facts as revealed by
science, as is the opposite materialistic view of creation of natural
process without divine will." He says further that the block to a
speedy reconciliation between science and religion is "not in the
head but in the heart—is not in the reason but in pride of opinion,
conceit, dogmatism."

A Roman Catholic parallel to this method of reconciling the
truth of science with the truth of Scripture is found in the report
of the Biblical Commission designated by the Vatican to deal with
the problem of relating Scripture to science. This report says:[32]
"On those matters which form the proper object of the physical and
natural sciences, God taught nothing to men by the intermediary
of the sacred writers since such instruction could not be of any
use for their eternal salvation." Hugh S. Taylor quotes this report
with the suggestion that it could well be emphasized by all science
teachers counseling students in such matters.

"Taylor's view is more typically Catholic than Protestant, for
he, like Lane and Poteat, recognizes the need for two spheres of
authority, he tends to regard the nature of religious authority more
in philosophical than in Biblical terms. Thus: 'Science seeks the
truth concerning the natural order. But there is a science outside
her scope, a higher physics, a metaphysics, the science of those
things which *are*, dissociated from material things, which can not
only be conceived without matter but which can also exist without
matter, the truths which man comprehends as the attributes of
God.' "

In contrast to the pseudoreligious enthusiasm for science and
invention is the attitude of Igor Sikorsky, the famous airplane
designer.[33] He emphasizes spiritual values to a surprising degree.
Sikorsky believes that the crucial issue between the devil and

Christ in the account of the temptation was whether Christ should take a material or a spiritual road to the establishment of His kingdom on earth. Long's criticism is that, in dealing with the material side of life, does Sikorsky feel that religion must contrast sharply with the concerns of his daily work? Sikorsky attributes the rise of Communism to the emphasis on the material side to the exclusion of the spiritual. The approach of Sikorsky to the problem is quite different from those of the other authors quoted.

Three paragraphs from Long's final chapter summarize his review of books from which he quotes: [34]"To suggest the necessity of two areas of concern and two types of knowledge is perhaps to run the risk of a new dualism. How can religious authority be made crucial to religion, and scientific authority crucial to science, without compartmentalism? The answer is a dialectical one: not the obscurantism of Kelly and Stine, but the constantly searching balance of Lane and Poteat should be our prototype. The line between science and religion cannot be eradicated. No satisfactory religious system can be based on the data of science. When religious authority is excluded, we land in chaos, and theology becomes the continuous reporting of the chaos—the unsatisfactory attempt to draw metaphysical conclusions from analogy to physical laws. Neither should a religious system be allowed to override science. When scientific facts are made subservient to dogmas, then truth itself requires the destruction of religious authority. Only when competent science handles scientific matters and competent religion handles religious matters and a dialectical attempt to relate both to a total world view bridges the gulf between them does a true reconciliation between science and religion result. How few of the credos in either part of this book really measure up to the dimensions of this standard!"

[35] "The compartmentalists are wrong not in their willingness to recognize two authorities but in their unwillingness to bring them together into a total outlook and in their failure to require rigorously that each side pursue its task in conscious recognition of the other. . . . One final element in the credos: the element of commitment. The scientists are ready to stake their lives for their faith. Existentialism is fond of pointing out the commitment involved in all thought; and we are in debt to its contribution at this point. We sometimes forget, in making generalizations about the existentialist movement, that this element of dedication does not necessarily destroy a scientific open-mindedness about scientific things. Our scientists are not poorer scientists for their willingness to commit

themselves in devotion to their high ideals; they are probably better scientists for doing so, and the point at which they make this commitment is indeed a boundary mark for their deep faith. . . .

[36]"The use of science in place of a 'religious' interpretation of all existence is as false as the use of Biblical revelation in place of a 'scientific' explanation of natural events. Christians who live in a scientific age need have no fear that ultimate loyalty to a Biblical perspective in religion *must* destroy the possibility of acknowledging the truth in science. Freedom to pursue the truth comes within devotion to a high and noble calling. We are measured neither by an ability to believe blindly nor simply to disbelieve, but rather by our ability to relate belief to experience and experience to belief. We must have our science—root honesty in experience and high skill in the control of nature. We must also have our religious credo—basic, though not blind, devotion to a truth beyond us and a deep commitment to a cause whose purposes we are constrained to serve. It is within this framework that Christians will face a scientific age, fully acknowledging the truth in science and ultimately loyal to God in Christ."

Long has thus summarized the views of the comparatively small number of scientists who have written books on the subject. What of the great majority of scientists who have not expressed themselves in papers or books? Acquaintance with a representative number of them leads to the opinion that they are as much divided as those whose ideas have been reported. Perhaps most of them have not given much thought to the subject; and there are others who have thought considerably about it but whose mental state regarding it is one of bewilderment. The few surveys that have been made indicate that scientists are just about as religious, as indicated by church attendance and membership, as the average person. I have heard reports of a survey made some time ago, but have not found a confirmative reference, in which it was shown that physical scientists are the most religious, biological scientists less so, and social scientists least of all. That result is probably to be expected, since social science attempts to treat social phenomena objectively. A more recent study of the scientific and technical employees of an atomic energy establishment has been reported in Chapter 2.

A book too recent to have been discussed by Long, has been read at first hand. Its author is both a scientist and a theologian. He is William G. Pollard, a physicist who has been Director of the Oak Ridge Institute of Nuclear Studies for a number of years, and also an Episcopal clergyman since 1952. His *Chance and Providence* was published in 1958 and *Physicist and Christian* in 1961. Pollard's underlying theme is the importance of the community both in science and in religion. In order for science to exist there must be not only a scientist but a community of scientists. Science must be communicated and shared. Each branch of science has its own community. Christianity has come to be regarded by many as a private and individual concern, but Pollard rejects and deplores that belief. He says: [37]"Any view of Christianity which does not make community its very essence is foreign to the spirit of the New Testament." Both science and Christianity, then, depend upon faith, the nature of which is widely misunderstood. He says about physicists: No matter how thorough their factual knowledge or how expert their technique, if they do not really believe in their bones that under the surface turbulence of recorded data there are really discoverable and operative realities, they cannot do physics. The gift of such a belief, however, is a matter of faith, not of knowledge or skill." Orthodoxy and heresy exist in science as well as in religion. Examples of heresy are osteopathy and parapsychology (study of extrasensory perception).

What are the primary experiences in religion? To answer this question Pollard first distinguishes between conceptual and non-conceptual knowledge. He compares total experience to a plum pudding in which the raisins correspond to the portion that can be conceptualized. Scientists and contemporary philosophers consider only the raisins and ignore or deny the presence of the rest of the pudding. His view is that that portion is just as real as the conceptual portion although inaccessible to the methods of science. Words also have a double function. Every word has a dictionary meaning, the purpose of which is to describe its conceptual content; but words also evoke non-conceptual experiences. This function of words pervades all literature and art; examples of the literature in which it is most evident are the poems of Poe.

"Holy" is a word that cannot be completely conceptualized. Pollard discusses Otto's book, *The Idea of the Holy* as an example of the treatment of non-conceptual experience. [38]Otto uses the word "numinous" to denote the non-conceptual aspect of the experience of the holy. Characteristics of the numinous include awfulness, overpoweringness, urgency, and fascination. The non-conceptual is a chief characteristic of other experiences, for instance beauty. Non-conceptual elements of experience occur even in science. [39]Pollard says: "Every one of the sciences is, for those who engage in it, shot through with experiences of great power and primary validity which never enter into the conceptual scheme that it is the primary task of science to elaborate. . . . These non-conceptual elements in the experience of engaging in science are of supreme importance in the teaching of science. . . . Moreover, it is a mistake to suppose that the purpose of laboratory experiments in science teaching is primarily one of developing familiarity with apparatus and with the methodology and techniques involved. Of much greater importance is the direct confrontation of nature by the student in situations which permit the conceptual content of the science to be known and experienced within its total context in nature herself. Only thus can the teacher share with his students the non-conceptual, and therefore non-teachable, content of his science, and permits them to experience for themselves something of the delight of it."

Spirit is the unifying power of a community. It is neither a mysterious, half-materialized entity, as it was regarded a hundred years ago, nor an attribute of the individual, as has been implied in the preceding chapter. It can exist only in a community. An example is the spirit of the Marine Corps. Spirits may be powerful factors for good or evil; examples of the latter are the spirits of Fascism, Nazism, and Marxist Communism. Similarly the Holy Spirit is the unifying power of the Church. Many Protestants will not agree with Pollard's contention that the Holy Spirit can exist effectively only in a unified Church.

Closely associated with the ideas of the spirit, the holy, and the beautiful is that of the transcendent or supernatural. Supernature is the non-conceptual part of experience; therefore rejection of the supernatural on the grounds of lack of scientific evidence is inconsistent. Formerly numinous experiences were pictured as entirely physical images, such as heaven above the clouds and hell under the earth. These pictures are no longer tenable, and we are led to Heim's use of additional dimensions in which our three-dimensional world is immersed, as a symbol more in accord with modern thought. Heim's ideas have been discussed in Chapters 3 and 6. The idea of God expressed in Psalm 139, that "God is everywhere" is an example of the additional-dimension view, as opposed to the narratives in Genesis in which God appears as a person. Even in science itself, thinkable concepts continue to fall short of total reality.

Returning to the subject of kinds of knowledge, Pollard discusses two in addition to the conceptual. Besides the non-conceptual, which has been discussed, the other is knowledge in encounter, which involves Buber's I-thou relation. Nearly always when the word "knowledge" is used in the Bible, this kind of knowledge is indicated. Just as conceptual knowledge results in the formation of concepts, so non-conceptual knowledge produces "intuents", which are known by intuition.

Pollard concludes with the subject of revelation. The knowledge gained by revelation is by encounter, and does not compete with that derived by the patient processes of science. God does not reveal facts; He reveals only Himself. Although the recipient acquires no new facts, he is able to translate his experience into language understandable to others. Pollard holds that the same living God revealed Himself to Mahomet, Zoroaster, and others, in addition to the prophets of Israel; the unique feature of the revelation to the prophets was the role played by the community. [40]"It took Israel many centuries of history, and extensive and varied contacts with other people, to become fully conscious of this special destiny and unique status. . . .It is this idea of a covenant between an entire people and God, experienced and acknowledged corporately in community and throughout a long history, which uniquely sets apart Israel and the Biblical revelation which came through her." The culmination of this revelation was in Jesus; Pollard emphasizes; [41]"*In* Jesus, not *through* Him."

I have here attempted to give a very brief exposition of Pollard's book, not a critical evaluation. Many of his points are highly controversial, as he himself admits; its value is in its fresh approach to the subject.

Chapter VIII

Human Effects of Scientific Progress

THE PROGRESS OF SCIENCE has markedly affected the daily life and thought of people in many ways, especially during the last one-hundred and fifty years. It is difficult to assess the relative roles of science and other influences. Religion in its broadest sense is an important factor in some of the changes. These changes will be discussed without regard to their importance, their desirability, or the extent to which science has been responsible for them. They include: (1) Better health and longer life; (2) Increased cleanliness; (3) Increased humanitarianism; (4) Changed attitude toward animals; (5) Increased leisure; (6) Overpopulation; (7) Depletion of natural resources; (8) More destructive wars; (9) Changes in morality; and (10) Changes in political systems.

Better Health and Longer Life

The great advances in medicine, all of which were preceded by and dependent upon research in biological sciences have resulted in the decrease in the numbers and virulence of illnesses and the consequent lengthening of the life span. Many of the most dreaded diseases have been controlled if not completely eradicated: tuberculosis, small pox, poliomyelitis have been nearly exterminated. Intensive research on cancer and other diseases will doubtless result in their control. The recent biological research on dioxyribonucleic acids, the molecular basis of life and heredity, promises to produce far-reaching results in the elimination of some diseases. Some of the credit for this progress is due to physicians and hospital personnel, even though they are too few for the task.

Longer life is not an unmixed blessing. It is attended by earlier and more general retirement, often compulsory, and has created the problem of the support of the retiree. The Social Security program, involving compulsory saving and at present providing outright gifts by the community, is a tentative solution. Also involved are the problems of overpopulation and the depletion of resources.

Increased Cleanliness

Man's brute ancestry was not conducive to habits of cleanliness. The apes have less desire to be clean than the cat and the dog. Moreover, man is not a natural swimmer. We have little information about man's cleanliness in prehistoric times, but we do know that in ancient and medieval periods, people were dirty to an almost unimaginable degree. The Roman baths were notable, but they were accessible only to at least the moderately affluent. In the Middle Ages there were practically no baths. Soap was known to Pliny as an import from Gaul and Germany, but in England no soap was produced commercially until the middle of the fourteenth century. The literature of that period has many references to the "unwashed multitude" and its odor.

The situation was accepted, not only as inevitable, but as divinely ordained. In an essay, Aldous Huxley writes; [1]"Dirt, then, seemed natural and proper, and dirt in fact was everywhere. But, strangely enough, this all-pervading squalor never generated its own psychological antidote—the complete indifference of habit. Everybody stank, everybody was verminous; and yet, in each successive generation, there were many who never got used to these familiar facts. What has changed in the course of history is not the disgusted reaction to filth, but the moral to be drawn from that reaction. 'Filth', say the men of the twentieth century, is disgusting. Therefore, let us do something to get rid of filth. For many of our ancestors filth was as abhorrent as it seems to almost all of us. But how different was the moral they chose to draw, 'Filth is disgusting', they said. 'Therefore human beings who produce the filth are disgusting, and the world they inhabit is a vale, not only of tears, but of excrement. This state of things has been divinely ordained, and all we can do is cheerfully bear our vermin, loathe our nauseating carcasses and hope (without much reason, since we shall probably be damned) for an early translation to a better place'. Meanwhile it is an observable fact that villeins are filthier even than the lords. It follows, therefore, that they should be treated as badly as they smell." As we had already noted, the Jews were an exception to the rule and thereby avoided epidemics; but the only recognition they received from Christians was persecution.

It is not known who first uttered the proverb, "Cleanliness is next to Godliness", but it is often attributed to John Wesley. It has also been attributed to Martin Luther, but the later date seems more probable. From Huxley's view, just given, it can easily be deduced that the non-Calvinistic theology of the Methodists would give the impetus to action to improve conditions that had previously been accepted with resignation. By Wesley's time science could not have demonstrated the extreme value of cleanliness, so without fuller knowledge of the facts we must give religion, particularly Methodism, credit. We know that scarcity of facilities was one of the reasons for infrequent bathing, and we do not know how much improvement followed Wesley's preaching. Older persons remember the weekly family bath, when all available vessels of water were heated on the kitchen stove. The great increase in cleanliness, therefore, is the result of a more easily available supply of water, brought about by scientific inventions. Both science and invention deserve credit for this element of progress.

White wrote on this subject in 1896; [2]"This development of sanitary science and hygiene in the United States has also been coincident with a marked change in the attitude of the American pulpit as regards the theory of disease. In this country, as in others, down to a period within living memory, deaths due to want of sanitary precautions were consistently dwelt upon in funeral sermons as 'results of natural sin' or as 'inscrutable providences.' That view has mainly passed away among the clergy of the most enlightened parts of the country, and we now find them, as a rule, active in spreading useful ideas as to the prevention of disease. The religious press has been especially faithful in this respect—carrying to every household more just ideas of sanitary precautions and hygienic living." This interest in medicine and sanitation is not confined to the "liberal" denominations. The ultra-conservative Seventh Day Adventists are very active in medical research, support of hospitals, and attention to sanitation. The recognition of the importance of medicine and sanitation by all denominations is shown in the support of medical missions.

Humanitarianism

An important development of the nineteenth and the present centuries has been the progress in humanitarianism. In the early stages of the industrial revolution children worked long hours in factories. Now, child labor is almost eliminated by law. Slavery was common in many countries; now it does not exist in any civilized country. Debtors were imprisoned for months and sometimes years; debtor's prisons are now a thing of the past. The feebleminded and the insane were imprisoned in wretched cells, chained to the walls, beaten and starved. A century ago women were considered morally superior to men; but it was taken for granted that they were inferior intellectually. They were permitted to work in factories, but not to practice law or medicine or to preach. The Army did not want them as nurses in the Civil War. A few courageous women, however, managed to force their way into the wretched prison camps and effected almost unbelievable improvement in conditions there. Women were equally unwelcome in politics; as late as 1912 intelligent men were gravely prophesying the disintegration of society and the collapse of morality if women were allowed to vote. Now women not only control their own property, but even own the major part of the wealth of the nation and are almost as active in politics as their brothers. Everywhere the double standard of morality was formerly taken for granted; now it is debatable, but the equality of the sexes is assumed. Another important field of progress is evident in greater religious, political and racial toleration. There is still room for improvement in all these areas, but the trend continues. Individually, our great-grandparents were as virtuous, as religious, as kindly and humane as we are, but they could not act so well collectively to achieve humanitarianism.

Is science responsible for these developments? It is difficult to see any direct relationship. Unquestionably from our standpoint these changes are applications of Christianity; collectively we have been doing to others in these respects as we would wish them to do to us. But why did it require more than 1800 years for the implications of the words of Jesus (and those of the noblest Jews) to be realized to so great an extent? The growth of humanitarianism was a development which followed the 18-19th century revolution in Christianity in which it was in process of triumphing over theology. We must admit, however, that fundamentalists are supporting the trend to humanitarianism as fully as their modernist contemporaries.

The discussion of humanitarianism should include the treatment of four classes of persons: (1) The hopelessly ill; (2) The physically and mentally abnormal; (3) The criminally insane; and (4) The "sane" criminals. For the first of these classes euthanasia has been advocated by many people. Riddle[3] reports that for many years the New York State Legislature has received petitions from thousands of physicians supporting the legalization of voluntary euthanasia; but it also received resolutions adopted by the National Catholic Women's Union, supported by many thousands stating the position that "The advocates of euthanasia disregard— the role which suffering can and does play in the achievement of sanctity. . . . Suffering is a blessing in disguise. . . .Many people would lose their souls if it were not for the suffering they are called upon to endure." That legislature, like others before and after it, found the religious argument—or the voting of the religious—the more persuasive."

There are, of course, other arguments against euthanasia. If the barriers against voluntary extinction of life were let down it would be difficult to draw the line where killing or suicide is permissible. Society is naturally hesitant to remove these barriers even when the religious question is disregarded. Then, too, no one can tell when the incurable disease may become curable.

Mental disease has for years been the nation's number one health problem; scientists are, in many ways seeking its causes. Although it has been reported that such cases are increasing it may be that they are noted and counted more completely than formerly.

In some ancient communities mentally defective children were allowed to die from exposure or neglect. In the Middle Ages and earlier in some countries their existence was considered as punishment by God or the handiwork of the devil. This view persists among children and unintelligent persons. Any abnormal child who associates with normal children has to undergo much suffering. For this reason such a child is much happier in an institution, where he is among those who are similarly afflicted.

Physicians and other scientists are conducting an urgent search for the causes of mental deficiency disorders in the belief that if they can find the cause they may eventually also discover new ways to alleviate the disease and even cure it. It is possible that some of the more common mental disorders are basically caused by chemical defects outside the brain. Phenylketonuria, which accounts for one percent of the mental disease, is a liver disorder.

The once popular theory that schizophrenia is caused primarily by parental neglect or other imperfections in the environment is now strongly doubted.

The same considerations apply to the criminally insane, because they include some of the same groups after they have reached maturity. The death penalty is not demanded if a criminal is proved insane according to arbitrary standards. For criminals who are not insane according to the same standards, and whose offense is severe, the death penalty is still exacted by law. The list of crimes calling for the death penalty, however, has been decreasing for the last two hundred years, at least. Punishment among the Hebrews and other ancient peoples followed the principle "eye for eye, tooth for tooth, life for life", which implies that the score is thus evened. More recently the principle of punishment as a deterrent has been applied. The trend now is away from capital punishment in the belief that "evening the score" is illogical, that the possibility of reform always exists, and that the rules against taking a life apply here as much as in the cases of the innocent, who are unable to distinguish right from wrong. Sometimes the case of the criminal has been over-sentimentalized; laxity in punishment has not been accompanied by scientific attempts to change the criminal. The many problems involved call for the cooperation of science, religion, common sense, and public interest. The last factor is important. Lack of progress is more often not the fault of the public, but rather of State Legislatures and other Government agencies who do not appropriate sufficient funds to employ competent personnel in penal institutions, or to apply scientific methods for the improvement of inmates. A prime difficulty is the small number of voters affected.

Also, under the head of humanitarianism is the matter of "welfare", which now includes old-age pensions, unemployment compensation, industrial medicine, socialized medicine, and various charities and institutions. No one can deny that these are worth while, but they must be so administered as to discourage idleness and needless dependence. Welfare plans are more advanced in several European countries than in the United States. Sweden is outstanding and Swedes are ready to defend their policies against criticism, in spite of their high suicide rate.

Conflicting reports are issued concerning the success of socalized medicine in Britain, but the predominating opinion is unfavorable toward it as a fundamental social improvement.

Changed Attitude Toward Animals

With the progress in humanitarianism during the past 150 years has come, also, a more sympathetic attitude toward animals.

Total disregard for the feelings of animals was the almost universal rule before that time. It is true that the Bible says: [4]"You shall not muzzle the ox when it is treading out the grain"; but Paul comments: "Is it for the oxen that God is concerned? Does He not speak entirely for our sake? It was written for our sake, because the plowman should plow in hope, and the thresher thresh in hope of a share in the crop." Although this was written as an argument for the support of missionaries, it is evident that kindness to animals was in itself a very minor consideration. There is not much evidence of regard for animals in other records of the ancient or medieval world except that pets were common. In the Roman gladiatorial combats there was equal lack of consideration for the animal and the human participants. Bull-baiting was one of the popular sports of the Middle Ages. Aldous Huxley, after describing a number of cases of cruelty to animals in that period, says: [5]"It was not until 1822 that the first piece of legislation in behalf of animals was enacted by Parliament. By 1876 the Royal Commission on Vivisection could state in its report that 'the infliction upon animals of any unnecessary pain is justly abhorrent to the moral sense of Your Majesty's subjects generally.' This was a far cry from Hogarth and St. Dominic, a change of heart and thought that marked perhaps a religious revolution. The old, all too human bumptiousness which had been consecrated by verse twenty-six of the first chapter of Genesis, the doctrine that man is a being apart from the rest of creation and may do with it what he pleases was giving place, under the influence of scientific knowledge, to a world much more realistic and charitable."

Human sympathy for animals is confined chiefly to the "higher" animals, but there is no definite dividing line. Cruel methods of slaughtering animals for food are now condemned. On the other hand, no one in the western world hesitates to swat a fly or a mosquito or to kill a higher animal in self-defense. Open and continuous warfare is waged against disease-producing organisms, large and small, simple and complex, animal and vegetable. A Hindu may not swat a fly because in so doing he may harm a departed ancestor, relative, or friend. Some others who have "reverence for life" will not harm any creature, but even their concern is limited.

The anti-vivisectionists go to extreme lengths in their objections to harming animals, no matter how humanely experiments on animals may be conducted. Medical Schools and biology departments in other colleges are in perpetual conflict with antivivisectionist groups before the legislatures in order to conduct experiments essential to the knowledge of biology and advances in medicine.

It is impossible to assess an exact role of science either in the development of humanitarianism or in its application to animals.

More Leisure

Invention is entirely dependent upon science; in fact it is almost synonymous with applied science. Many inventions have resulted in the substitution of automatic, mechanical action for human effort. This change may enable more goods to be produced by the same effort and will give the worker added leisure time. Since there is a limit to the amounts of various goods that can be utilized, the inevitable result of automation is unemployment. Many workers must then be retrained in order to enter some other field, or they must depend upon savings or charity, private or governmental. In some cases the result of automation may be shorter work hours. Through his union, the worker demands higher wages per unit of product and is usually successful in his effort. The result leads employers to develop additional automation and the process may be repeated again and again, with higher prices and unemployment as the ultimate consequences.

Only routine workers are directly thus affected by automation. Their employers must work harder in order to meet the problem of higher costs. The professions are not directly affected, at least in theory. But in the case of the medical profession the reply is: "Just try to find a Doctor on a week-end!" Lawyers may have their work organized so that most of it can be done by employees, although there is no automation there. Teachers have to work as hard as ever. So do clergymen, although the amount of work they do depends largely on the individual conscience. Probably scientists who are employees of a corporation have reduced work hours; but those who are interested in vital research problems cannot be tied to a definite schedule. All members of professions and non-union workers, as well as housewives, generally share in the increased leisure, but the routine workers constitute a new special leisure class. That is beneficial if the additional leisure time is spent in educational, intellectual and social activities. For others, however, the leisure will be spent in watching television, attending sports events and other thought-stifling pursuits, none of which are objectionable in moderate amounts, but which in excess detract from mental activity.

Overpopulation

With the advent of better health and a consequent declining death rate and a rising or even constant birthrate comes the threat of overpopulation, the import of which is being realized at the present time. The population of the world is now increasing at the rate of 2.3 million per year. Overpopulation is inevitable unless the birthrate falls noticeably with the rising standard of living as it has done in Europe and in this country. Everyone is familiar with the idea of "family planning", and of the arguments for and against artificial means for lowering the birthrate. Certainly, the factors that determine birthrate need to be studied carefully by biologists, social scientists, public-health experts, religious leaders, and others. In the past the Malthusian doctrine operated; that is, as population increased, destructive influences such as wars, famines, and other catastrophies, operated to check population growth. It is now argued that we need not worry about overpopulation; a few atomic bombs will take care of it. On the other hand, with the great amount of attention the matter is receiving some solution will eventually be reached.

Depletion of Natural Resources

Concern is widely expressed that the increasing use of our natural resources, due to population growth and scientific advances, will soon lead to their exhaustion. We have seen, however, that exhaustion does not usually occur as early as predicted, because new resources are continually being discovered. It is generally agreed that each generation should conserve available resources, with the needs of future generations in mind. On the other hand, no one knows what future generations will need or lack. A few decades ago the coal supply was a subject for anxiety; but now many coal mines are idle because of the substitution of other fuel, and the present problem is the unemployment of miners. About twenty years ago it was predicted that our natural gas supply would soon be depleted; but gas fields then unknown are now operating. The same is true of petroleum. The supply of water is limited but has not yet become a serious problem in most localities. The possibility of the inexpensive preparation of pure water from sea water has been widely explored, and has been realized in a few localities. The development of atomic energy has upset all calculations about sources of power, and at this time no one can predict its future capabilities. Improved agricultural

methods have put part of our land out of production as a reserve
for future expansion. Does this mean that man will find new
resources as fast as he needs them? We do not know. The obligation remains to make the best use of what we have.

More Destructive War

All the benefits that science has brought us may be canceled by
the use of atomic weapons in warfare. Large proportions of the
world's population and wealth could be wiped out. This possibility
is at present a deterrent to war, but how long it will remain so is a
question. The chief deterrent to war is good will. Can we have
good will toward an organization that is frankly hostile to our way
of life? The American Revolution is said to have been the last "war
between gentlemen". Economic and cultural aid to backward countries without regard to political relationships is coming to be considered one of the nation's obligations, as important as our military
strength and even as our power to reach the moon. The direction of
human progress should be, and we can almost say must be, toward
the furtherance of good will. Science can contribute little toward
that aim other than to make communication easier. Mistakes are
being made in this conduct of good will and will continue to be
made until all factors are understood. The aid to nations might be
directed away from disaster by evincing the state of mind which the
study of science creates.

A number of religious sects and other organizations have had
as an objective the abolition of war. It has been suggested that
scientists, having been to a considerable extent responsible for the
possibility of greatly increased harm to mankind, should exert any
influences they might command to prevent war. They might not be
more successful as speakers or writers than others who are today
reaching large numbers of the people through publications and
through radio and television speaking and personal appearances as
lecturers. The crying need is for all persons to forget petty differences of procedure and to unite in an all-important cause. The time
may come when we shall have to do just that.

Changes in Morality

Literally, according to the Bible and the beliefs of many religious persons, the principles of morality in its highest sense, were
promulgated directly by God in the Ten Commandments and elsewhere, and were summarized in the teachings of Jesus. On the other

hand the scientists find their source in a growing awareness throughout history and pre-history; morality originated even longer ago than human history, because its genesis is to be found among animals. Riddle says:[7] "A denial by theology or religion of the purely natural sources of morality and of values is a bold and crude pretention. It is clear, however, that the so-called religious impulse may, if it will, usefully contribute to the readiness and willingness of men to think and act within acceptable forms of morality and value. All human populations must persistently strive to make the moral also the acceptable and satisfying, and a good life must be both satisfying and productive. But, in advanced societies, a religion based on revelation, or indeed one that looks to any intervention of the supernatural in human affairs, mainly offers confusion to jobs that call for fact, clarity, and unchallenged logic. In presenting an account of unmitigated evolution, the natural sources of morality and values—or at least their non-requirement of a separate and a 'spiritual world'—must now be particularly emphasized because this point is so uniformly denied in religion, because it is shamelessly surrendered by many scientists, and because the entire structure of evolution has neither consistency nor any deep significance without it."

Certainly Riddle is correct to the extent that morality has been a gradual development which began before the appearance of man. But of what value is that knowledge in dealing with a particular situation? Does that instinctive morality apply to human issues? Is the existentialist "personal hypothesis" which puts one in the other's place a product of evolution? Whether we call it supernaturalism or prenaturalism it is not within the field of science.

It is difficult to determine whether there has been a decrease or increase in morality over any given period. The definition of morality must be considered. Customs change, as do definitions. Over the last few decades the crime rate has increased. It would be almost impossible to assess the causes of this increase or to relate it to the complex structure of present-day society. In general, in the history of any religion, morality has little to do with holiness in the early stages, but after a time the demands of the gods include a moral life. Christianity came when Judaism had already established a high scale of morality which was not mentally separated from a ritual. Jesus completed the establishment of morality on the basis of putting one's self in the other's place. Many of His followers were sincere in their attempt to do so, but others made a fetish of the religion without becoming better morally. The latter were in the majority, at least among the leaders, when Christianity became the dominant religion; and they were most ardent in furthering the spread of Christianity by the sword.

The effect of science on morality is hard to estimate. The idea that greater knowledge of one's self and others will result in betterment, especially in dealing with matters related to sex, has been exploited. The evidence at present is that such an idea is wrong.

To repeat what was said in an earlier chapter, during the first two or three centuries of the Christian era, there was a high standard of morality and disregard of physical conditions; also good will toward one another. Then, and in subsequent years there were probably many unrecorded examples of saintly generosity, purity, and mutual help toward pagan as well as Christian.

When Christianity became dominant, or was conquered by its superficial reception, the trend was opposed to independent thinking, pity for humanity as such, and regard for animals. The command, "Love one another," was buried in a mass of theology and ritual. At the time of the Crusades the official attitude was that the highest service a man could perform for the Church was to join a Crusade and kill as many infidels as possible. There must have been many personal opinions to the contrary, but there is no record of them. Physical occupancy of the Holy Land was more important than individual goodness. Later the hatred of Catholics was directed toward Protestants and was fully reciprocated. Still later the persecution of so-called witches took place. Race prejudice is still strong. The progress of Christian principles has been very slow indeed. Science cannot be credited with improvement in morals, whatever may be the reason for its failure.

Changes in Political Systems

No political system, either extinct or extant has been based on scientific principles. The function of political science has been to describe political systems as they are, with some reference to their origin and effects. On the other hand, scientific thinking has been affected by political systems, because some systems have afforded a better atmosphere for scientific work than others. Without doubt, the great advance of Western civilization since the sixteenth century was made possible by the development of the physical and biological sciences; but neither was democracy a consequence of this reform nor did it contribute to the reform more than other forms of government. The first democratic government in Europe, following the French Revolution, which was inspired in part by the

American Revolution, beheaded Lavoisier, the father of modern chemistry. His scientific work was not the direct cause of his execution, but it did not save him. Conversely, much of the scientific work in the seventeenth and eighteenth centuries was made possible because benevolent despots in some European countries chose to defy religious leaders and support scientific work.

At present we cannot say that a totalitarian state contributes greater or less impetus to the progress of science than a free republic. Soviet Russia is graduating more scientists than we are because there is no alternative to science in their educational courses. In America, where science study is optional, the scientific spirit should be more firmly entrenched because the study has been chosen, not accepted under compulsion. In the totalitarian states science is a means to physical world supremacy, but in America it is only one of the means of meeting that challenge. The danger exists that accomplishments in the field of warfare may outweigh those in medicine and other areas where progress is needed most.

In summary, the effects of science on man's welfare are favorable to improvements in his physical condition, but dangers are involved. Science provides means for man's destruction, barely possibly by accident, but more likely by widespread effects of the unleashing of his natural tendency to destruction. The greatest danger, however, lies in the provision of greater material comforts, with less effort. Struggle against adversity is an important factor in the progress of any race of living beings, including man. When that struggle is no longer necessary the energy that is required to conduct it must have other outlets, and this upsetting of balance is usually detrimental to the organism. Theoretically, in the case of man, other outlets can be found, but in practice such outlets are hard to find and slow to develop.

Some of the improvements listed in this chapter can be attributed to science alone, but credit for others must be shared, chiefly, with religion. The effects of science on man's thoughts are not discussed here, because the religious aspects of that subject have been considered in Chapter 5.

Two extreme view-points of the effects of science are: first, that the world's problems can be solved by the application of science, and therefore all we need is more science; second, that scientific knowledge is leading to man's downfall. These two views, and possible intermediate ones can be discussed after a study of the present state of the conflict between science and religion.

Chapter IX

Is There Still A Conflict Between Science And Religion?

THERE IS A "conflict between science and religion," in the sense that science is concerned with the intellect and religion largely involves the emotions. Without elaboration we may say that theology is thought applied to religious problems, and therefore an intellectual conflict can arise; as we have seen, even in Darwin's time, there was unanimity of opinion neither among scientists nor among theologians regarding evolution. Since then, considerable thought has been given to various aspects of the subject, whether or not they concern evolution, but no generally accepted conclusion has been reached. It is safe to say that there is no single conflict between two forces but a number of conflicts between various viewpoints, both scientific and religious.

By definition, there can be no differences of opinion regarding scientific facts; but a science composed only of facts is non-existent and logically almost impossible. In astronomy, for instance, the approximate distances, compositions, masses, and other properties of many of the stars and nebulae are well enough known to be considered facts. On the basis of simple measurements of their spectra and a minimum of deduction, it is generally accepted as fact that the nebulae and the stars are moving away from each other at high velocities. But astronomers are not willing to stop there. Beyond those facts, there are two theories regarding the origin of the universe: some astronomers believe that the universe began at an instant in a very small space, from which it has been expanding ever since; others think that matter is constantly forming to fill the intervening space as the universe expands. (I am avoiding the word "create" as used by some astronomers,

merely to avoid the theological implication at this point.) Astronomers hope that the question will be answered within a few years
through a further knowledge of space; but at present there are no
facts to support either view. The question probably will be settled eventually; but by that time, there will be other questions.
Similar situations exist in other fields of knowledge. Though established facts are not questioned, there are always questions about
their interpretations. Moreover, the suppositions of today may
become facts tomorrow, outmoded beliefs the next day, and super-
stitions next week.

Turning for a moment to the religious viewpoint, since there
are no facts in theology, the tendency for beliefs to diverge is
much greater than in science. Among Protestants there are now
the three general beliefs that have been briefly described: fundamentalism, modern orthodoxy, and liberalism, whose boundaries
are somewhat blurred. The general attitude of fundamentalists is
that any scientific theory that conflicts with the literal interpretation of the Bible is wrong. Some fundamentalists, however, accept
a modified theory of evolution which includes the belief that God
directs its course. Modern Orthodox and liberal thinkers accept
the results of science, believing that they have no effect on the
fundamental principles of Christianity. In general they do not
consider the records of miracles historical, and the orthodox regard
them as myths with a spiritual meaning. I am not attempting to
elucidate the Roman Catholic position, but it is close to that of the
fundamentalists, but with more reliance on the infallibility of the
Church than on that of the Bible. Divisions in Judaism are somewhat similar to those in Protestantism.

Purpose in the Universe

The most important question which divides religionists as
such from scientists as such is whether the universe is subject to a
Purpose. We know that persons have purposes; in fact, the earliest
experiences of childhood are the purposes of the child himself and
of the people around him, which may conflict with his own purpose and force him to do things he does not want to do. With
many memories of restraint by someone else's purpose, the child
attributes purposes to its impersonal surroundings. A similar situation arises in the history of the race. Purposes are found in
natural forces, and phenomena, such as the sunshine and the
storm. There are three directions which the idea of purpose may
take. First, purpose may be attributed to the higher animals, then

to the lower animals, and then to inorganic nature. Second, unseen beings are assumed who have purposes. This conception reaches its highest form in the idea of a purposeful God. A third, more sophisticated belief is that of "goal-seeking." An illustration of the first form of naive belief is given by Pollard. A beginning student in biology was examining a small organism through the microscope. It was held by his dissecting needle, but was in motion as if trying to escape. [1] "It's trying to get away from me!" the student exclaimed. His professor admonished him that such language is not permissible in science; that he was only to report what he saw, without assuming any purpose in any organism that he was studying. I can conceive an experiment on a person by a behaviorist psychologist, in which the same exchange of words might take place. The emphasis upon objectivity is correct; although many scientists would not express it this way, science must be forever limited to the it-world; any trespass into the I-world or the you-world would lead to vagueness on the part of the scientist, and therefore would not be science. The stone wall between the worlds is impregnable. Science is not only a product of the human mind; it is its captive. Personality eludes science, but science cannot escape from personality.

The progress of science has led to the conception of an it-world independent of purpose or consciousness. Most biologists have extended this no-purpose world into the animal kingdom, and behaviorist psychologists have included human beings in its scope, and have tried to ignore the last vestige of purpose. According to that view, animals are subject to biological drives; so is the human animal. There is no need to assume a "soul" under any name or with any definition; every action can be explained on the basis of physical drives and other physical entities. At least one psychologist has attempted to show how consciousness may have appeared in the course of evolution. Its functions, however, could be served just as well by further complexities of the nervous system, just as increasingly complex problems can be solved by the invention of more complicated mechanical computers.

If I were a detached consciousness somewhere outside the universe observing the material of science, I have no doubt that I should be thoroughly in agreement with this materialistic view. My objection to it is that here I am, in the middle of the world which is studied, and my consciousness does not fit into the picture. The conclusive answer to the statements of such materialists, then, is that of the existentialist: "But here I am." Here I am, with the definite purpose of learning more about biology and psychology, and thinking and writing about them. The most materialistic scientist has the purpose of studying his subject and making his ideas known. No matter how materialistic or mechanistic his viewpoint may be, he tacitly assumes his existence as a thinker and the existence of personal readers who, he hopes, will understand what he has to say.

This does not imply that all human actions are the result of conscious purpose. The explorer replies to questions about why he climbs a difficult mountain peak: "Because it is there". Many actions are confessed not to result from the conscious will. The criminal admits compulsion to follow drives outside his conscious purpose. There are, however, still many of our actions which we attribute to conscious choice. It is also true that one can turn over the picture and objectify the scientist and convert his purposes into drives; but he can still reply: "Here I am."

Most biologists believe that all biological phenomena can be described by the application of the laws of physics and chemistry. Bergson, who was a philosopher, not a biologist, introduced the concept of the *elan vital,* or vital energy, which is peculiar to living things and which operates to produce effects which the physical forces alone cannot do. His views have been followed by similar ones, some of which have been held by some biologists. This *elan vital* has been called vitalism, cellular consciousness, aristogenesis, nomogenesis, holism, hologenesis, entelechy, telefinalism, and telism. Two of the more recent biologists holding such a view are Lecomte du Nouy and Sinnott, who are discussed because of the popularity of their books and the violence of the attack against them.

Sinnott says that goals rather than drives are evident even in the low scales of life, and become most important in man. [2] "Goal seeking and directiveness in organisms should be recognized as a basic fact and life's most characteristic quality. About it center the basic problems of biology and philosophy." [3] "This power as a general property of life, and not as the result of local entelechies or directive agents, is therefore, it seems to me, the basic problem. We must admit that our ignorance about it is essentially complete. There are two positions in this difficult matter, however, that should be avoided. One is that the problem is insoluble and that no rational inquiry into it is possible. The other is to maintain, in the face of all evidence to the contrary, that a living organism is no different in character from a lifeless physico-chemical mechanism, and that mind as a direct factor is inconceivable. A more reasonable attitude is . . . what might be called biological agnosticism."

The idea of purpose just quoted does not necessarily imply religion, but Sinnott concludes: [4] "The conception that life is goal-seeking and that spirit is its highest expression may serve as the basis for an essentially religious personal philosophy for those who value intellectual integrity but are convinced that the universe makes sense only if interpreted in spiritual terms. Life, manifest in organisms, is integrating, purposeful, and creative. We cannot yet explain these qualities, but through them we may gain a clearer spiritual insight into man's nature and his relation to the universe than through intellect alone. If man continually seeks to elevate his goals they can lift him up to heights not dreamed of now. If he debases them he will destroy himself."

Although Sinnott emphasizes the individual, it is evident that such a purpose on a world-wide scale would direct the course of evolution. Lecomte du Nouy lays emphasis on purpose in evolution as contrasted with mere chance. He finds purpose throughout the history of evolution. He regards the second chapter of Genesis as a figurative but essentially correct account of the beginning of the history of man. If there is a vital force or goal-seeking independent of physical forces, the process of evolution becomes more understandable. One phase of the dispute about evolution is whether chance would give time for the slow changes wrought by evolution. Du Nouy presents the argument of the physicist [5] Charles-Eigene Guye, that the synthesis of a single molecule of a protein on the basis of the forces of inorganic chemistry would require immeasurably longer than the calculated period of the existence of the universe. Therefore there must have been a purpose in constructing this first molecule and all the other molecules which finally culminated in life. Opponents reply, and du Nouy admits the validity of the argument, that no matter what the chances are against any occurrence, it sometimes happens. Mainx has said: [6] "Structures which are improbable when considered from the point of view of inorganic models are formed by the special biochemical and biophysical situation in the organism and are thus very probable." Some modern developments, moreover, indicate that the chances against the formation of heavy organic molecules are very much smaller than was believed earlier. Carbon compounds of high molecular weight have been found in meteorites, and in rocks, but the possibility that they have originated in terrestrial sources is not entirely excluded at present. Also, it has been found very easy to synthesize one of these compounds which are the building blocks of protein.

Vitalistic views like those of du Nouy and Sinnott have been severely criticized by a number of other biologists. A paper by Leo Francis Koch summarizes several books and papers which present the mechanistic side of the question and oppose the vitalistic view. A strong point against the idea of purpose is the principle of Occam's razor. Occam was a medieval philosopher to whom is credited the dictum that entities should not be multiplied unnecessarily; that is, if a principle or set of principles is sufficient to support a particular conclusion, no additional arguments should be applied. He used this principle freely to slash away many of the statements of the Scholastics who preceded him; hence the word razor. Koch thus restates the principle in its modern application: [7] "A theory which has no other basis than speculation serves a useful function only if it leads to hypotheses which can be tested experimentally or by observation." According to scientists who support the belief that physical causes are sufficient to account for the course of evolution, there is no use for the assumption of a purpose. So far as present knowledge goes, these objectors are right. Koch urges a second objection closely akin to the first. [8] "Teleological explanation is an abandonment of the means of inquiry which enabled man to obtain his exalted position in the animal kingdom. A teleological argument is a confession of the acceptance of an extra-scientific principle to explain the existence of conscious behavior or conscious existence." The reservation might be made that there could be a set of biological principles, unknown at present, which could be as scientifically coordinated as are the physical principles now accepted as the basis of the existence of living matter; but since no such principle is known or indicated, we shall not linger at this point, but shall tentatively accept Koch's statement. If the answer to any question that comes under the domain of science is, "because God has so willed it," there is no further inquiry to be made. In tracing down scientific causes, do we not similarly finally arrive at a point where no further inquiry is possible? Science does not really explain; it merely describes.

Koch concludes: [9] "A justifiable conclusion seems to be that the vitalistic-mechanistic controversy in its original formulation is now almost meaningless for scientists. However, mechanism has proved to be a fruitful hypothesis in research, and for that reason the label has been conserved for modern ideas which have little resemblance to the original 'mechanism'. Vitalism, on the other hand, under the most elaborate pseudonyms, has tended to sterilize research as well as the thinking of its ardent devotees." Koch quotes from L. K. Frank, [10] "Much of the customary denunciation of science has become meaningless and irrelevant since science is no longer mechanistic or materialistic but is dynamic." Still, the substitution of dynamism for materialism or of energy for matter, does not affect the main point at issue.

A second argument for Purpose in the Universe is based on twentieth-century physics. The earlier theory of the "billiard-ball universe" stated that any cause could produce only one result. This word "cause" is the source of much discussion; it may mean a series of causes or occurrences, but it will be used in the generally accepted sense. The whole history of the universe, then, could be predicted if we had sufficient knowledge, and there were no room for man's free will or God's planning. A miracle would consist in God's stepping in to upset this inevitable sequence. This possibility was asserted by most theologians, at least up to the twentieth century, but was naturally denied by scientists of the materialistic school. Since the discoveries of the present century, most physicists have abandoned the deterministic or "billiard-ball" view. According to the new conception, one cause may produce several effects, in relative proportions subject only to the laws of chance. No longer is it believed by many scientists that the history of the universe can be or could have been predicted. Human free will could choose one of the possible results as the actual one. On a larger scale, God could select one of the possible outcomes, and still it would be no miracle because the laws of nature were still valid.

A philosophy of evolution may be developed on this basis of indeterminacy. No matter how slight the probability that a highly complex organic molecule would be formed from simpler ones, divine purpose would cause its formation. Through all the steps leading to the beginning of man, and on to the development of our present civilization, God would tilt the scale to achieve the desired result, and still there would be no conflict with natural law. The same reasoning could be applied to the answering of prayer. It is no longer necessary to assume a vital force independent of physical forces. The place for purpose is in the application of principles already evident in the study of the physical world.

This theory provides an easy way out of the dilemma of determinism vs. purpose. The objection, however, is that this way out is too easy. The theory is attractive at first sight; but it has been attacked, not only by scientists of the mechanistic school, but also by philosophers and theologians with theistic beliefs. Promient among these are William G. Pollard, who is both scientist and theologian, and John Dillenberger, an astute theologian well grounded in science.

Pollard's book, [11]*Chance and Providence,* deals with the reconciliation of the ideas of chance, accident, and providence. He rejects, however, the application of the physical principle of indeterminism. He says: "We must, however, proceed with great caution in drawing conclusions from the statistical character of quantum mechanics and the existence of the indeterminacy principle . . . Some have . . . seen in the Heisenberg principle the basis for human freedom of the will. No such argument will, however, form any part of the thesis to be developed here. Indeed, I have great doubt that there is any relationship between them." By inference from this and other passages, the argument for confirmation of divine purpose is equally unsupported.

The following points, I believe, summarize Dillenberger's exposition of the difficulties in the [12] application of the indeterminacy principle: (1). The principle of indeterminacy is not accepted by all physicists. Einstein and Schrödinger remained consistently deterministic, while Bohr and Heisinger advocated randomness, as did de Broglie at first, though he later changed to the other opinion. (2). Even by its advocates, it is not believed that the principle is final. Further progress in physics may demonstrate an entirely different principle. (3). Indeterminacy is evident only in the submicroscopic range; it does not hold in the size range with which we are ordinarily concerned. (4). Even if the principle were fully established in the field of physics, it would not necessarily be applicable in other fields.

The entire reasoning of both Pollard and Dillenberger in agreement with many others, could be summarized by saying that science can tell us nothing about God. The attempts to justify religion by the use of scientific principles, whether indeterminism or vitalism, are neither good science nor good theology. These attempts may be classed with other attempts at natural theology, none of which has ever held its ground.

The use of teleological expressions in scientific literature is generally condemned, but they are often used unwittingly. Although Koch is definitely against the use of such expressions, the following sentence appears in his first paragraph: [13] "Yet, in every case, the death of an organism or species marks the end of an evolutionary experiment involving the ability of a set of hereditary factors (genes) to utilize the substance of an environment in perpetuating its kind." An experiment by whom or what? [14] Bernatowicz has written a paper strongly protesting against such teleological statements and gives a number of examples in which they have been used, always or almost always unwittingly. Still, Bernatowicz does not present the fundamental reason why such statements appear. The reason is that a large part of the environment of each of us is human, that is, it consists of people who have purposes. Thus purpose is one of the most common elements of our experience, and it is not surprising if it is occasionally attributed to the non-human features of our environment. The idea of purpose is like a pet dog which is allowed to wander freely over our surroundings, but must be kept strictly out of the little garden enclosure which we call science. Sometimes it gets into the enclosure and causes havoc there.

Can Science Save the World?

Some mechanists maintain, not only that the claims of vitalism and indeterminacy are refuted, but also that science is the only true guide for mankind, in ideals and morals as well as in physical activities. The paper by Koch, although mainly directed against those philosophies, also advocates the supremacy of science, and he cites a number of authorities to support his position. According to Otto, [15] "What is needed is more science, a great deal more science" to enable man to achieve his highest good. The principal obstacle to the achievement of this goal by science is entrenched superstition, by which these authors apparently mean all religion. Koch says: [16] "The supernaturalistic and antiscientific ideas which still dominate so many of our social amenities are often clearly irreconcilable with scientific theory. The paradox is that the material aspects of our existence are operated largely in accordance with the dictates of research, but, outside the scientific fraternities, the ideological aspects of our existence are still preponderantly governed by dogmatic, unscientific concepts." ". . . Foremost among the antagonists of science are the religionists of supernaturalistic faiths and the philosophers of dualistic or idealistic convictions . . . The battle lines are drawn between the advocates of scientific inquiry (not all scientists) as a universal method of solving problems and their opponents (not all non-scientists), who would virtually destroy science as a social force by divorcing it from values and morality. The stakes are high, no less than survival versus possible extinction." Koch does not deny the importance of artistic truth, but believes that scientific truth is more important because it can be verified. He says further: [17] "The views of scientists as a group, in contradistinction to those of Bergson, du Nouy, and Sinnott, have not captured the imagination of a great number of readers. Partly this may be the result of the usually drab presentation employed by scientists, perhaps because in their tranining they were taught to avoid langauge with emotional impact. Furthermore, the necessarily tentative nature of conclusions drawn by scientists is unpalatable to those reared in a cultural milieu governed by dogma which claims to be absolute, and which is acknowledged to be so by many persons in responsible position in their communities. To advocate any doctrine derived solely by speculation as an inflexible guide to thought and behavior is directly opposed to any scientific attitude. An abstract, scholarly admonition is unlikely to replace the devil as a symbol of hell-fire and damnation in any concrete contest of persuasion among the great masses of people."

Unquestionably the thinkers of this school are correct in some of their implications. One can devoutly wish that a much larger number of persons would think and act scientifically; that is, that they would observe and reason about their environment and experiences. The question arises, however, whether religion and superstition are altogether responsible for their lack of thinking, or whether stupidity and mental laziness are more responsible for their unthinking attitude toward both religion and science. As Koch implies, their contact with scientists is very limited. Most people do not read even the most diluted popular science magazines; they read the still more diluted and often misleading articles about science in the newspapers; and they hear the claims of "science" supporting a nostrum or gadget on television. Many believe the "science" they see or hear thus as implicitly as others believe blindly in their religion; often they are the same people. Some venturesome souls buy the article in question and find that it falls far short of its claims; then they blame the so-called "scientist" whom they have not been able to distinguish from the true scientist. This situation has been blamed upon the "ivory-tower" attitude of scientists, probably to some extent justly; but the writers in these popular science magazines go a long way to make themselves clear to the layman. The unthinking attitude is prevalent all over the world, no matter what the official religion or non-religion may be. In the Communist countries it is furthered by compulsion from above.

If we were to assume that more science is all that people need, the question arises as to which science is most needed and the manner in which it shall be presented or applied. Before attempting to answer this question, it will be well to discuss some other views in addition to those just presented. Julian Huxley and others have advanced the view that up to the present time the evolution of man has been accomplished by forces outside him, but that now to an increasing extent man is assuming the direction of his evolution, and will continue to do so to an even greater extent. All evidence points to lack of progress in man's physical development since the cave-man period some 100,000 years ago, when a slight unknown change may have occurred. All progress since then has been in social environment; the originally slow but continuous and accelerating invention of tools has now culminated in the scientific age. Huxley does not go to the extreme of claiming that science alone will enable man to continue the desired evolutionary changes. He says: [18] "It is clear that man is only at the beginning of evolutionary dominance, and that vast and still undreamt-of possibilities of advance still lie before him . . . We can justly extrapolate some of the main trends of progression into the future, and conclude that man should aim at a continued increase of those qualities which have spelt progress in the biological past—efficiency and control of environment, self-regulation of outer changes, individuation and level of organization, wholeness or harmony of working, extent of awareness and knowledge, storage of experience, degree of mental organization. In particular, man is likely to fulfill his destiny more successfully if he exploits to the full those improvements which have given him his position as the latest dominant type, notably his properties of reason, imagination, and conceptual thought, and his unique capacities of accumulating, organizing, and applying experience through a transmissible culture and set of ideas. These include the capacity to construct religions in the broad sense—systems of attitude, in which knowledge can be combined with ideals and imaginatively fused with our deep spiritual emotions to form a stable framework of sentiments and beliefs, which will in turn influence behavior and help to determine moral and practical action."

The question is debatable whether man can construct his own

religions; but that is part of the subject of Huxley's book, "Religion without Revelation." The point to be noted here is that Huxley does not entirely equate religion with superstition and antiscientism. He also says: [19] "There should no longer be any talk of conflict between science and religion. Between scientific knowledge and certain religious systems, yes; but between science as increasing knowledge of nature and religion as a social organ connected with destiny, no. On the contrary, religion must now ally itself wholeheartedly with science . . . Meanwhile science must not allow any ancient prejudices against certain aspects of previously established religions to hold it back from giving its aid when called upon."

In a recent paper on the subject of man's progress, Jean Rostand, another biologist, says that man has still far from exhausted all his initial possibilities. The question which he discusses, however, is whether these possibilities can be enlarged by biological means, especially whether man can become more intelligent, more clever, more sensitive, more disposed to solidarity and altruism—in a word, more human.

The means for such a change would be: (1) the use of hormones known at present or new ones that can be synthesized in the future; (2) surgical procedures; (3) operations on the embryo. Rostand refers to Aldous Huxley's *Brave New World* as an example of what might be done. In this book Huxley describes a state in which the population is totally controlled. All babies are born outside the body; the growth of the embryos is carefully watched by technicians; the children are all educated alike, with attention to every need, and all social acts of the persons fall naturally into grooves. The possibility of doubling the pyramidal cells where the thinking is done, is discussed by Rostand, who thinks that such a procedure is possible.

A number of authors, beginning with Plato, have advocated improvement of the race by selection of parents. The effects of radiation and of certain chemicals on gene mutation are known, but changes thus induced in experimental animals have never been improvements, and such mutagenic treatments cannot be applied to the human species. It is questionable whether the production of "supermen" by such means would be desirable. Quoting Rostand, [20] "Up to now, biology has scarcely impinged upon our lives, except through the intermediary of its daughter—medicine; but it will not keep up this discretion." Cries of alarm have been raised, especially by Catholic authorities, and there is some foundation for the uneasiness of those who protest. "Part of my idea of man," Rostand continues, "is my idea of his boldness, of his determination to rise higher and become more. For this reason I shall not say, as many do, that man is not good enough as he is. I shall take it as a postulate that man must aim at surpassing himself, at drawing from himself something better than himself. But, however legitimate and magnificent such a dream may seem to us, one is nonetheless fully conscious of the formidable difficulties that are raised by the idea of evolution controlled by man."

Lewis Mumford, who is not a biologist, amplifies this idea. He uses the term "post-historic man" first coined by Seidenberg, as a characterization of man after more changes are accomplished as the future results of science. Among the possibilities that he mentions besides space travel and increased use of the automobile and other means of transportation are: production of food from inorganic materials, frontal lobotomy on children, grinding down the mountains, and production of uniformity of seasons. He says: [21] "Only one problem would remain: Why should anyone, even a machine, bother to keep this kind of creature alive? But post-historic culture goes further; it tends to make all activities automatic, whether they are sterile and servile or creative and liberal . . . Totalitarian conformity springs from the machine, in fact every department it touches; the standardized agent exacts a standardized response. This fact is not confined to the totalitarian states . . . Post-historic man's starvation of life would reach its culminating point in interplanetary travel by rocket ship, or in the creation and utilization of a satellite space station . . . His end is to turn himself into an artificial homunculus in a self-propelling capsule, traveling at maximum speed, and depressing to the point of extinction of his natural gifts, above all, eliminating any spontaneous trace of spirit. The triumph of post-historic man would, one may confidently say, do away with any serious reason for remaining alive. Only those who had lost their minds already could contemplate, without horror, such mindless experience; only those who had forfeited the attributes of life could contemplate, without despair, such a lifeless existence. By comparison, the Egyptian cult of the dead was overflowing with vitality; from a mummy in his tomb one can gather more of the attributes of a full human being than from a spaceman."

In the light of actual experience of spacemen, it is evident that they have plenty to do; moreover, space flights have the goal of landing on a planet or other location where exciting adventures will happen on arrival; but Mumford's criticism still expresses the ultimate in self-limitation. Naturally the alternative to this depressing outcome is the creation of a new self, adequate to command the forces that now operate aimlessly but compulsively. Mumford believes that something in the nature of a miracle is called for. He comes to the same conclusion as have Huxley, Rostand, and others, that science without religion in the broadest sense will destroy man, not benefit him. Religion of some kind, at least its elements, is as fully necessary as science.

Some objections to the viewpoint represented by Koch may now be considered more fully. First, what sciences will be useful in improving man? The physical sciences? Admitting that their underlying principles are also valid in biology, just where do they connect with everyday thought? The biological sciences? They give some information about man's fundamental drives and about his body; they assist in formulating the laws of health; but they say nothing about his relations to other people. Psychology? The farther the distance from the physical sciences, the less exact a science is. Psychology has many noteworthy achievements to its credit; but there are several schools of psychology, and none of them can be assumed to give the exact truth. There remain the social sciences—sociology, economics, anthropology, etc. Their devotees do not agree among themselves, because they are still farther from the exact sciences. Ethics is still farther away; it is not ranked as a science. Again, there are different bases for ethics in the different schools of thought. It is true that anyone will profit greatly by being familiar with any of these subjects; and to some extent would regulate his conduct according to what he learned; but human nature is not so simple that he would simply always do so. Plato was the first to suggest that knowledge is the sufficient cause for good conduct, and he has had many followers; but history shows that the idea is not generally correct.

Let us suppose that ethics had developed to the status of a science. Laws could be formulated which would state that a given course of conduct would be followed in 65 per cent of the known cases by a better understanding among people, and therefore by greater peace. If the dry facts were presented to the intelligent public; how much response would result without an emotional appeal? Suppose that social scientists should agree; how would they secure obedience or conformity of the rest of humanity?

This brings us to the next question. How can science be applied so as to enable man to achieve his highest ideals? The mechanistic school has given no answer. Neither does Huxley suggest a method. Rostand's methods imply complete control of the populace by scientists, who resort to physical methods. Mumford provides the reductio ad absurdum to control of people by science.

Plato, in his *Republic,* describes a utopian state governed by philosophers. Their suggested modern counterparts are the scientists. Scientists from the Soviet Union and from Western countries have been mutually cooperative, and have not shown the animosity toward each other that politicians have. Most scientists are free from the delusions of politicians and other people; why not give over the rule of the world, or at least of nations, to the scientists? The answer is that they rarely have the needed executive ability to accompany their knowledge. Moreover, to the ranks of the scientist-governors would quickly be added a host of pseudo-scientists whose object would be political control rather than the application of science to government. Most of the schemes for the improvement of the race would depend upon control by scientists or groups served by scientists; such a plan would be entirely foreign to our conception of liberty. It would surpass the wildest dreams of the Soviets.

Improvement of the race, whether merely physical or also moral and cultural, depends upon either education or control by a minority group. The educational process would be very slow. Neither of these possibilities is likely to occur for many years, unless some current predictions of early domination by Communists or extreme socialists are fulfilled.

Role of Existentialism

None of the authors contributing to the discussion just reported mentions the existentialist position. Existentialism recognizes dualism and pluralism; science does not. Dualism says that two entities that are not interpretable in terms of each other can exist side by side. Pluralism adds the idea that more than two such independent entities can exist. Examples of dualism are body and mind, spirit and matter, I and it. Pluralism recognizes the independent existence of many persons as egos to themselves. Neither dualism nor pluralism has any place in science or in scientific philosophy, because it would be very confusing to have two or more unrelated systems; they would unquestionably interfere with each other. When an apparent dualism is present it is the obligation of science to eliminate it. Dualism, however, necessarily enters the picture as soon as we step outside the narrow wall which bounds science, even so far as to say that there must be a scientist in order to have science. Materialistic scientists or scientific philosophers, however, may go to extremes to oppose dualism or existentialism. They can say that even science is a matter of nerve cells and therefore of atoms. Psychologists have postulated that "the thoughts are the thinkers". Existentialists will reply that the idea of the *I* is not thereby touched. If the thoughts are the thinkers, "very well, I am the thoughts". It has been shown in Chapter 3 that the self, the ego, the *I,* is not a matter of direct experience and that we have to depend upon the I-hypothesis; but that hypothesis is necessary for all thinking; it is not a part of science, but an assumption underlying all science. Koch says: [22] "Because of the operational and pragmatic basis, scientific truth is more easily verified among persons of different cultural backgrounds and therefore, its potentiality for universal communication, understanding, and brotherhood is unique. Admittedly, art and philosophy can be very important aids in this progression, but they cannot serve as substitutes for science." This and other statements supporting the mechanist position cross and recross the line between subject and object many times, apparently without the author's awareness.

There are many kinds of dualism. The kind I have been discussing is that concerned with the individual; I and it, the thinker and the thoughts. Possibly I have been setting up a man of straw; possibly the antagonism of the mechanistic writers is only toward a more general being than the individual, whether called God or an intelligence outside man. This idea is suggested by another quotation from Koch: [23] "Unlike atoms and some molecules in gaseous or liquid form, knowledge does not diffuse autonomously; nor do I believe that it radiates from some 'reservoir' of 'limitless creative power.' Man creates knowledge just as truly as he does machines. But, even if we acknowledge the reality of non-material events and thus apparently abandon 'rigid' or 'pure determinism,' the strict necessity of empirical methodology must be emphasized explicitly, as stressed by Frank: [24] 'The most successful scientific investigation has generally involved treating phenomena as if they were purely materialistic, and rejecting any metaphysical hypotheses so long as a physical hypothesis seems possible. The method works.' " That is, although there is a limitless reservoir of matter and energy, there is not one of thought or creative power.

With emphasis on the personal side, [25] Dillenberger says:

"Existentialism stands for the affirmation of the vitality and personal nature of man against all that objectifies him. Whether in the Christian or atheistic form, existentialism declares that man is subject, not object. Objectivization, of course, is related to man both as value and as animal. In either case, he becomes 'thing'."

Observation and experiment are the deciding factors in science (except in mathematics and logic), but life is often given to science by speculative ideas which precede the observation or experiment; and in private thought such ideas should not be neglected, so long as they are not mistaken for knowledge confirmed by observation. Occam's razor should not be applied to private thought; it is well to let one's mental beard grow as long as it will; but one should appear clean-shaven when appearing at the jousting field with other scientists or philosophers. Even to the busiest and most fully committed scientist, his science is but a small part of his life. It must always be remembered that he is human.

In conclusion, by all means let us have more science, more widely dispersed knowledge of science, and more interest in science; but let us also remember that science alone will not save the world; to change Otto's plea, what we need is more than science, much more than science. We need more appreciation of the purposes, character, and needs of others, more sympathy with others; in other words, more love. The extreme mechanists do not deny personality; they simply ignore it. If we take personality into account materialism, naturalism, positivism, dynamism, and all similar philosophies reduce to humanism, which is the real alternate to theism. Their conflict will be considered in the next chapter, after attention to some other phases of the conflict.

Revelation vs. Study of Facts

Christians up to the time of the development of science naively accepted the Bible as the literal word of God. This was the more true of Protestants, since an unchallengeable authority had to be substituted for that of the Church. Even the early scientists tried to make their findings conform to a literal view of the Scriptures. At the present time, however, only fundamentalists believe in revelation in the sense that God once revealed *facts* which would otherwise belong in the domain of science, and that any scientific pronouncement is wrong if it conflicts with a statement in the Bible. The Sunday School studies in use for adults in the principal denominations distinctly say, for instance, that

the stories of Job and Jonah are allegories, but fundamentalist
teachers even in adult classes either do not read the commentary
or ignore it. On the other hand, a minister may, and sometimes
does, make a statement based on evolutionary thought without
raising too much opposition, although fundamentalists in his congregation do not agree with him. The question of verbal revelation is rarely raised in churches.

Scientists do not unanimously maintain that there are no
other methods of learning facts than the common ones of direct
observation and induction. Experiments on ESP (Extra-sensory
Perception) have been conducted at Duke University in which
the investigator holds cards with pictures, letters, or other characters. The subject has no way of seeing the cards or being aware
of their contents. It has been found that some persons give the
right answer, by no means always, but very much oftener than
the laws of chance would call for. In a few cases the subjects
were aware of the right character shortly before it was presented.
These results are granted enough validity to upset any dogmatic
assertion that there is no such method of learning. Also, investigations of numerous cases of clairvoyance and telepathy have not
given a satisfactory common-sense explanation for all of them.
The question is being studied whether there is an unknown method
of transmitting something physical which may account for the
phenomena rather than any purely mental process. Some of the
apparent miracles of the Bible might be explained on such
grounds; but the inconsistencies in Biblical accounts, as well as
disagreement with scientific statements, have rendered them vul-
nerable as sources of facts.

Most liberal and modern orthodox Christians take the position that the knowledge imparted by God to man in the Bible and
in preaching and contemplation is simply knowledge of God, not
knowledge of facts. Many of the facts stated in the Bible may be
wrong; but what survives is knowledge of God Himself, and with
it spiritual truth that cannot be imparted by the methods of science.
They include the existence of love, the forgiveness of sins, and
God's purpose in the world. God has a purpose for man, difficult
as it is to give it verbal expression. Two quotations from the
existentialist theologian and philosopher Bultmann illustrate that
view: [26] "It is the word of God which calls man away from his
selfishness and from the illusory security he has built up for himself. It calls him to God, who is beyond the world and beyond
scientific thinking. For the self of man, his inner life, his personal

existence is also beyond the world and beyond rational thinking. The word of God addresses man in his personal existence and thereby it gives him freedom from the world and from the sorrow and anxiety which overwhelm him when he forgets the beyond." Also, [27] "God's word is a real word spoken to me in human language, whether in the preaching of the Church or in the Bible, in the sense that the Bible is not viewed merely as an interesting collection of sources for the history of religion, but that the Bible is transmitted through the Church as a word addressing us. This living word of God is not invented by the human spirit and by human sagacity; it rises up in history. Its origin is a historical event, by which the speaking of this word, the preaching, is rendered authoritative and legitimate. This event is Jesus Christ." This does not imply that morals may not have an evolutionary origin.

This direct relation of man to God is called mysticism. A mystical belief, however, if carried too far, may lead to a doctrine of infallibility. Hocking says: [28] "As a matter of natural history, the mystic in practical affairs is apt to carry his assurance too far. The defect of his virtue may be that he becomes absolute on too slight provocation. The worshiper, by the nature of his profession, must first humble himself before his object, and with all his strength suppress his strength, until it begins its assertions at the zero of all historical content. None but God can teach the all-mighty word in its solitary origins. It is the destiny of religion to find that difficult and all-important center of a just infallibility, which curbs and defines all abstract assurance, without disastrously abolishing it." Hocking also describes the assurance of the mystic in four words: "Sure of too much." The scientist, also, may be "sure of too much," but he can be recalled from his over-assurance by being asked to state the facts on which his statements are based.

Facts, Myths, and Lies

Niebuhr, the neo-orthodox theologian, makes frequent use of the term "myth" in dealing with the Bible, and has been followed in that usage by other neo-orthodox and modern orthodox authorities. Hordern thus explains Niebuhr's position: [29] "The relation of man to God, the finite to the infinite, cannot, says Niebuhr, be expressed in purely rational or logical terms. It can only be expressed in myths such as the Genesis story of the creation and the fall. In religion, he believes, we are dealing with the

mystery and depth of life which elude our efforts to catch them in
neat rational descriptions. Niebuhr compares theology to a painter
who, working upon a flat surface, tries to create the illusion of
another dimension, depth. This is a deception, but a deception
that describes a truth about reality. Similarly, the theologian must
describe God and His ways in the thought forms of our space-time
world. But God transcends the world so that none of the things
we say can be adequate. On the other hand, God does not simply
transcend the world; He is also immanent and active within it, so
theology can say something about Him. Since our earth-born logic
can speak, but not adequately, about God, it must, like the painter,
use symbols that point to another dimension of reality. Theology
is the attempt to express the dimensions of depth in life. Niebuhr
applies the term "myth" to this form of thinking. The term is
perhaps unfortunate, as "myth" implies a fairy tale to most people.
But by myth Niebuhr means that which, although it deceives, none
the less points to a truth that cannot be adequately expressed in
any other form. It is deceitful and yet true, just as is the deception
of depth which is attained by the artist."

Hartshorne's views on the New Testament miracles as myths
have been stated in Chapter 6. The existentialist philosophers
[30]Karl Jaspers and Rudolf Bultmann have conducted a debate on
the use of myth, which runs through several volumes. Jaspers
agrees with Niebuhr about the usefulness of myths and is opposed
to demythologization. He believes that no other mode of language
can adequately express the meaning of myth, and that the myths
in the Bible should be retained as they are. Bultmann, on the other
hand, advocates expressing their meaning in factual language.

The best known of meaningful myths is that of Santa Claus.
The young child is told that this jovial personage brings him
Christmas gifts. He learns a few years later that Santa has no
objective existence but that his spirit prevails at Christmas time
and should endure for a longer time. This myth involves deception, but objection to it has been limited. With Santa Claus, however, is also introduced the Christ-Child myth. According to one
variation of the myth, three astrologers (the word translated "Wise
men" really means astrologers) from the East see a star which
they recognize as being associated with the King of the Jews, so
they go to Jerusalem. There they learn that the King is to be born
in Bethlehem. The star's motion is accommodatingly kept within
their range of speed and finally rests over the place where Jesus
lies, without causing any astonishment at the peculiar behavior of

the star. King Herod, alarmed at the idea of a rival King of the Jews, orders all infants in Bethlehem under two years of age to be killed. Mary and Joseph have been miraculously warned to flee to Egypt. This action would be entirely in accord with Herod's character, but strangely there is no mention of it outside the Scriptures.

In the other legend, Joseph and Mary go from their home in Nazareth to Bethlehem to be enrolled for taxation. History records such an enrollment under the governor who is mentioned, but it was several years later, after Herod had died, and also at a time out of line with later recorded events. (This point has been disputed by some recent scholars.) According to the story Jesus was born in a manger, which according to some traditions is in a cave, because "there was no place for them in the inn." His birth was heralded by throngs of angels who were visible to shepherds. The irony of his humble birth would be still greater if, according to humanist and liberal views, he was born in Nazareth or some other obscure Galilean village, unannounced by angels and unvisited by Wise men; the place and circumstances of His birth would make little difference to present-day Christians. To some early Jewish Christians, however, His birth. in Bethlehem was very important in establishing Him as the rightful King of the Jews according to their understanding of prophecy.

Fundamentalists and many other Christians retain a literal view of these accounts, without considering the discrepancies; many Jews, Unitarians, other liberals, and atheists take part in Christmas celebrations although they regard the story as mythical. It is proper that they should, because it is the vision, not the facts, that counts.

Liberal and modern orthodox thinkers make little effort to argue the implausibility of the stories as recorded, and properly so. A well-known story concerns an artist who was told by an observer of one of his pictures: "I never saw a sunset like that." The artist replied: "Don't you wish you could?" The story of the Christ-Child takes us into a world in which we should all like to be; a world where good will and gift-giving prevail; where we are all in the presence of a Supreme Being. After all, the question of the historicity of the story is not important. The legends are among the finest pieces of literature and have become the theme for the basis of some of the world's greatest music and paintings. For every mother they idealize her child. They give us a glimpse of things as they ought to be under adverse conditions. The central theme is God's love, which according to most theology is the basis for human love.

The Santa Claus myth as a historical fact can be easily disproved; the Christ-Child myth cannot, whatever we think about its probability. Children become mature enough to disbelieve in Santa Claus and still retain the significance of the myth. Can people in general become mature enough to disbelieve the Christ-Child stories as historical fact and still accept thoroughly the underlying meaning? If not, should they be kept in ignorance of the improbability of the myth, while an esoteric belief is concealed from them? In short, can the Pastor or teacher be entirely honest regarding the subject?

Two small boys in my neighborhood were talking together; imaginative and contemplative Manuel was telling literal-minded Eddie about a fairy tale he had read. Eddie ran shouting: "Manuel is telling lies!" Some modern atheist critics of Christianity regard some of the Biblical accounts neither as facts nor myths, but as deliberate lies to bolster the importance and support of the "priesthood." The statement made by some fundamentalists, "Either the Bible is all true or it is a lie," may contribute to the view that it is a lie. Plato saw nothing wrong in an esoteric disbelief in the Greek gods although the common people believed in them, and several Roman authors thought that if the lower classes were kept in subjection by their religious beliefs, so much the better. So far as I know, no such opinion has been published by any official or leader of thought in any Christian country, although it is quite probable that some persons have held one in private. In these days of publicity through the press it would be dangerous to express them. It is only the enemies of Christianity who speak of it as an opiate of the people.

If religion has its myths according to the definition given, does not science also have its myths? Are molecules and electrons myths? The answer is that although all visual conceptions of the molecule and electron are deceitful, it is a recognized deception. Perhaps one might say that the things that we see are deceitful, and that the molecules and electrons are a partial explanation of the method of deception. We can look back on discarded theories and call them myths—for instance the phlogiston theory and the luminiferous ether of the nineteenth century. The word that we use for these explanations is not myth but hypothesis. The difference is that a hypothesis is (or should be) recognized as such, while a myth may be accepted as fact by those who do not take the trouble to investigate.

Fundamentalists and others who accept the stories of the Bible and other religious sources as facts may be in error in doing so; but among the most vocal in calling them lies are the Marxists, who after demolishing the stories build up an atheistic caricature of religion, the falsity of which is transparent. The utter lack of freedom under Communist rule is disguised as freedom from Capitalism. There is deception here also, but it is a different kind of deception from that described by Niebuhr and his school. Instead of a deception which enables the viewer to interpret a myth, it is a deception which suppresses freedom. Whether some of the Bible myths should be demythologized or not, they have an indispensable place in human education and thought.

The subject of myths may be illustrated by a quotation from [31] G. R. Harrison: "Some scientists are so overwhelmed by the discoveries that animal bodies are mechanisms that they tend to be literal in their assessment of vitalism, and act like a child who has just learned that there is no Santa Claus. Though the child's earlier concept of Santa Claus was limited and incorrect, it is better that he believe in a false Santa Claus for a time than that he never grasp the spirit of Christmas at all. When the wife of one eminent scientist asked him what she should say in reply to their young son's question about whether God really exists, he said, 'Of course the answer is yes, because this will come much closer to what we consider the truth than if you were to give the answer no.' Yet this man was what would be called an agnostic, or one without knowledge, which does not conflict at all with the fact that he was a deeply spiritual person."

Is there a possibility of reconciliation between the scientific and the theological views? Just as the theory that light consists of corpuscles and the one that it consists of waves can be combined in an all-embracing theory of radiation, may not the theological and the scientific accounts of the universe somehow be combined into a consistent set of ideas? May it not be true that design or purpose on the one hand and determinism or chance on the other are aspects of a yet unknown truth? The answer is that in all the cases mentioned both conceptions are objective, but the concepts of God, of purpose or design, are not objective, and there is little hope of reconciliation.

This much may be said toward the establishment of a unified statement; the universe from the beginning has had potentialities as well as actualities. If the electrons, neutrons, protons, etc., existed before the atoms, they had the potentiality of being combined into atoms. The outer electrons in the carbon atom had the potentiality of enabling the carbon atoms to be linked with each other to a degree possessed by no other atoms. This linking of the carbon atoms gave the possibility of the formation of very complex compounds such as the proteins, enzymes, and all the other building blocks of living matter. Life, once established, had the potentiality of becoming more and more complex as its environment permitted. This complexity had the potentiality of freedom and consciousness which came to its full fruition in man. Primitive man had the potentiality of developing all the complexities that we call civilization, and man as he is has the potentiality of further development to a degree unknown to us. In brief, the first material, electrical, or energetic particles had the potentiality of becoming the universe as it exists now and for man's present and future development. It may be objected that potentiality means nothing except that what was potential has happened. That is all that can be said on a scientific basis. But is there not a shadow of a purpose in a potentiality?

What I have attempted to indicate in this chapter is that, with the possible exception mentioned in the preceding paragraph, to the mind there is no solution to the many phases of the conflict between science and theology and that none is in sight. The victory can be conceded to neither side. That is, if it is to be called a conflict, it is one that cannot be resolved by reason, but depends upon different unrelated outlooks. Those outlooks constitute the difference between theism and humanism.

Chapter X

Humanism And Theism

THE PRECEDING CHAPTER has shown that even the advocates of naturalism, positivism, mechanism, or whatever an atheistic philosophy may be called, assume the existence of a knower, an "I". Science is impossible without a scientist; philosophy is impossible without a philosopher. It is also necessary for the scientist or philosopher to have another person to whom he may communicate his ideas. Therefore the "I-and-you" hypothesis, which was mentioned in Chapter 3, must be assumed. The humanist stops with this hypothesis, but the theist adds the "God-hypothesis", which includes the other; it could be called the "I-you-God hypothesis". Must the choice be made between these two, or are there other possibilities? The story is told of a professor of philosophy who announced to his class: "There are some who believe in God; there are others who do not; probably the truth is somewhere between the two." Fanciful as the story sounds, there are many who would like to see a compromise made, and it cannot be said that such a solution is impossible.

Another philosophy is panpsychism, which means that all material entities, even down to the atom and its constituents, have a sort of life and consciousness.

In practice we try to be neutral on the subject, but without success. Most religious groups believe that the Bible should be read in the public schools and that some reference should be made to God in history. Catholics, however, want the Catholic version of the Bible read and references to God expressed in Catholic form. Protestants are equally insistent on the Protestant versions. Jews do not want the New Testament read. Atheists desire to have no religious matter read and no reference made to the existence of God. Sometimes, as a compromise, the Bible is not read and religious matters are not discussed, thus practically settling the question in favor of the atheists. As in the alignment of nations, there is really no neutral ground. The possibility remains, how-

207

ever, that the way is left open for the idea that both humanism and theism are aspects of a truth that thus far is unattainable, and that at some distant day there will be neither theists nor humanists but people whose belief is different from either. Since that day has not arrived, we must turn to the present aspects of the situation.

Humanism has been defined and characterized in Chapter 5. Webster's third definition is: "A system, mode, or attitude of thought or action centering upon distinctively human interests or ideals, especially as contrasted with naturalistic or religious interests." The fourth definition is "A contemporary cult or belief calling itself religious but substituting faith in man for faith in God." Its scope as a belief, if it exists as a cult, is much wider. Although there may be a set of beliefs which may be called "atheistic humanism", it constitutes a borderline case, and it can be said that the difference between humanism and atheism is one of emphasis. Humanism emphasizes man, while atheism emphasizes the absence of God.

A picture of theism in terms of Heim's metaphor has been given in Chapter 6. The numerous prison cells which represent human individuals are open at the top to the space which is God. Humanism could say that instead of an opening at the top, there is a rather fuzzy mirror closing the cell. The individual looks upward and thinks he sees an unbounded space, whereas he really sees an imperfect reflection of himself. In rejecting the God-hypothesis the humanist denies supernaturalism, miracles, and revelation in either the fundamentalist or the modern sense. He denies the existence of purpose in the universe except human purposes, which become all-important. The possibilities of man are limitless. They are not confined to achievements in science, marvelous as these are, and still more marvelous as they are expected to become; achievements in humanitarianism and personal relations will be even greater.

An extreme case of humanistic belief is reflected in Henley's poem *Invictus*. Aldous Huxley comments thus on this poem and the idea it represents: [1] " 'I am the master of my fate,' poor Henley wrote at the end of a celebrated morsel of rhetoric, 'I am the captain of my soul.' Nothing could be farther from the truth. My fate cannot be mastered; it can only be cooperated with and thereby, to some extent, directed. Nor am I the captain of my soul; I am his noisiest passenger—a passenger who is not sufficiently important to sit at the captain's table and does not know, even by report, what the soul-ship looks like, how it works or where it is going."

Most humanists would find ground somewhere between Henley and Huxley, while theists of most religions would agree with Huxley, except that they would assert that the passenger has been given a little information about the boat and has some choice about its destination. The humanist idea which was prevalent early in the present century, that man will increasingly improve himself and has done pretty well thus far, was rudely shaken by the two world wars and subsequent conflicts. They at least indicate that the road is much longer and more difficult than anyone had predicted. Against this view theists argue that man is not fundamentally good, and cannot accomplish his improvement alone. This denial had its climax in the doctrine of total depravity which many theologians held until fifty years ago, and which is still found among extreme conservatives. According to that view man accomplishes goodness only by yielding to spiritual forces, or, in strictly Calvinist doctrine, only the grace of God can help him. "Unbelievers" have been able to achieve humanitarian ends only because they have been influenced by Christianity; and their accomplishments count them nothing. The present general belief is that man is neither wholly good nor wholly bad. According to theism man can choose the good only through God's grace"; that is, when directed or assisted by God. The humanist can say with Polonius: "To thine own self be true." The theist can reply that man's own self is not good enough to warrant this devotion. Both might agree that man should be true to the Holy Spirit, but they would be maintaining their separate definitions of the Holy Spirit: the humanist's, that it is an unconscious attribute of man; or the theist's, that it is not part of man but "abides in him".

We may imagine the case of a young child who has been taught the lesson of God's care, in the Sunday School: [2] "Are not two sparrows sold for a penny? And not one of them will fall to the ground without your Father's will." Later the child finds a dead sparrow and wonders why God let that particular sparrow die. The fullest possible explanation would lie far beyond his comprehension; for example the survival of the fittest and the role of accident. More inclusively, he would learn that no amount of goodness or faith would completely protect him from harm; that even Christ had to suffer. As he grew more mature, he would wonder what would be the advantage of having an all-powerful and loving Father, over the kind of supreme rule that seems deducible from science, with no concern for him as a person. He would find, as Job did, that the difference would lie in being reconciled to the will of a personality mysteriously like himself rather than to an inanimate and cruel impersonal reality. His choice, as affected by his subsequent experience, would lie or vibrate between the two.

I have had several humanist friends. They were all reared in fundamentalist Christian families, except one who was a generation removed from Christianity. They were much alike in character, scrupulously honest intellectually and personally; of unimpeachable morals; aware of obligations to their families, to other people, to the community, and to the State, but not to God in any form. Nearly all of them were scientists. Their objections to Christianity were, first, that Christian beliefs as they understood them were contrary to scientific facts; and second, that Christians did not act in accordance with their professed beliefs. They had a certain pride in their attitude and did not consider themselves sinners. In so far as I can judge, the attitudes of a number of humanists whose writings I have read are similar. These friends rejected liberalism and modern orthodoxy as fully as they rejected fundamentalism; but if their environment in their younger days had been liberal it is possible that they would have called themselves Christians. It is of such people that Tillich has written that in rejecting formal religion they have really become converted to religion.

One of these friends told me that in a personal crisis he simply "took hold of himself" and finally solved the problem, and he thought that in similar cases when help seems to come from a "higher power" it is really from one's self; that is, as Huxley put it, from one of the non-selves which is the Holy Spirit. Is it an aspect of the individual or a manifestation of a unity including all humanity? Humanism says, "man looks out into the universe and finds—himself." The theist says that he can find God if he knows how to look.

In all cases of genuine faith healing, including the many cures of alcoholism in which members of Alcoholics Anonymous have assisted, the healing help seems to come to the patient from without. Some light may be thrown on the subject by research in extrasensory perception. That field is being investigated extensively by the Society for Psychical Research. Its investigators have found much fraud among "spiritualists" and other "mediums," but on the other hand they have found phenomena which are not explicable by fraud or other known means, so far as they can determine. There are on record thousands of answers to prayer; the objection made to their admission is that cases of unanswered prayer are not equally thoroughly reported. Christians would then answer that God often gives negative answers to prayer. The researches on extrasensory perception are viewed skeptically by materialists and to some extent by most scientists, and it has been alleged that not all possibilities of fraud have been eliminated. If the so-called proofs are to be accepted as truth, they signify that in special cases one person can learn what is in the mind of another without having received that information through the senses (telepathy) or can discern real objects not yet perceived by any person (clairvoyance). There are two ways of regarding these phenomena. One is that there are as yet unrecognized physical means, for instance some unknown types of waves, which carry an impression from an organ of one person to that of another. Some experiments on insects by a Russian scientist give a hint of that possibility. The other is that minds are in direct communication with each other without any intervening material or space. It is possible that at some future time these questions will be answered and the science of extrasensory perception will blossom forth into totally unanticipated consequences.

Our main interest in these discussions, however, is in their contributions to a possible decision between humanism and theism and whatever intermediate philosophy there may be. A humanist will admit the reality of non-conceptual thinking and even the I-thou relationship; but he will assert that all types of thinking had to await the evolution of an organ capable of thinking, whether conceptual or non-conceptual. The theist insists that spirit and thought preceded the physical world and physical relationships. The panpsychist believes they grew up together. All these beliefs in their simplicity imply the fundamental reality of time; they are all thrown out of focus if we consider time as one of a number of dimensions which is emphasized in our way of life.

On a practical basis a variety of opinions exists on the subject. Since there is no way of applying science to the subject as a whole, mental attitudes can and do vary widely. It would be difficult but interesting to know the beliefs and attitudes of the members of even one religious congregation to even one subject just discussed in a sermon. The mental backgrounds of people differ so much that a surprising variation in belief and application to daily life would be found. One point to be considered is intellectual honesty as related to religion, a subject that has been postponed from an earlier chapter.

Intellectual Honesty in Religion

There is no Biblical commandment which says: "You shall be intellectually honest." The Ten Commandments prescribe an individual's relations to God and to others, not to himself; but intellectual honesty underlies obedience to all the Commandments. Many cases of intellectual honesty and of its absence occur in the history, poetry, and fiction of the Bible. The most noteworthy example in the Old Testament is that of Job. He was not satisfied with the philosophy that good conduct is always rewarded by happiness and prosperity. That philosophy had been proclaimed by priests and prophets and some of the psalmists and writers of proverbs and was dinned into his ears by his "friends", but it had not been confirmed in his own experience. In the New Testament the climax of the parable of the Prodigal Son is his realization of intellectual honesty when he "came to himself". The injunction is given, "Test all things; hold fast that which is good." The emphasis in the teaching of Jesus and the Apostles is always on honest personal experience.

Coe devotes a chapter to intellectual honesty in Christianity. Some pertinent quotations are: [3] "There is no calamity, no unrighteousness, more dreadful than that of bringing our intellect into slavery to our desires. There is no more momentous aspect of our freedom than our ability to form a habit of regarding as true whatever we desire to have true. On the other hand, there is no more exalted function of the human will than that of maintaining judicial rectitude in the inmost thought." "The process of self-deception is of a kind to conceal even its own nature from us. We may degrade ourselves to almost any extent at the same time that we regard ourselves as good churchmen or even as saintly characters. We then become, to use a paradoxical term, unconscious hypocrites. The worst kind of hypocrite is not the one who tries to appear to others what he is not, but the one who deceives himself concerning himself. This is a vice before which both the victim and his friends stand helpless . . . Strangely enough, some of these self-deceived persons, through the very completeness of the deception, make such an impression of sincerity as to become or remain leaders of the people. The question is often a difficult one, whether this or that person who is doing great harm in the name of religion is conscious of insincerity or of imposture. It is not improbable that in most of these cases the standards of self-judgment have been so far destroyed as to make genuine self-knowledge practically impossible." (Coe 149, 152)

Although intellectual honesty is a fundamental Christian virtue, it is not always found in Christians, including theologians and pastors, conservative and liberal as Coe has just implied. Naturally it should be added that it is often absent in non-Christians in their opposition to Christianity. One would expect it to be more prevalent among theologians than among pastors, because the theologians' statements can be questioned by other theologians, but the pastor's audience is not usually in a position to question him.

A reason for a fundamental tendency toward intellectual dishonesty in Christianity in the present age is that there is an aura of unreality about the words of the Bible, in the minds of most readers except the very young, in all cases where the supernatural is involved. To a certain degree this aura of unreality is present when any new subjects are studied or new ideas are presented; but as the subject becomes assimilated in the mind, the apparent unreality disappears. The story of Columbus at first sounds unreal; but the student eventually reasons that here we are in America, and there are many facts which make it evident that the story is true. Likewise the American Revolution finally seems real because there are so many things to remind us of it; and so on throughout history. Fiction is recognized as fiction almost from the child's youngest days, but in most stories the reader can see himself in the story. The sense of unreality is very evident in the beginning of the study of science, including mathematics; most students soon realize the impact of the subject on their ordinary experience, but some do not; they never care for science because they have not assimilated it as part of themselves. In religion the reaction to this aura of unreality may take any one of several courses: the supernatural may be rejected as part of actual life, and with it all accounts implying the supernatural (materialism and atheism); the supernatural may be accepted without realizing that it makes a cleavage in the personality (compartmentalism); it may be accepted at the expense of the conception of the material world (fanatical idealism); it may be accepted to the limited degree in which it appears in the Bible (fundamentalism); or it may lead to a realization of both the material and spiritual elements in life with the determination to resolve conflicts as nearly as possible, either by demythologization or retention of symbols and myths as such (enlightened theism).

The early Christians did not have this problem. Although the supernatural was not an item of their daily experience, they ac-

cepted accounts of it as facts. They believed in the Second Coming
in their time, which did not come to pass, and in immortality, the
existence of God, the divinity of Christ, which have been neither
proved nor disproved. As the history of Christianity progressed
and theology became more complicated, and especially after
Christianity became subordinated to politics, the intellectual honesty of its adherents deteriorated. Religion is not objective; there
are no scientific facts in theology; and therefore there is no opportunity to check with facts, as there is in science. The historical
facts associated with any religion cannot be checked with certainty. A theologian may begin with assumptions which he thinks
are based on revelation. In so far as these assumptions are
followed logically and revelation and fact are not confused, the
theologian may be considered intellectually honest; but another
theologian may begin with different assumptions which he thinks
are warranted by revelation. His conclusions may not agree with
those of the first theologian.

Theological doctrines may have some consequences in human
morals, and if one of these assumptions is found to result in better
morals than the other, it may be judged the more nearly correct;
but this is not absolutely logical. Although the substance of theology may be in an un-physical dimension, any statement made in
theology may have consequences in the scientifically comprehensi-
ble world. Differences in theological belief do not result merely in
academic discussions; wars have been fought over such differences.
Those wars, of course, did not settle the questions, but they did
give a strong indication that both sides were wrong and both sides
were dishonest. To Christianity's credit it may be said that the
most flagrant cases of dishonesty, intellectual and otherwise, are
found in unchristian Communist governments; but brain-washing
is just as obnoxious in Christianity as it is in Communism, and as
foreign to the spirit of Christianity.

George Albert Coe wrote sixty years ago: [4] "Men who fancy
themselves in this predicament" (what Long calls compartmentalism) "generally see an escape by yielding up one side of the
nature as a sacrifice to the other. In nearly every case it is the
religious side that is sacrified, and for a very obvious reason. The
methods of the sciences are more definitely organized than the
corresponding modes of religious thought. Religion cannot measure
and weigh the objects of its thought, or experimentally reproduce
its facts for purposes of investigation. Again, religious thought has
clung longer and more tenaciously to authority and to dialectical

and speculative schemes. Whenever evidence has failed, its tendency to assert that faith can take the place of evidence in producing a reasonable conviction has also given it the appearance of double dealing. Finally, religious thought has, not unnaturally, assumed the attitude of an attorney rather than that of an investigator. While the man of science is required to find out something that he does not know, the religious thinker knows his conclusion in advance, and merely seeks means of proving and defending it. The very preciousness of religion has rendered difficult the absolute candor that gives to all facts and considerations the exact weight that belongs to them, irrespective of their bearing upon a conclusion that we desire to establish. When the dearest things of the heart plead on any side of a question, one would have to be almost superhuman not to render a prejudiced decision. There are, of course, scientific as well as religious prejudices, yet they have no such eloquence as that of the religious instinct."

A quotation from Geddes MacGregor is also pertinent: [5] "The religious philosopher, in his singlemindedness and fidelity to the pursuit of truth for its own sake, is in the same case as any other philosopher. Far from taking sides, all genuine philosophers are on the alert for prejudice which, lurking at the back of their minds, might vitiate the impartiality, and consequently the success, of their enterprise. This constant vigilance ought to be a background for all their thinking; as much so, to say the least, as that of a clever detective in a murder case who takes account of all possible motives among his suspects. The religious philosopher is no exception; indeed his scent for prejudice is likely to be particularly sharp, for he usually has more experience than other men in encountering and detecting it." All persons are to a slight degree religious philosophers and the obligation to be intellectually honest rests upon them to some extent."

Daniel Jenkins says on the same subject: [6] "Religion is a most embarrassing subject. Nowhere is it more difficult for men to be honest than when they are approaching religion. Nothing is easier than to imagine that one is seeking objective truth, when all that one is doing is either seeking ready confirmation of a truth one is too timid or lazy to scrutinize, or looking for a justification to continue in uncritical disbelief. To imagine that our own reasons are the only reliable courts of appeal in trying to discover grounds for belief in God, covers up the fundamental difficulty, which is that we are not disinterested persons in this matter. . . .

"There is nothing on which the self-consciously modern people pride themselves more than their sincerity and their integrity. Yet mature psychological study has made clear the extent to which our thinking is motivated, not by what we consciously assert, but by deep urges of pride and timidity, and by desires for security and conformity. This fact has often been used, sometimes with considerable justice. But those who have been the quickest to point out these things in relation to the religious have not always seen that the same influences may be at work in their own attitudes." It is dishonest for the Christian to discount anything that science or criticism says; but it is also dishonest for the atheist to neglect any element of his own experience that is not in accord with a materialistic view. Both are then in the position in which Cavendish would have been if he had neglected the "small bubble".

E. Z. Mozley says about Albert Schweitzer's written works: [7] "One feels in reading the 'Mystery' and the 'Quest' a sense of truthfulness, of entire absence of any partisan attempt to select the facts to suit past orthodox teaching. Dr. Schweitzer's picture of Jesus and exposition of His thoughts are as beautiful as they appear to be true. Perhaps the strongest evidence for Schweitzer's theological position is the rarity of its public discussion by clergy. Ask, as I have done, some Anglican or Free Churchman what works to consult *against* the last pages of the 'Quest' and you will meet little more fortune than met my own search. I myself was offered nothing of value."

Unfortunately Schweitzer's action in leaving the seminary when he could not sincerely teach what he was expected to teach was the exception rather than the rule. Many others remained in their positions masking their beliefs with a show of orthodoxy. A flagrant case of dishonesty was that of a theological professor, H. G. Mitchell, who "some years ago" signed the declaration of his acceptance of the Doctrines and Disciplines of the Methodist Church and later gave his private interpretation of them. The declaration read (numbers added for clarity): (1) "I accept the Old Testament as divinely authoritative, recognizing a supernatural element manifested in miracles and prophecy. (2) I accept the Gospel statement respecting Jesus' advent into the world. (3) I believe in the Trinity including the deity of Jesus Christ and the Holy Spirit. (4) I believe that the death of Jesus was necessary for the salvation of mankind. (5) I have never had any sympathy with the doctrines of Universalism." In his autobiography he interpreted the declaration as follows: "The first (statement) neither declares nor implies that the entire Old Testament is divinely authoritative. In the second I took care to say that I accepted the teachings of the Gospel, not the Apostles' Creed or any version but the concordant testimony of evangelical tradition which of course remains to be determined. The third did not commit me to any form of the doctrine of the Trinity. The fourth question was so indefinite that I might have answered in the affirmative or in the negative or in both ways. In my fifth statement I confined myself to the denial of the doctrine of retribution."

The Present Situation and Future Goals

As we have seen, there are many shades of religious opinion; but the most important is that between orthodoxy and liberalism. Among the areas in which they differ are: revelation or experience as a source of truth; the relation of faith to religion; the immanence or transcendence of God; the nature of the divinity of Jesus; the nature of Christian hope, whether for the future or for both the present and the future; attitudes toward social issues; and attitudes toward other faiths than Christianity.

Potthoff expresses some of these differences thus: [8] "Theology sets forth ideas about human nature and the human situation. The good news of Christianity is good news for human beings involved in existence. But how shall we describe and interpret human nature? To what extent is a man bound by a sinful nature? Is man really free to make basic decisions, or is his life largely determined by forces beyond his control? Does it have growth potential? In what sense does man need to be redeemed? Is man subject to death? What of immortality and eternal life? In the main, the orthodox tradition has tended to stress the doctrine of sin and man's inability to work out his own salvation. Liberalism, on the other hand, has frankly faced the fact of sin but has attributed greater power to man on his own creative renewal at the same time that he needs to draw on divine resources. We have said that Christians share a common loyalty to Christ. However, we find differences in thinking as to what constitutes the divinity of Jesus and what his chief work of salvation is. Is Jesus primarily a revealer of God? If so, how are we to understand the revelation in Christ? Is his redemptive work done by paying a debt or ransom, or is it by changing the hearts of men? To be a Christian involves not only belief, but a distinctive way of life. How would you describe that way of life? What are the marks of a Christian? Doubtless there—is not agreement on what constitutes 'right and wrong', and there is disagreement on many ethical issues. Likewise, there is not agreement as to how Christian faith involves one in the great social issues of our world. Is the Christian life purely a private matter, or does it have implications for issues in the political, economic, and international fields? Sincere Christian people approach these questions from somewhat different 'perspectives'."

Notwithstanding all these differences, there are many areas of unity among Christians, as distinguished from atheistic humanists. They have in common the history of the Christian church. They share belief in the sovereignty of God. They believe in the existence of sin and the necessity for redemption, however these terms may be defined. They find a fellowship with other Christians wherever they are and whatever minor differences there may be in their beliefs.

Again quoting Potthoff: [9] "Ours is a life-affirming philosophy. In contrast to some eastern faiths, we affirm the meaningfulness of history and human experience. There is a depth dimension to it. God is in it. We are called to be responsible participants in the created world."

In his final paragraph Potthoff says: [10] "Thus far we have been discussing what other people think. Perhaps the time has come for us to recognize that every Christian is a theologian in his own right. To be sure, we cannot all be technical theologians, but we can ask the great questions of theology and try to clarify our own perspective."

It may be asked why, since personal relations are so all-important, theology should exist at all. The answer is, that just as in the cases of science and philosophy, the mind must rationalize. As in philosophy, there are areas in which we have no first-hand knowledge and can have none. But there is an insatiable craving for intellectual consistency which can be appeased only by thinking as far as possible into the unknown. So far as I know, no one has criticized Dr. Schweitzer for abandoning of the field of theology for practical service, but we can hope that, if not now, at some time in the future, someone will try to penetrate further into the mysteries with which theologians are concerned. The fault of theologians, generally has been to consider their subject a closed field, as science was considered several hundred years ago. A virtue of the ideas and works of some contemporary theologians is that they do not believe that theological questions have been settled, but that they open up new vistas of progress. They show that not learned authorities only, but even the amateur may speculate.

The question of humanism versus theism cannot be satisfactorily solved by the assumption of additional dimensions, because the idea is too indefinite. Humanism cannot be accepted as a final solution. "Where do I come from; what is the explanation of existence" are not answered. The alternative has been thus expressed by Heim: [11] "Either it is a frivolous chance which has washed me up at this precise point on the shore of the world, in which case my whole life is arbitrary and meaningless, or I have been set at this point by an eternal Thou. In that case I am under a divine commission. I can base my whole life on faith in the One who put me here." If humanists deny that their lives are "arbitrary and meaningless," probably the reply would be that they have an unconscious and inexpressed faith in the eternal Thou.

According to Heim neither compromise nor tolerance is possible between secularists and theists. That does not mean that there can be no tolerance on the part of Christians toward secularists. There must also be at least equal tolerance toward fundamentalists and other extremists in spite of their inconsistencies, excesses, and misapplications. Heim suggests that the whole of reality in its present form is not in its normal state but in an unresolved intermediate state which bears the character of a "Paradise Lost" and is directed toward a consummation in which these riddles will be solved which in the present form remain insoluble. He believes that this is the underlying thought of the New Testament.

The argument for theism is well put by Toynbee: [12] "In this mysterious universe there is one thing of which Man can feel certain. Man himself is not the greatest spiritual presence in the universe. He understands the Universe only partially, he can control it only slightly, and manifestly he did not bring it into existence. His own presence in the Universe is, for him, an accomplished fact which has not come about through any choice or act of his.

"There is a presence in the Universe that is spiritually greater than Man himself. This presence is not contained either in the phenomena or in the sum total of them. . . .

"Man's goal is to seek communion with the presence behind the phenomena, and to seek it with the aim of bringing his self into harmony with the absolute spiritual reality.

"A human self cannot be brought into harmony with Absolute Reality unless it can get rid of its innate self-centeredness. This is the hardest task that man can set himself; but, if he accomplishes it, his reward will be far more proportionate to the toil and pain of the spiritual struggle."

But these are for the future. What can we believe for the present day? Fundamentalism presents much that is intellectually unacceptable, but it is clear-cut in contrast to much liberal literature which is often fuzzy. How do you present liberalism to the relatively uneducated person or to the child? I confess that I have never studied the Sunday school teaching methods of a liberal church. Atheistic humanism is also clear, clearer than Christian liberalism. But its attitude is to exclude certain points of view almost as completely as fundamentalism excludes other points of view. Both stop too short to be satisfying.

How much harm does fundamentalism do when accepted. It breeds intolerance. Too Much? It produces good character. Too much on the basis of fear? On the other hand there are good atheists; but what is the result when atheism is the belief of a country? One has only to look at Russia.

As a future goal for humanity, the Christian leader would greatly wish that all were converted to Christianity. The scientist and the educator would equally strongly wish that they would become practically intelligent; that is, would have a reasonably correct understanding of the world and its people and would have the common sense to act upon that knowledge. Are these goals compatible? There are many who believe not only that they are, but also that they imply each other. At least it will be generally admitted that there is room for great improvement of humanity, both mentally and spiritually. It is easy to see that the progress of science during the last two hundred years has been a small step into the knowledge of the great world around us, and that we can expect greater progress in the future. No similar progress has occurred in religion; the changes in doctrine and opinion are those in which some aspects of religion agree more nearly with developments in science. May we not, however, at some time in the future expect a "Great Awakening" more thorough than the "great awakenings" of the past, not merely of our emotions but of our whole beings. That is, people may see the outer, scientific universe, their personalities, and their dreams as part of a great whole, at the center of which is God. Will this be something beyond Christianity or will it still be Christianity?

Bibliography

Ref.	Page	**Preface**
1	IX	KNOX, JOHN. *Criticism and Faith.* Abingdon-Cokesbury Press. 1952.
2	X	SMITH, ROY L. *Commentator,* International Sunday School Lesson. 1962.
3	XIII	HORDERN, WILLIAM. *A Layman's Guide to Protestant Theology.* The Macmillan Co. 1955.

Chapter 1

1	4	Quoted from *Reader's Digest,* October 1959. Credited to Erdmans.

Chapter 2

1	5	CONANT, JAMES B. *On Understanding Science.* An Historical Approach. Yale Univ. Press (1947), p. 98.
2	5	DELAHAY, PAUL. *Reflections on the Cultivation of Science.* Am. Scientist **48**, 20 (Mar. 1960).
3	6	SIMONS, JOSEPH H. *Scientific Research in the University.* Am. Scientist **48**, 81 (Mar. 1960).
4	6	DU RUEN-SHEING. *Great Progress Made in the Natural Sciences in China during the Last Decade.* Scientia Sinica **8**, 1196-1217 (Nov. 1959); reprinted in Science News-Letter **78**, 386 (Dec. 10, 1960).
5	7	SIMONS, ibid. p. 81.
6	8	WALKUP, LEWIS E. *Individual Creativity in Research.* Battelle Tech. Rev. **7**, 3-8 (Aug. 1958).
7	9	DELAHAY, ibid., p. 28.
8	10	BRIDGMAN, PERCY W. *The Way Things Are.* Harvard Univ. Press (1959), p. 320.
9	10	HUXLEY, THOMAS H. *Letter to Charles Kingsley,* Sept. 23, 1860. Printed in *His Life and Letters by his Son, Leonard Huxley* (**1**, 219, 1900). From SARTON, GEORGE. *The History of Science and the New Humanism,* George Brazilier, Inc. (1957). This quotation has also been given in toto or in part in a number of publications.
10	11	Reference to original quotation not found. From BECK, WILLIAM S., *Modern Science and the Nature of Life,* Harcourt, Brace & Co., New York (1957), Flyleaf.
11	12	SIMONS, ibid., p. 82.
12	15	BRIDGMAN, ibid., p. 324.
13	16	HARRISON, GEORGE RUSSELL. *What Man May Be. The Human Side of Science.* Wm. Morrow & Co. (1956), p. 215.
14	17	*New York Times,* Magazine Section (Oct. 9, 1960), p. 72.
15	17	HARRISON, ibid., p. 250.
16	19	STANDEN, ANTHONY. *Science Is a Sacred Cow.* E. P. Dutton & Co. (1950), pp. 59-61.
17	20	STANDEN, ibid., pp. 77-78.

Ref. *Page*
18   20   STANDEN, ibid., pp. 98-99.
19   23   SCHMIDT, PAUL F. *Some Merits and Misinterpretations of Scientific Method.* Sci. Monthly **82,** 23 (Jan. 1956).
20   24   WHITTAKER, EDMUND TAYLOR. *What Is Science?* Simon & Schuster (195-), pp. 37-38.
21   24   STANDEN, ibid., p. 175.
22   24   STANDEN, ibid., p. 184.
23   26   STANDEN, ibid., p. 4. Quoted from Cole Stewart. *Liberal Education in a Democracy,* Harper & Bros.
24   26   STANDEN, ibid., p. 16. Quoted from Hendren. *Survey of Elementary Physics,* University Press, Athens, Ga.
25   27   STANDEN, ibid., p. 19.
26   28   FADIMAN, CLIFTON. *Reader's Digest,* Feb. 1960.

Chapter 3

1   29   FRAZER, SIR JAMES G. *The Golden Bough, a Study in Magic and Religion.* Macmillan (1922).
2   30   KAUFMANN, WALTER. *Existentialism from Dostiievsky to Sartre.* Meridian Books (1956), p.11
3   32   BUBER, MARTIN. *I and Thou.* Translated by Ronald Gregor Smith. Scribner. Second Edition (1958). Translator's Introduction.
4   32   BUBER, ibid., p. 33.
5   32   HEIM, ibid., pp. 53-55.
6   34   ABBOTT, EDWARD. *Flatland, a Romance of Many Dimensions, by A Square.* Little, Brown & Co., Boston (1927). Fourth Edition Blackwell, Oxford (1932).
7   35   HEIM, ibid., p. 84.
8   35   JAMES, WILLIAM. *Principles of Psychology.* From Philosophy of William James, Modern Library, p. 139.
9   36   BRIDGMAN, PERCY. *The Way Things Are.* Harvard Univ. Press (1959), p. 223.
10   37   BRIDGMAN, ibid., pp. 203-206.
11   38   BODIAN, MARTIN. *What Do the Color Blind See?* A Report on Monocular Color Blindness. Am. J. Opthalmol. **35,** 1471-1479 (Oct. 1952).
12   39   BRIDGMAN, ibid., p. 245.
13   40   HEIM, ibid., pp. 74-76.
14   40   TOYNBEE, ARNOLD. *An Historian's Approach to Religion.* Oxford Univ. Press (1956), p. 292.
15   42   KILLIAN, JAMES R., JR. *Eleven Ways to Make Science a Vital Force in Foreign Policy.* Tech. Rev. **63,** No. 14, p. 8 (Feb. 1961).
16   44   BUBER, ibid., pp. 125-126.
17   45   POLLARD, WILLIAM GROSVENOR. *Physicist and Christian.* Seabury Press, Greenwich, Conn. (1961), p. 131.
18   46   BUBER, ibid., pp. 7-8. Quoted by Pollard, ibid., p. 133.

Chapter 4

Ref.	Page	
1	48	SARTON, GEORGE. *The History of Science and the New Humanism.* Brazilier, Inc. (1956), pp. 65-67.
2	49	BERNAL, J. D. *The Social Function of Science.* Macmillan (1937), p. 17.
3	49	SEDGWICK, W. T., and TYLER, H. W. *A Short History of Science.* Macmillan (1935).
4	50	SARTON, ibid., pp. 76-77.
5	51	WHITE, ANDREW D. *A History of the Warfare of Science with Theology in Christendom.* D. Appleton (1896), Vol. **2,** pp. 3-4.
6	52	WHITE, ibid., **1,** p. 73.
7	53	SARTON, ibid., p. 83.
8	54	SEDGWICK AND TYLER, ibid., p. 156.
9	55	SEDGWICK, W. T., and TYLER, H. W. *A Short History of Science.* Revised by H. W. Tyler and R. P. Bogelow. Macmillan (1939), p. 250. Quoted from Fahie, Life of Galileo.
10	56	WHITE, ibid., **1,** pp. 129-130.
11	56	SEDGWICK AND TYLER, ibid. (1935 edition), Appendix E, pp. 414-420.
12	59	HESSE, MARY B. *Science and the Human Imagination.* SCM Press Ltd., 56 Bloomsbury St., London (1954), p. 34.
13	59,60	WHITE, ibid., **1,** pp. 135-137.
14	61	TAYLOR, F. SHERWOOD. *Science, Past and Present.* Wm. Heinemann, Ltd. (1945), pp. 80-81.
15	64	NOYES, ALFRED. *The Unknown God.* Sheed & Ward (1949), p. 44.
16	64	NOYES, ibid., p. 54.
17	65	DARWIN, CHARLES. *Descent of Man and Selection in Relation to Sex.* Second Edition, D. Appleton & Co. (1925), pp. 627-628.
18	65	WHITE, ibid., **1,** p. 68.
19	68	POLLARD, WILLIAM G. *Physicist and Christian.* Seabury Press (1961), p. 104.

Chapter 5

1	74	DILLENBERGER, JOHN, and WELCH, CLAUDE. *Protestant Christianity, Interpreted through Its Development.* Scribners (1953).
2	75	MILTON, JOHN. *Paradise Lost,* Book VIII. From F. SHERWOOD TAYLOR, *Science Past and Present.* Wm. Heinemann Ltd., London (1945), pp. 191-192.
3	76	HORDERN, WILLIAM. *A Layman's Guide to Protestant Theology.* Macmillan (1955), p. 44.
4	77	WISH, HARVEY. *Society and Thought in Early America.* Longmans Green & Co. (1950), Vol. **1,** p. 159.
5	77	HORDERN, ibid., p. 44.
6	77	WISH, ibid., **1,** p. 158.
7	78	LOETSCHER, LEFFERTS A. *A Brief History of the Presbyterians.* Westminster Press (1958), p. 59.
8	78	WISH, ibid., p. 159.

Ref.	Page	
9	78,80	WHITE, ANDREW D. *A History of the Warfare of Science with Theology in Christendom.* D. Appleton & Co. (1896), Vol. **1**, p. 8.
10	80	WHITE, ibid., **1**, p. 9.
11	82	WHITE, ibid., **2**, p. 396.
12	82	DILLENBERGER AND WELCH, ibid., p. 190.
13	83	WHITE, ibid., **2**, p. 294.
14	83	WHITE, ibid., **2**, p. 305.
15	84	WHITE, ibid., **2**, p. 310.
16	84	HORDERN, ibid., pp. 45-46.
17	84	WHITE, ibid., **2**, p. 317.
18	85	WHITE, ibid., **2**, pp. 331-332.
19	85	WHITE, ibid., **2**, p. 336.
20	85	WHITE, ibid., **2**, p. 367.
20a	86	WHITE, ibid., **2**, p. 365.
21	89	DILLENBERGER, JOHN. *Protestant Thought and Natural Science.* Doubleday & Co., Inc. (1960), p. 201.
22	90	HORDERN, ibid., p. 52.
23	90	HARNACK, ADOLF VON. *What Is Christianity?* Translated by T. B. Sanders. Putnam (1903).
24	91	DILLENBERGER AND WELCH, ibid., pp. 227-228.
25	92	MACHEN, JOHN. Typical books: *Christianity and Liberalism,* Macmillan (1923); *What Is Faith?* Macmillan (1935).
26	92	HORDERN, ibid., p. 67.
27	93	Issued at Auburn Seminary, Auburn, N. Y., January, 1924.
28	94	LOETSCHER, ibid., p. 88.
29	94	FOSDICK, HARRY EMERSON. Typical books: *As I See Religion.* Harper (1937); *A Guide to the Understanding of the Bible,* Harper (1938); *The Man from Nazareth,* Harper (1949).
30	96	HORDERN, ibid., pp. 73-74.
31	97	DILLENBERGER AND WELCH, ibid., pp. 230-231.
32	98	HARTSHORNE, CHARLES. *Beyond Humanism.* Essays in the New Philosophy of Nature. Willett, Clark & Co. (1937), p. 2.
33	99	TILLICH, PAUL. *Dynamics of Faith.* Harper Torchbooks (1957), p. 62.
34	99	HORDERN, ibid., p. 96.
35	100	HORDERN, ibid., pp. 95-96.
36	100	HORDERN, ibid., p. 103.
37	101	HORDERN, ibid., pp. 147-148. Typical books by Niebuhr: *Interpretation of Christian Ethics,* Harper (1935); *The Children of Light and the Children of Darkness,* Scribner (1944); *Christian Realism and Political Problems,* Scribner (1953).
38	102	HORDERN, ibid., p. 149.
39	102	HORDERN, ibid., pp. 163-164.
40	102	HORDERN, ibid., pp. 174-175.
41	103	HORDERN, ibid., p. 209.
42	103	Typical books: LEWIS, *Mere Christianity,* Macmillan (1929); BUTTERFIELD, *Christianity and History,* Scribner (1950); WALSH, *Stop Looking and Listen,* Harper (1947).

Ref. Page
43   104   Webster's New International Dictionary. 3d Edition.
44   105   Webster's New International Dictionary. 3d Edition.

Chapter 6

1   109   HUXLEY, JULIAN. *Religion Without Revelation.* Second Edition. Max
            Parrish, London (1957), p. 103.
2   109   HUXLEY, ibid., p. 102. Quoted from WHITEHEAD, A. N. *Religion in the
            Making.* Macmillan (1926), pp. 15-19.
3   110   HUXLEY, ibid., p. 105.
4   110   HUXLEY, ibid., p. 100.
5   110   GATLAND, KENNETH W., and DEMPSTER, DEREK D. *The Inhabited
            Universe.* An Inquiry Staged on the Frontiers of Knowledge.
            David McKay Co., N. Y. (1958), p. 156.
6   113   ROYDEN, MAUDE. *The Idea of God in the Mind of Man.* In *Man's
            Destiny in Eternity* (The Garvin Lectures). The Beacon Press
            (1949), pp. 45-47.
7   114   HEIM, KARL. *Christian Faith and Natural Science.* Translated by
            N. Horton Smith (1953), p. 212.
8   114   HEIM, ibid., p. 219.
9   116   TILLICH, PAUL. *The Courage to Be.* Yale Univ. Press (1952), pp.
            186-190.
10   118   STRAUSS, DAVID FREDERICK. *Life of Jesus.* (1835).
11   118   SCHWEITZER, ALBERT. *The Quest of the Historical Jesus.* Critical
            Study of the Progress from Reimarus to Wrede. Translated by
            W. Montgomery. Macmillan (1948).
12   119   SCHWEITZER, ALBERT. *Psychiatric Study of Jesus, Exposition and
            Criticism.* Translated by Charles R. Joy. Beacon Press (1948).
13   119   HOLTZMANN, N. J. *Messianic Concept of Jesus.* (1907).
14   119   BAUMANN, H. *Character of Jesus.* (1908).
15   120   SMITH, HOMER W. *Man and His Gods.* Little, Brown, and Co. (1952),
            Grosset & Dunlap (1956), p. 197. (The preceding paragraphs
            summarize pp. 187 ff.)
16   121   COE, GEORGE ALBERT. *The Religion of a Mature Mind.* Fleming H.
            Revell Co. Second Edition (1903), pp. 403-438.
17   123   SMITH, ibid., p. 204.
18   124   LOETSCHER, LEFFERTS A. *A Brief History of the Presbyterians.* West-
            minster Press (1959), p. 13.
19   125   SMITH, ibid., p. 251.
20   127   HUXLEY, ALDOUS. *Tomorrow, and Tomorrow, and Tomorrow, and
            Other Essays.* Harper & Bros. (1952).
21   127   POLLARD, WILLIAM G. *Physicist and Christian, a Dialogue between
            the Communities.* Seabury Press (1961), p. 62.
22   128   POLLARD, ibid., p. 70.
23   129   New Testament, Revised Standard Version, I John 4: 2-3.
24   129   COMPTON, ARTHUR H. *Science and the Supernatural.* Sci. Monthly
            63, 441-446, (Dec. 1946).
25   129   HUXLEY, J., ibid., p. 31.

Ref.	Page	
26	130	HORDERN, WILLIAM. *A Layman's Guide to Protestant Theology.* Macmillan (1955), p. 21.
27	130	HEIM, ibid., p. 213.
28	131	PARKER, WILLIAM R., and ST. JOHNS, ELAINE. *Prayer Can Change Your Life.* Prentice-Hall, Inc. (1957), p. 8.
29	132	BRIDGMAN, P. W. *The Way Things Are.* Harvard Univ. Press (1959), p. 72.
30	133	TILLICH, PAUL. *Dynamics of Faith.* Harper Torchbooks (1957), p. 1.
31	133	TILLICH, *Dynamics,* ibid., p. 108.
32	134	New Testament, Revised Standard Version, Mark **11**:23.
33	135	HARTSHORNE, M. HOLMES. *The Promise of Science and the Power of Faith.* Westminster Press (1958), pp. 93-95.
34	136	OTTO, RUDOLF. *The Idea of the Holy.* Translated by John W. Harvey. Second Edition, Oxford Univ. Press (1950), pp. 207-210.
35	138	POLLARD, WILLIAM G. *Chance and Providence.* Scribner (1958), pp. 116-117.
36	140	GATLAND AND DEMPSTER, ibid.,
37	141	OTTO, ibid., pp. 228-229.
38	142	JENKINS, DANIEL. *Believing in God.* Westminster Press (1956), pp. 46-47.
39	146	JAMES, WILLIAM. *Varieties of Religious Experience.*
40	146	REA, FREDERICK B. *Alcoholism, Its Psychology and Cure.* Philosophical Library (1956), pp. 126-127.
41	147	REA, ibid., p. 125.
42	148	REA, ibid., p. 127.
43	150	HEIM, ibid., p. 110.
44	151	TOYNBEE, ARNOLD. *A Historian's Approach to Religion.* Oxford Univ. Press (1956), p. 4.
45	153	SARTON, GEORGE. *The History of Science and the New Humanism.* George Brazilier Inc. (1956), pp. 117-119.

Chapter 7

1	155	EINSTEIN, ALBERT.
		Cosmic Religion. Covici Friede (1931).
		The Meeting Place of Science and Religion., In *Has Science Discovered God?* Edward H. Cotton, Ed. Thomas Y. Crowell Co. (1931).
		Out of My Later Years. Philosophical Library (ac. 1950).
		JORDAN, DAVID STARR.
		Standeth God Within the Shadow. Thomas Y. Crowell Co. (ca. 1901).
		The Higher Foolishness. Bobbs-Merrill Co. (ca. 1927).
2	155, 156	LONG, EDWARD LEROY, JR. *Religious Beliefs of American Scientists.* Westminster Press (1952), p. 22.
3	156	REUTERDAHL, ARVID. *The God of Science.* The Arya Co. (1926).
4	156	COMPTON, ARTHUR H.
		The Freedom of Man. Yale Univ. Press (1935).
		The Religion of a Scientist. Pamphlet. Jewish Theological Seminary of America (1938).

Ref.	Page	
4	156	CURTIS, HEBER D.

Modern Physical Science—Its Relation to Religion. In *Has Science Discovered God?* ibid.

STANDEN, ANTHONY. *Science Is a Sacred Cow.* E. P. Dutton & Co., Inc. (1950).

RICE, WILLIAM NORTH
Christian Faith in an Age of Science. A. G. Armstrong & Son (1903).
Science and Religion. Abingdon Press (ca. 1925).

5   156   RICE, ibid., (Christian Faith), p. 338. LONG, ibid., p. 42.

6   157   Reprinted in *Science and Life,* R. A. Millikan, pp. 86-90. The Pilgrim Press (1924). Quoted from Long, ibid., pp. 45-46.

7   157   OSBORN, HENRY FAIRFIELD. *Evolution in Science and Religion.* Charles Scribner's Sons (1926).

DU NOUY, PIERRE LECOMTE *Human Destiny.* Longmans Green & Co. (1947).

MILLIKAN, ROBERT ANDREWS
Science and Life, Pilgrim Press (1924).
Time, Matter, and Values. Univ. North Carolina Press (1932).
Evolution in Science and Religion. Yale Univ. Press (1935).

PUPIN, MICHAEL. *The New Reformation.* Charles Scribner's Sons (1927).

8   157   WHITEHEAD, ALBERT NORTH. *Science and the Modern World.* Lowell Lectures, 1925. Macmillan Co. (1925).

9   157   MATHER, KIRTLEY. *Science in Search of God.* Henry Holt Co. (1928), p. 77.

10   158   LONG, ibid., p. 59.

11   158   MILLER, WALLACE. *A Scientist's Approach to Religion.* Macmillan Co. (1947), p. 65, Quoted by Long, ibid., p. 63.

12   158   MILLER, ibid., p. 125. Quoted by Long, ibid., p. 64.

13   158   CONKLIN, EDWARD GRANT. *Man, Real and Ideal.* Charles Scribner's Sons (1943).

DOOLEY, DONALD. *As Intelligent as Science,* in *Faith of the Free,* by W. E. Garrison. Willett, Clark & Co. (1940).

14   158   LONG, ibid., p. 70.

15   158   BUSH, VANNEVAR. *Modern Arms and Free Men.* Simon & Schuster (1949). LONG, ibid., p. 71.

16   159   BRIDGMAN, PERCY W.
The Logic of Modern Physics. Macmillan Co. (1927).
Reflections of a Physicist. Philosophical Library (1927).
The Way Things Are. Harvard Univ. Press (1959).

17   159   Webster's New International Dictionary. 3d Edition.

18   159   LONG, ibid., p. 78.

19   159   FRANK, PHILIPP
Between Physics and Philosophy. Harvard Univ. Press (1941).
Modern Science and Its Philosophy. Harvard Univ. Press (1949).
Relativity: A Richer Truth. Beacon Press Inc. (1950).

20   159   LONG, ibid., p. 83.

21   159   COMPTON, KARL TAYLOR
Science, the Soul of Prosperity. Address, 1940.
Scientists Face the World of Life. Rutgers Univ. Press (1942).

KETTERING, CHARLES F. *Short Stories of Science and Invention.* General Motors Corp.

Ref. *Page*

22   159   HUXLEY, JULIAN. Religion Without Revelation. Second Ed. Max
            Parrish, London (1957).

23   160   HOOPER, E. RALPH. *Does Science Support Evolution?* Defender Pub-
            lishers (ca. 1931), Evangelical Publishers, Toronto.
            MARSH, FRANK LEWIS. *Evolution, Creation, and Science.* Review and
            Herald Publishing Assn. (1944).

24   160   KLOTZ, J. W. *Genes, Genesis, and Evolution.* Concordia Publishing
            House, St. Louis (1958).

25   160   MOORE, LOUIS TRENCHARD. *The Dogma of Evolution.* (Vanuxen Lec-
            tures). Princeton Univ. Press (1925).

26   160   Constitution of the American Science Affiliation, Article II. Quoted
            by Long, ibid., pp. 107-108.
            American Science Affiliation. *Modern Science and Christian Faith.*
            Van Kampen Press (ca. 1948, 1950).
            KELLY, HOWARD ATWOOD. *A Scientific Man and the Bible.* Harper &
            Bros. (date of first publication 1925).

27   161   STINE, CHARLES M. A. *A Chemist and His Bible.* Sunday School
            Times (1943).

28   161   LONG, ibid., p. 121.

29   161   PACK, FREDERICK J. *Science and Belief in God.* Deseret Press (1924).
            SAJOUS, CHARLES E. DE M. *Strength of Religion as Shown by Science.*
            F. A. Davis Co. (ca. 1926).

30   161   POTEAT, WILLIAM LEWIS. *The New Peace.* Richard G. Badger (ca.
            1926).

31   162   LANE, HENRY HIGGINS. *Evolution and Christian Faith.* Princeton
            Univ. Press (1923), p. 167. Quoted by Long, p. 129.

32   162   Quoted by TAYLOR, HUGH S., in *Religious Perspectives of College
            Teaching in the Physical Sciences.* Pamphlet, Edward Hazen Co.
            (1951). Long, ibid, p. 134.

33   162   SIKORSKY, IGOR IVAN
            The Invisible Encounter. Charles Scribner's Sons (1947).
            The Message of the Lord's Prayer. Charles Scribner's Sons (1942).

34   163   LONG, ibid., p. 148.

35   163   LONG, ibid., p. 151.

36   164   LONG, ibid., pp. 151-153.

37   165   POLLARD, WILLIAM G. *Physicist and Christian.* Seabury Press (1961),
            p. 9.

38   165   OTTO, RUDOLF. *The Idea of the Holy.* 2nd Ed. Oxford Press, N. Y.
            (1950).

39   165   POLLARD, ibid., pp. 91-93.

40   167   POLLARD, ibid., pp. 156-158.

41   167   POLLARD, ibid., p. 173.

Chapter 8

1   170   HUXLEY, ALDOUS. *Tomorrow, and Tomorrow, and Tomorrow, and
            Other Essays.* Harper & Bros. (1952), pp. 154-155.

2   171   WHITE, ANDREW D. *A History of the Warfare of Science with Theol-
            ogy in Christendom.* D. Appleton & Co. (1896), vol. 2, pp. 94-95.

3   173   RIDDLE, OSCAR. *The Unleashing of Evolutionary Thought.* Vantage
            Press, Inc. (1954), p. 342.

Ref. *Page*

4   175   Bible, Rev. Standard Version, I Cor. **9**:9-10.

5   175   HUXLEY, *Adonis and the Alphabet,* ibid., pp. 191-192.

7   179   RIDDLE, ibid., p. 92.

Chapter 9

1   185   POLLARD, WILLIAM G. *Chance and Providence.* Scribner (1958), p. 161.

2   186   SINNOTT, EDMUND W. *The Biology of the Spirit.* Viking Press, N. Y. (1955), p. 102.

3   186   SINNOTT, ibid., p. 111.

4   187   SINNOTT, ibid., p. 123.

5   187   DU NOUY, PIERRE LECOMTE *Human Destiny.* Longmans, Green & Co. (1947), p. 34.

6   187   MAINX, F. *Foundations of Biology,* in International Encyclopedia of Unified Science. Univ. of Chicago Press (1955), p. 633. Quoted from Koch.

7   188   KOCH, LEO FRANCIS. *Vitalistic-Mechanistic Controversy.* Sci. Monthly **85,** (Nov. 1957), p. 250.

8   188   KOCH, ibid., p. 249.

9   188   KOCH, ibid., p. 255.

10   189   FRANK, L. K. *Nature and Human Nature.* Rutgers Univ. Press, New Brunswick, N. J. (1951), p. 17. Quoted from Koch.

11   190   POLLARD, ibid., p. 53.

12   190   DILLENBERGER, JOHN. *Protestant Thought and Natural Science.* Doubleday & Co., Inc. (1960), pp. 273 ff.

13   191   KOCH, ibid., p. 245.

14   191   BERNATOWICZ, A. J. *Teleology in Science Teaching.* Science **128,** 1402 (Dec. 5, 1958).

15   191   OTTO, M. *In Honor of John Dewey on His Ninetieth Birthday.* Univ. of Wisconsin Press (1951), p. 17. Quoted from Koch.

16   191   KOCH, ibid., p. 246.

17   192   KOCH, ibid., p. 252.

18   193   HUXLEY, JULIAN. *Religion Without Revelation.* Second Edition, Max Parrish, London (1957), pp. 217-218.

19   194   HUXLEY, JULIAN, ibid., p. 210.

20   194   ROSTAND, JEAN. *Can Man Be Modified?* Sat. Eve. Post, (May 2, 1958), pp. 97-100.

21   195   MUMFORD, LEWIS. *The Transformations of Man.* Harper & Bros. (1956), pp. 164-166.

22   198   KOCH, ibid., p. 246.

23   198   KOCH, ibid., p. 253.

24   198   FRANK, ibid., p. 131. Quoted from Koch.

25   198   DILLENBERGER, ibid., pp. 264-265.

26   200   BULTMANN, RUDOLF. *Jesus Christ and Mythology.* Charles Scribner's Sons (1958), p. 40.

27   201   BULTMANN, ibid., pp. 79-80.

Ref. *Page*
28   201   HOCKING, WILLIAM ERNEST. *The Meaning of God in Human Experience.* Yale Univ. Press (1948 Ed.), pp. 455-456.

29   201   HORDERN, WILLIAM. *A Layman's Guide to Protestant Theology.* Macmillan (1957), p. 147.

30   202   JASPERS, KARL, and BULTMANN, RUDOLF. *Myth and Christianity.* An Inquiry into the Possibility of Religion without Myth. Noonday Press, N. Y. (1958), p. 15.

31   205   HARRISON, GEORGE RUSSELL. *What Man May Be.* The Human Side of Science. Wm. Morrow & Co., N. Y. (1956), p. 228.

Chapter 10

1   208   HUXLEY, ALDOUS. *Knowledge and Understanding.* In *Tomorrow, and Tomorrow, and Tomorrow, and Other Essays.* Harper & Bros. (1952), p. 63.

2   209   New Testament, Revised Standard Version, Matt. **10**:29-30.

3   212   COE, GEORGE ALBERT. *The Religion of a Mature Mind.* Fleming H. Revell Co. (1902), pp. 50-52.

4   Ibid.

5   215   MACGREGOR, GEDDES. *Introduction to Religious Philosophy.* Houghton Mifflin Co. (1959), p. 315.

6   215   JENKINS, DANIEL. *Believing in God.* Westminster Press (1956), pp. 31-32, 36.

7   MOZLEY, E. Z. *The Theology of Albert Schweitzer for Christian Inquirers.* Macmillan Co. (1951), p. 82.

8   217   POTTHOFF, H. H.

9   218   Ibid.

10   218   Ibid.

11   219   HEIM, KARL. *The Transformation of the Scientific World View.* Translated by W. A. Whitehouse. Harper and Bros. (1953).

12   219   TOYNBEE, A. J.

OCCUPATIONS OF SCIENTISTS MENTIONED